Beginner's ASSEMBLY LANGUAGE AND HARDWARE for the IBM®-PC Series

Dr. P. K. Mahanti
Indrajit Mukherjee

CENTRAL

Beginner's ASSEMBLY LANGUAGE and HARDWARE for the IBM®-PC SERIES

Dr P. K. Mahanti

Department of Computer Science & Engineering
Birla Institute of Technology
Mesra, Ranchi

Indrajit Mukherjee

Faculty & In-charge, Computers,
Ranchi College, Ranchi University

New Central Book Agency (P) Ltd

LONDON

HYDERABAD ERNAKULAM BHUBANESWAR

DELHI KOLKATA PUNE GUWAHATI

NCBA

REGD OFFICE

8/1 Chintamoni Das Lane, Kolkata 700 009, India
ncbapvtltd@eth.net

OVERSEAS

NCBA (UK) Ltd, 149 Park Avenue North, Northampton, NN3 2HY, UK
ncbauk@yahoo.com

EXPORT

NCBA Exports Pvt. Ltd, 212 Shahpur Jat, New Delhi 110 049
ncbaexports@ncbaindia.com

BRANCHES

208B Peacock Lane, Shahpur Jat
New Delhi 110 049
ncbadel@ncbapvtltd.com

House No. 3-1-315, 1st Floor
Nimboliadda, Kachiguda, **Hyderabad** 500 027
ncbahydb@ncbapvtltd.com

Shop Nos. 3 & 4, Vinayak Towers
681/B Budhwar Peth, Appa Balwant Chowk
Pune 411 002
ncbapune@ncbapvtltd.com

GSS Shopping Complex, 1st Floor
Opposite College Post Office, Convent Road
Ernakulam 682 035
ncbaernk@ncbapvtltd.com

Shop No. 15, Bharati Towers, Ground Floor
Forest Park, **Bhubaneswar** 751 001
ncbabub@ncbapvtltd.com

Radhamayee Complex (Second Floor)
Opp. SBI, Panbazar, Jaswanta Road
Guwahati 781 001
ncbaguwahati@ncbapvtltd.com

BEGINNER'S ASSEMBLY LANGUAGE AND
HARDWARE FOR THE IBM®-PC SERIES • Dr P. K. Mahanti, Indrajit Mukherjee

First Published: 1998
With Additions: 2008
Reprinted: January 2013

PUBLISHER AND TYPESETTER
New Central Book Agency (P) Ltd
8/1 Chintamoni Das Lane, Kolkata 700 009

PRINTER
New Central Book Agency (P) Ltd
Web-Offset Division, Dhulagarh, Sankrail, Howrah

PROJECT TEAM
Prabht Jas, and Somenath Ganguly

ISBN 81 7381 207 1
978 81 7381 207 1

Price ₹ 385.00

Preface

Computer world, today, has overheartedly endorsed the IBM®-PC Series. The present state of affairs claim that the PC Series, instead of getting obsolete is marching full steam ahead. This wonderful achievement sustained for the last fifteen years is undoubtedly credited to the three giants—**Intel, IBM** and **Microsoft**. To any average computer use the name "COMPUTER" gives a vision of the IBM®-PC. This cosy desktop marvel has become almost omnipresent. It is for this reason the authors chose to put effort howsoever little, into bringing that corner of the PC into focus which is usually in eclipse. Here we are talking of Assembly Language and Hardware.

Most of the people we have met in the computer circle are either afraid of Assembly Language or have misconceptions about it. On the contrary, Assembly Language could become one of the choicest if one puts little effort to understand it. Afterall, it is the sole language that is nearest to the hardware that made the above mentioned miracles possible.

We have tried to deal with both Assembly Language and the PC Series hardware, as fairly as possible, so that neither the reader is overburdened with unnecessary deep technical jargon nor any injustice is done to the subject itself by withholding necessary and important information.

We are yet to come across a book that helps people understand computer hardware in the context and relationship of software. It is only when both are revealed in tandem, a book becomes wholesomely useful.

The first three chapters introduce the computer hardware and teach 8086/8088 Assembly Language programming. Material is given on the latest Macro Assembly (Masm 6.X) and a comparison has been done with the previous versions. The next chapters explain the different hardware models of the computer. We have added reports of four projects carried through in our Institute, and related to Hardware and Networking. These projects will be very useful for engineering students in getting practical exposure to methods of linking Assembly Language, high level language and the computer hardware. They also give an insight into communication standards. We have added some exercises at the end. Thus, this book can be taken as a text book covering the syllabus of **COMPUTER HARDWARE & PERIPHERALS** which is a common elective subject in both **under-graduate and post-graduate engineering courses** as well as in **Master of Computer Application Courses** in Technical colleges and Universities in India.

Suggestions and criticisms are always welcome from readers because that would make us improve the book in the next revision. It is our sincerest hope that after going through this book, readers would come much closer to this amazing machine that we call a **Computer**.

AUTHORS

Acknowledgements

The authors wish to express their profound appreciation to the following students, who helped with research materials, corrections and illustrations in the different sections of this book.

Hardware Section : Anirban Mahanti, Abhinav Garg—93 batch B.I.T., Mesra.

Assembly Language Section : Neetu Kumani, Aparajita, Sunil Verma, Anupama, Sujata, Binod Kr. Sinha, Manisha Pandey and Neeraj Chandra—91 batch, B.I.T., Sindri.

Project Section : Sunaina Pande, Priyam Hora, Anshu Agarwal, Sandeep Chatterjee, Amit Biswas, Manisha Sinha, Soumyajit Sen and Supriya Bose—91 bach, B.I.T., Mesra.

Illustrations : Manjit Singh—92 batch, B.I.T. Mesra.

Text Processing : Bidyut Chanda, Dept. of Computer Science, B.I.T., Mesra.

CONTENTS

Chapter One
INTRODUCTION

1.0 INTRODUCTION

August 12, 1981 stands as a testimony to the birth of the first IBM PC.It wasthe first step by the giant IBM (International Business Machines) Company towards the microcomputer market. Needless to mention that their debut itself changed the markets perception of the microcomputer and its usage as a versatile machine.

It was during the early eighties that IBM seriously planned to make it to the microcomputer arena. A division of IBM, Entry Systems, was given the responsibility of designing an IBM microcomputer. No one exactly knows what actually happened at Entry systems, as the details have been held back by IBM. What is presented here is purely an estimate based on the informations that slipped out of IBM to find itself on the pages of magazines and various books published around the early eighties.

Engineers at the Entry Systems were surely confronted with a myriad of problems. From the late seventies itself, microcomputer or micros in short, were available in the market. At that time, that is around early 1980s,the micros were primarily aimed at the hobbyists. Professionals didn't prefer using the micros and business didn't like its name at all.Going around with the ideology of the micros available in the market wouldn't have been beneficial for the IBM in any aspect. So they had to work out some sort of alternative, while maintaining the micro standards prevailing then. What actually made the IBMs micro different from the pack of micros already available will be clear during reading of the subsequent sections. But it was probably IBMs design without purpose, which made its micro so much popular. While IBM was stili working with its design, micros were being described as personal computers by some of their patrons. IBM took this evolving name as its product label, and stamped its first micro, which rolled out on August 12, 1981, as the IBM PC. This first PC was popularly known as the PC-I. Personal Computers signified homely feelings,which became a substantial reason for its popularity. Now, fourteen years since the PC-I, IBM stands as a kingpin in the micro scenario. IBMs success with the PCs have long been considered as a beacon for all aspiring PC manufacturers.

1.1 PRECURSORS OF THE IBM PC

The advent of microcomputers is very much related with the commercialization of microprocessors. The first microprocessor chip was conceived by Dr. Ted Hoff of Intel Corporation in late 1969. Commercially the chip was available in the market by 1971. It was only after the commencement of commercial production of microprocessor chips that the microcomputer idea cropped up.

The concept of a microcomputer with a microprocessor as its brain originated from a paper by Allan Kay, Published in 1972. By that time Intel had come out with a full 8 bit microprocessor chip called Intel 8008, which had a clock speed of 0.75 MHZ and an estimated throughput of around 1. Around late 1974, an article published in a magazine called Radio Electronics, outlined the design of a microcomputer using the Intel 8 bit processors then available. It was only in early 1975 when the first microcomputer called MITS Altair rolled out. It used the Intel 8080 chip which was an advanced version of the 8008 chip, having a clock speed of 3MHZ and an estimated throughput of about 10.

Before IBMs entry into the microcomputer market,quite a few micro manufacturer were already there. Apple computers was the leader in the micro industry. Apple II made by Stephen Woznaik and Steven Jobs was ready by 1977. It was the first single board microcomputer, with a dedicated expansion bus, eight bit Rockwell 6502 microprocessor and 1 MHZ speed. Apple II used tapes as an auxillary storage and was easy to operate.

Radio-Tandy was another important player in the micro market. It used the Zilog Corporations Z80 eight bit microprocessor keeping the remaining features resembling the Apple computers. Some other manufacturers used the hybrid type of computers, lifting some features from Apple and Tandy computers.

1.2 GENEALOGY OF THE IBM PC

When IBM was taking decisions on its design of the IBM PC, its first hassle was opting for the right microprocessor. Already its predecessors were using the eight bit microprocessors. The 6502 had a throughput less than the Z80 based machines. Opting for the Z80 would have made its micro a copy of the Tandy machine. To get around with this identity crisis, IBM opted for the 8088 chip, which externally worked on eight bits, but internally manipulated sixteen bits. This significantly contributed to the original IBM PCs speed, while keeping the cost low. The 8088 offers greater memory addressing. The next step was to opt for a proper memory chip. IBM used the 16k RAMs. Since these were one dimensional memories, (eg. 16384 x 1 bit RAM) it was necessary to use atleast 8 such RAMs to make up 16kb of memory. Instead of using eight 16k RAMs, IBM used nine RAMs. The extra ninth bit was used as a parity check. IBM also introduced the concept of empty sockets for increasing memory of the machine when required. The original PC-I had a 5.25" Floppy drive, a cassette port, and a BASIC compiler loaded in its ROM. With these features (to name a few only) the IBM PC, popularly known as **PC-I**, rolled out of the IBM castle on August 12, 1981.

The PC-I is an Intel 8088 based computer that operated at a fequency of 4.77 MHZ. It used a single sided floppy drive.

Around 1982, IBM lauched an advanced version of the PC-I, called **PC-II**. It was again an Intel 8088 based machine having two 5.25 inch floppy drives. It also had an operational frequency of 4.77 MHZ.

Early 1983 saw IBM'S first addition to the PC family the XT model. It was a personal computer with Extended Technology, with a hard disk drive added. It was again an Intel 8088 based machine, with the operating frequency increased to about 8 MHZ. It also introduced the concept of double density diskettes.

In the summer of 1984, the AT (Advanced Technology) was introduced. The processor used was the new Intel 80286 chip, which communicated both externally and internally with 16 bits, making the AT a true 16 bit computer. It was having an operating frequency of 1O MHZ, had two-floppy drives, and a hard disk. It is also known as the **AT-286** machine.

By late 1986, another AT machine known as the **PC-AT 386** came up. It used the Intel 80386 chip, thus introducing 32 bit computing in the micros. Originally it had a processor speed of 20 MHZ, but the newer 386 machines work at speeds upto 40 MHZ. Another new feature introduced was the 3.5 inch floppy drive.

During the begining of ninties, **PC-AT 486** was made available. It used the Intel 80486 chip, which introduced true 32 bit computing. Processors have speeds of 33 MHZ, 40 MHZ and even 66 MHZ.

Recently the Pentium P-5 chip (Intel 80586) has come up. Details of Pentium and the underdevelopment Pentium P-6 chip is covered in the chapter covering microprocessors (chapter Two) and appendix C.

Since 1988 IBM has come up with a new series of advanced personal computers known as the **PS/2**. PS/2 series uses Intels 8086, 80286, 80386 and 80486 chips as the microprocessor. The PS/2 uses **MCA** (**M**icro **C**hannel **A**rchitecture) and allows high speed operation. Typically Bus speed is around 80MB/sec compared to the others 10 MB/sec. This new architecture allows multiple bus masters. Memory and I/O units are all "bus-masters", because they independently control the bus without loading the processor. These new PS/2 machines unleash the full power of the newer chips like the 486.

PC-I	**8088 microprocessor, 4.77 MHZ, Floppy Drive 1981**
PC-II	**8088 microprocessor, 4.77 MHZ,2Floppydrives,1982**
PC-XT	**8088 microprocessor, 8 MHZ, 20 MB Hard disk, 2 Floppy Drives, 1983**
PC-AT/ 286	**80286 microprocessor, 6-15 MHZ, Hard Disks, 2 Floppy Drives, 1984**
PC-AT/ 386	**80386 microprocessor, 16-40 MHZ, Hard Disk, 5.25" floppy drive, 3.5" Floppy drive, 1986**
PC-AT/ 486	**80486 microprocessor, 33-66 MHZ, Harddisk, 5.25" Floppy drive, 1990**

Table 1.1 : IBM PC Tree At A Glance

1.3 THE IBM COMPATIBLE OR CLONES

The so called IBM compatibles come in different levels of compatibility. There are basically two levels of compatibles. They are :

Hardware Compatibles

Software Compatibles

The hardware compatible system are those which are a replica of the original IBM system. They look and work exactly like the original IBM system. All softwares written for the IBM systems work on these systems without any problem.

The software compatible systems are those systems which are not exactly a copy of the IBM's system hardware set. The design and appearance of these systems differ from the original IBM system. But the systems are so designed that they run all the softwares written for the original IBM systems.

Various popular brands of systems are available, viz. HCL, WIPRO, SIVA, ICIM, PCL, ETC.

1.4 OPERATING SYSTEM

Why do we need the operating system (OS in short) ? The operating system is a system software that provides an interface between the application programs and underlying hardware. This interface provides better management of computer resources like CPU, RAM and disk space.

A Computer is regarded as a machine formed from six layers of virtual machines. Layer 0 is called **digital logic level**, layer 1 is called the **microprogram level**, layer 2 is the **machine level**, layer 3 is the **operating system level**, layer 4 is the **assembly level** and layer 5 is the **application level**. Most users work at layer 5 writing application programs in different programming languages. Each computer level has some set of defined functions.

The major functions of the operating systems are :

1. Process Management : The operating system defines that program as the process which runs under the OS. The resources are provided to the process by the OS.

2. Input/Output : Input/Output resources are also scheduled by the OS. This is very important in multi-tasking environment.

3. Memory Management : The way the processes are assigned memory is also determined. Efficient memory management enhances the system's quality.

4. File system : The OS also determine how a file is to be kept and used. It determines the way files are organized.

Examples of popular operating systems are CP/M, DOS, Window N.T, UNIX, and OS/2. We consider the DOS and OS/2 next.

1.5 GENEALOGY OF DOS

Over the years, MS-DOS has evolved as the most popular operating system for the microcomputer using the Intel 8086 family of microprocessors. The progenitor of the **MS-DOS** was an operating system called **86-DOS**. 86-DOS was written by Tim Patterson and was a product of Seattle Computer Products. When IBM was designing its PC, it looked for an operating system that could run all the softwares already available and running on the CP/M based machines. 86-DOS worked very much like CP/M but had brought out some changes in the file structure and operating modes. IBM approached Microsoft for an operating system that could be used with its system (IBM PC). In the early 1981, Microsoft purchased all the rights of 86-DOS and made some changes to it and labelled its product as the MS-DOS 1.0. This first version of Microsoft DOS was offered as the primary operating system for the IBM PC (PC-I) on its release on August 12, 1981. Since then, IBM and Microsoft have maintained very intimate relations.

A point to be noted. IBM calls the DOS provided in its systems as PC-DOS. Microsoft came up with MS-DOS 1.25 to fix the bugs discovered in its original version. This revised version came out as PC DOS 1.1 when IBM released the IBM PC-XT. Microsoft released MS-DOS 2.0 (PC DOS 2.0 is equivalent to it). It brought in many new features, and we mention a few below :

1. Support for Hard disks.
2. Support for larger capacity floppy disks.
3. Installable device drivers.
4. Concept of background printing.
5. Maintenance of environment blocks.
6. Concept of heirarchy of directory in disks.

With the IBM PC-AT 286, MS-DOS 3.0 was released. It allowed many enhanced features while maintaining downward compatibility. The major features are :

1. Direct control of printer spooler.
2. Larger hard disk support.
3. Enhanced memory management.
4. Support for 1.2 MB floppy disks.

Version 3.2 added the 3.5 inch floppy support. It was released with PC-AT 386 machines. Other versions released are version 3.3.

MS-DOS 4.0 was released in 1988. It allowed the user to declare partitions of sizes larger than 32MB. Restrictions on hardware and software limitations were removed. It also introduced a user friendly shell feature for the first time in personal computing level.

MS DOS 5.0 was released in 1991. The unutilized memory space in the previous versions was faithfully used. The shell feature was enhanced to make it more user friendly. In addition to the line editor, a new full screen text editor was also introduced. Hard disk partition of 2 gigabytes is allowed. Also the Quick Basic Interpreter has been made an integral part of the operating system. It also allows the user to use two hard disk systems.

MS DOS 6.0 was released in April 1993. It has added a whole new range of commands and features. A concept known as Microsoft Double space has been introduced, which increases the available space on the hard disk and floppy disk. A memory optimizing program known as MemMaker allows better memory management on an 80386 or higher processor. An anti-virus program known as Microsoft Anti-Virus is provided. This utility can detect, clean and destroy 800 different computer viruses. An improved defragmentor program is also bundled into the operating system. Many more features are available. To get a full list better consult the MS-DOS user's Guide available with a new PC, or any other book listed in the bibliography.

It has just been about two years with the DOS 6.X versions. Already we have started hearing about MS-DOS 7.0 which along with windows 4 is popularly described as Chicago by Microsoft.

Some experts have already started saying that doom's day has arrived for DOS. According to them DOS is essentially a 16 bit operating system,and they have to give way to 32bit operating systems which are custom built for 32 bit Intel processors. Seeing 32 bit operating systems gaining ground, IBM introduced the PS/2 series with an operating system called OS/2. We see the added advantage of 32 bit operating system and the OS/2 briefly in the next section.

1.6 32 BIT OPERATING SYSTEM

DOS being a 16 bit operating system cannot fully leverage the 32 bit processors inside our latest PCs. DOS never delivers true protected-mode operation, multitasking in the real sense and even does not support multithreading. Workarounds emulating these features are available but are more prone to crashes. The memory model supported by most 32 bit operating systems is essentially flat in nature, a single unified 4 GB of addressable memory. You are simply working with it, without worrying about upper memory, high memory, extended memory and expanded memory.

With the advent of the 32 bit processors, IBM decided to look for alternatives to DOS. It had started working on an operating system known as OS/2 in collaboration with Microsoft. It uses 16 MB memory and supports multitasking, multiuser and networking. The requirement of about 16 MB of RAM turned out to be the first hurdle. When IBM planned its launch around 1988 prices of RAM chips went up, delaying OS/2's release. Then differences between IBM and Microsoft widened, delaying the quick instalment of OS/2. Now, both develop OS/2 independently. Repeated design changes also hampered its acceptance in the micro scene. Originally it was developed as a 16 bit operating system. But the popularity of 386 processors prompted IBM and Microsoft to change the original design and implement OS/2 as a 32 bit operating system, unleashing the full powers of today's processors.

1.7 MODEL OF A MICROCOMPUTER

Basically the microcomputer can be thought to be made up of four key parts (fig. 1.1) : the microprocessor, input device, output device and memory. We have further divided the memory into RAM and ROM.

The microprocessor is the brain of the computer. In the model of big machines, this is often refered to as the Central Processing Unit, or CPU. For our model of the micros we call this the microprocessor. The microprocessor chip contains an Arithmetic Logic Unit(ALU), control and timing circuits, instruction registers and decoders and many other working registers. The working and details of the microprocessor internals is considered in the chapter Two which is devoted to microprocessors and motherboards.

Next we consider the memory. RAM is the memory to which data is written and read from. From ROM data is only read. Thus ROM contains certain control programs and BIOS routines.

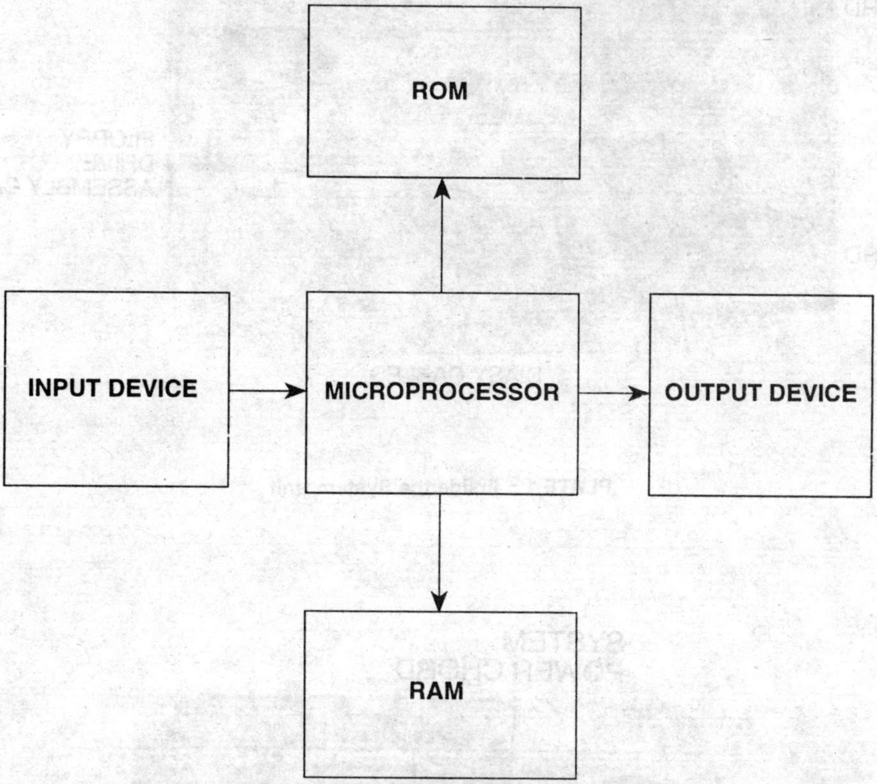

Fig 1.1 A Microcomputer Block Diagram.

Input and output devices allow us to interact with the computer. The Input device which is most commonly used is the keyboard. Nowdays mouses are also used for some window applications. Output devices are used to see the output obtained after processing is done. Popular output device is the video display unit, or VDU,Printer is another output device, used to get a printed result. With this discussion on the micro model, we can proceed to see what is inside the IBM PC.

1.8 IBM PC HARDWARE OVERVIEW

The basic microcomputer configuration was discussed in sec 1.7. In this section,the emphasis is to try to get an overview of the IBM PC hardware. In this endeavour emphasis is laid to understand what's inside the system box. Refer plate 1.

The raw PC configuration can be given in terms of the display unit, system box and keyboard. The display unit is the output device, while keyboard is the input device. Most of the PC's hardware is inside the system box. So this section is devoted towards understanding the internals of the system box briefly.

PLATE 1 : Inside the System Unit

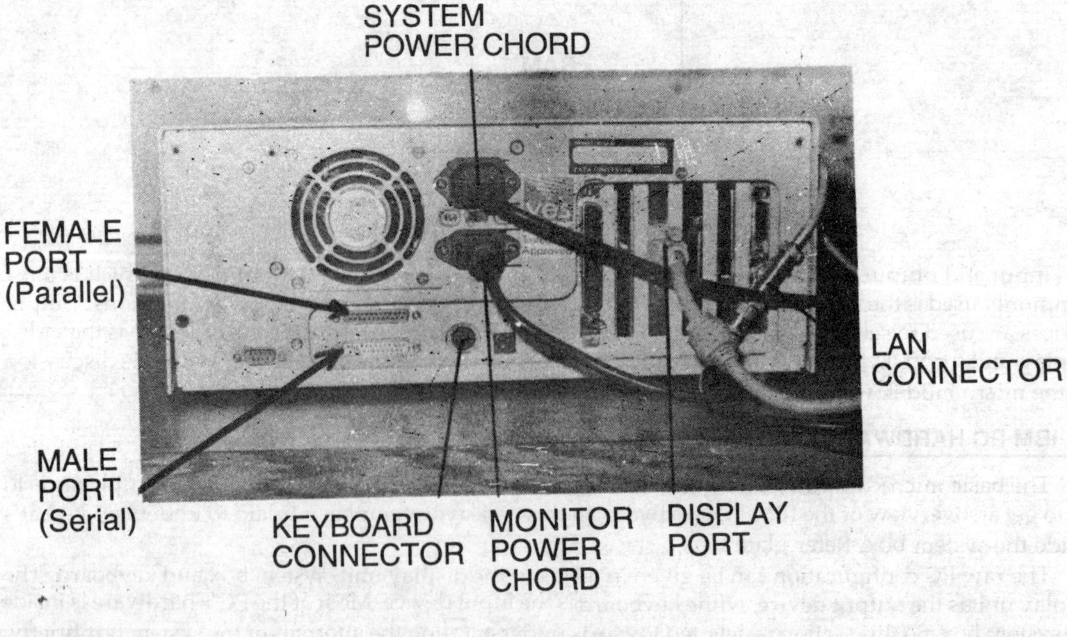

PLATE 2

The PCB covering the major portion of the system area is called the system board. It is the main board with all the important chips and electronics placed on it. Most important, the microprocessor is placed on this board. It is also known as the motherboard.

Power Supply unit is generally located on the right rear end of the system box. It is responsible for converting A.C. to D.C. power. PC systems generally use ±12V and ±5V inside its system. Power supply unit does all the necessary conversions in the supply of power. **FIGURE 1.2.**

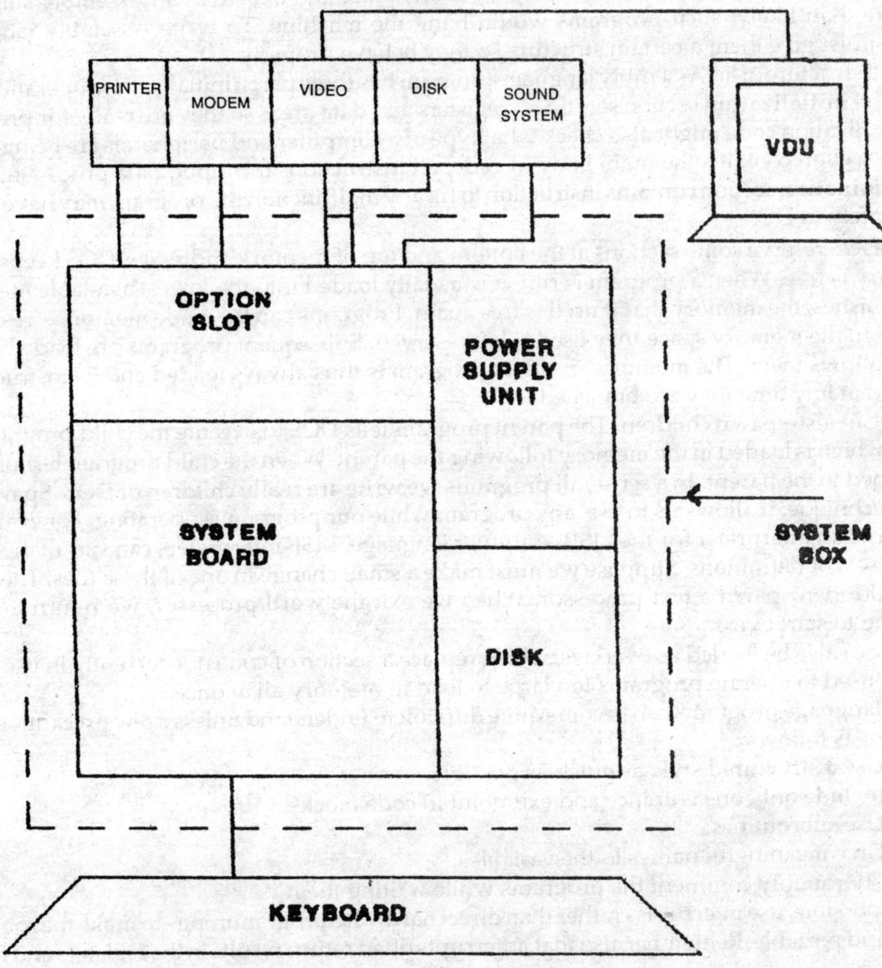

Fig 1.2 : PC Hardware Overview.

The disk slot is generally located on the front right side of the system box. It is the place where hard disk and floppy disks are placed. Some newer systems provide a floppy disk slot near the front left side of the system box.

In the earlier PCs, most peripherals like printer, video display unit etc. were implemented using additional card. This means that the interface between the PCs, motherboard and these peripherals is provided by these cards. To install these cards, the expansion/option slot was provided. Nowadays, most motherboards come with the functions of the most essential peripherals integrated on it. But the expansion slot is still provided to add additional peripherals.

With this introduction, you are now ready to launch your self into the essentials of the PC – its hardware and how to program the microprocessor chips. Bon Voyage.

## Chapter Two

ASSEMBLY LANGUAGE FOR 8086/8088

2.0 ASSEMBLY LANGUAGE

Introduction : **Assembly Language** is the most elementary computer language available to programmers. It is composed of short mnemonics that translate directly into numbers that instruct the computer to execute very basic instructions, such as "add two bytes" or "read a byte in memory".

Assembly Language Programs are collection of Assembly language instructions. Any set of numbers can be loaded into the computer's memory at any place and treated as an Assembly language program. More than likely, such programs would hang the machine. To write Assembly language programs, we must give them a certain structure so they behave properly.

The overall structure of an Assembly language program has three parts: initialization, operation and termination. The **initialization** section sets up all registers and data areas so they are ready for program operation. Initialization code might also check what type of a computer and peripherals are being used. The **operation** section contains the main body of code, all instructions for input, data processing, and output. The **termination** section contains instruction to fix any malfunction the program may have made and to return safely to DOS.

BIOS and DOS reserve some sections at the bottom and top of memory addresses. DOS keeps track of what memory is free. When a program is run, it is usually loaded into the lowest available memory slot. When it finishes, the memory that it used is free again. Programs can be made memory - resident; when they finish, the memory space they used is left reserved. Subsequent programs are loaded in the memory that follows them. The memory - resident program is thus always loaded and its instructions can be executed at any time they are branched to.

Programs can also spawn children. The parent program tells DOS to execute the child program (or subprogram), which is loaded in the memory following the parent. When the child program terminates, control is returned to the parent. In a sense, all programs we write are really children of DOS. Spawning is a powerful technique; it allows us to use any program while our program is operating. For example, suppose we write an interpreter for the LISP computer language. LISP interpreters can simultaneously read in several sets of definitions. Suppose we must make a small change in one of these files. The LISP interpreter could then spawn a text processor. When we exit the word processor, we return to LISP without needing to start over.

Programs can also be loaded as overlays, which replace a section of code not currently in use. This method can be used to operate programs too large to load in memory all at once.

Assembly language programs can become quite difficult to understand unless a few precautions are taken, which are as follows :

1. Use a structured style as much as possible.
2. Include only one entrance and exit point in code blocks.
3. Use subroutines.
4. Give meaningful names to the variables.
5. Thoroughly comment the programs while writing them.

Whenever possible, use interrupts - rather than direct hardware programming - to make the routines more readable and portable. Remember also that, interrupts often return results in the registers and flags.

2.1 NUMBER-SYSTEM

Number Systems can generally be classified into positional (binary, octal, decimal, hexadecimal, etc.) and non-positional (Roman) number systems. Only positional number systems are suitable for arithmetic operations. All positional number systems have a base and a weight accorded to each position by some power of this base. For example, in decimal number system (base 10) the weight of each position is some power of 10.

Computers use three number systems more often. Namely, binary, decimal and hexadecimal and it uses octal occasionally.

2.1.1 Binary Number System :

The binary number system uses only two symbols 0 and 1. The base of this number system is 2. Each position of a binary number stands for a power of 2.

2.1.2 Binary - Decimal Conversion :

We can convert a binary number into its decimal equivalent by multiplying the co-efficients of each position of the binary number by the weight of the position.

Example : (110101.01101) = ?

$$(110101.01101) = 1 \times 2^5 + 1 \times 2^4 + 0 \times 2^3 + 0 \times 2^2 + 0 \times 2^1 + 1 \times 2^0 + 0 \times 2^{-1} + 1 \times 2^{-2} + 1 \times 2^{-3} + 0 \times 2^{-4} + 1 \times 2^{-5}$$

$$= 32+16+4+1+0.25+0.125+0.03125$$

$$= (53.40625)_{10}.$$

2.1.3 Decimal - Binary Conversion :

For conversion of decimal integer to a binary integer, divide the decimal integer by 2 repeatedly and note the remainders. And for decimal fraction multiply it by 2 repeatedly and note the carries to the left of the decimal point.

Example : Convert$(121.34375)_{10}$ to binary.

First we convert the integer part :

121/2 =	60 +	remainder of 1
60/2 =	30 +	remainder of 0
30/2 =	15 +	remainder of 0
15/2 =	7 +	remainder of 1
7/2 =	3 +	remainder of 1
3/2 =	1 +	remainder of 1
1/2 =	0 +	remainder of 1

$$(121)_{10} = (1111001)_2$$

Now for the fractional part :

0.34375 × 2 =	0.68750
0.6875 × 2 =	1.3750
0.375 × 2 =	0.750
0.75 × 2 =	1.50
0.5 × 2 =	1.0

$$(0.34375)_{10} = (.01011)_2$$

Thus, $(121.34375)_{10} = (1111001.01011)_2$

2.1.4 Binary Addition :

The rules for binary addition are :

0 + 0 = 0
0 + 1 = 1
1 + 0 = 1
1 + 1 = 10 where 1 is carry bit.

Example : Addition of 110101 $(53)_{10}$

+101111 $(47)_{10}$

1100100 $(100)_{10}$

2.1.5 Binary Subtraction :

The rules for binary subtraction are :

0 - 0 = 0
1 - 0 = 1
1 - 1 = 0
10 - 1 = 1

Example : Subtraction of (101011) 43_2
-(110100) -52_2

-9 As,

```
 101011     2's Complement    010101
-110100                      +110100
-------                      --------
                             1)001001   = 1001.
```

carry indicates (-) ve sign.

2.1.6 Multiplication :

The rules for binary multiplication are :

0 × 0 = 0
0 × 1 = 0
1 × 0 = 0
1 × 1 = 1

Example : Multiplying 1101 by 1001

```
      1101          (13)10
    × 1001        × (9)10
    ------        --------
      1101         (117)10
     0000
    0000
   1101
-----------
 (1110101)2       = (117)10
```

2.1.7 Binary Division :

The rules for binary division are :

0 / 1 = 0
1 / 1 = 1
1 / 0 = meaningless.

Example : Divide 1001111 by 1011

```
1011)  10001111  (1101 In decimal 143/11 = (13)
        1011
       -----
         1101
         1011
       ------
        001011
          1011
        ------
            x x
```

2.1.8 Octal Number Systems :

In this system each position of an octal number stands for a power of 8. The octal number system uses 0,1,2,3,4,5,6 and 7.

Octal numbers are used in machine language programming for many minicomputers because they are shorter and easier to use than their binary equivalents.

2.1.9 Decimal - Octal Conversion :

The simplest way to convert decimal into octal is to divide decimal by 8 and note the remainders as in binary.

Example : $(139.43)_{10}$

```
8 | 139
  |  17    3        0.43 * 8 = 3.44      ∴ (139.43)10 =
  ------            0.44 * 8 = 3.52
      2    1        0.52 * 8 = 4.16        (213.334)8
                    0.16 * 8 = 1.28
                    0.28 * 8 = 2.24
```

2.1.10 Octal - Decimal Conversion :

We can convert an octal number into decimal by multiplying the coefficients of each position of an octal number by the weight of the position.

Example : Conversion of $(423.15)_8$

$$\begin{aligned}(423.15)_8 &= 4 \times 8^2 + 2 \times 8^1 + 3 \times 8^0 + 1 \times 8^{-1} + 5 \times 8^{-2} \\ &= 256 + 16 + 3 + 0.125 + 0.015625 \\ &= (275.203125)_{10}\end{aligned}$$

2.1.11 Binary - Octal Conversion :

Conversion between binary and octal numbers is simple. To convert a binary number to octal we separate the number at the binary point into its integer and fractional parts. Then we group the binary number into groups of 3 to the left and right of the binary point. We may have to add 0's at the far left and right ends.

Example : Conversion $(11101.10101)_2$

```
011101. 101010
  3 5    5 2
```

$\therefore (11101.10101)_2 = (35.52)_8$

2.1.12 Octal - Binary Conversion :

Here we substitute equivalent binary groups of three for each octal digit.

Example : Conversion of $(273.16)_8$

```
      273. 16
--------------------
 010111011.001110
```

$\therefore (273.16)_8 = (1011011.00111)_2$

2.1.13 Hexadecimal number system :

The hexadecimal number system is another positional number system. Each position has a weight that is a power of 16. Hexadecimal number system uses 0,1,2,3,4,5,6,7,8,9, A,B,C,D,E,F.

2.1.14 Decimal - Hexadecimal Conversion :

To convert a decimal into hexadecimal number system the integer parts is divided by 16 and fraction part is multiplied by 16, repeatedly as in other cases.

Example : Conversion of $(123)_{10}$

123 / 16 = 7 + remainder of 11 (B)

7 / 16 = 0 + remainder of 7

$(123)_{10} = (7B)_{16}$

2.1.15 Hexadecimal - Decimal conversion :

We can convert a hexadeciamal number into decimal by multiplying the coefficient of each position of a hexadecimal number by the weight of the position.

Exampie : Conversion of $(47A.3D)_{16}$

$$
\begin{aligned}
47A.3D) &= 4 \times 16^1 + 7 \times 16^0 + A \times 16^{-1} + 3 \times 16^{-2} + D \times 16 \\
&= 4 \times 256 + 7 \times 16 + 10 \times 1 + 3 \times 0.0625 + 13 \times 0.0039 \\
&= 1024 + 112 + 10 + 0.1875 + 0.0507 \\
&= (1146.2382)_{10}
\end{aligned}
$$

2.1.16 Binary - Hexadecimal Conversion :

We can easily convert binary numbers to hexadecimal. We simply group the binary number into groups of four, starting at the binary point.

Example : Conversion of $(1011110.1101011)_2$

01011110. 11010110

5 E . D 6

$\therefore (101110.1101011)_2 = (5E.D6)_{16}$

2.1.17 Hexadecimal - Binary Conversion :

Conversion of a hexadecimal number to binary is equally easy. We substitute equivalent binary groups of four for each hexadecimal digit.

Example : Conversion of $(23D.7E)_{16}$

$(23D.7E)_{16}$

001000111101 . 01111110

$\therefore (23D.7E)_{16} = (1000111101.0111111)_2$

2.2 MACHINE LANGUAGE

A computer uses only binary digits for its operations and understands information composed of only zeros and ones. Hence, the instructions are coded and stored in the memory in the form of zeros and ones.A program written in the form of zeros and ones is called a machine language program. In the machine language there is a specific binary code for each instruction and each machine has its own set of instructions based on the design of its CPU or of its microprocessor.

The machine language is preferred for the following situations :

1) For small and simple program.
2) Simple control applications where less computation is required.
3) Applications where prototype is the final product.

The demerits of the machine language programs are :

1) It is very difficult to understand or debug a program.
2) Since each bit has to be entered individually the entry of a program is very slow.
3) Programs are long.
4) Program writing is difficult and tiresome.
5) Chances of careless errors in writing the program are more.

2.2.1 Machine Language Implementation :

To have a better idea of how the parts of a computer function together, we now describe the actions a simple computer might go through to carry out (execute) a simple program. Now let us consider a simple program which does the following.

1. Input a value from a keyboard connected to the port at address 07H.
2. Add 9 to the value read in. 3. Output the result to a display connected to the port at address 04H.

For this example assume that the CPU fetches instructions and data from memory one byte at a time. Also assume that the binary codes for the instructions are in sequential memory locations starting at address 00100H. Figure given below shows the binary codes that would be required.

Memory Address	Contents (Binary)	Contents (Hex)	Operation.
00100H	10100010	A2	INPUT FROM
00101H	00000111	07	PORT 07H
00102H	00000101	05	ADD
00103H	00001001	09	09H
00104H	10100101	A5	OUTPUT TO
00105H	00000100	04	PORT 04H

in successive memory locations to execute this program on an 8086 or 8088-based micro computer. The first action a computer will do is to fetch the first instruction byte from memory. To do this the CPU sends out the address of the first instruction byte, in this case 00100H, to memory. The CPU then sends out a memory read signal on the control bus. This causes the memory to output the first instruction byte (A2H) on the data bus. The CPU reads in the byte from the data bus and decodes it. By decode we mean that the CPU determines from the binary code, brought in, what actions it is supposed to take. In this case the CPU determines that code read in represents an input instruction. Also from decoding this instruction byte, the CPU determines that it needs more information before it can carry out the instruction. The CPU must fetch from memory the input port address. To do this the CPU sends out the next sequential address (00101H) to memory. The CPU also sends out another memory read signal on the control bus. This enables the memory to put the addressed byte on the data bus. When the CPU reads in this second byte, 07H in this case, it has all the the information it needs to execute the instruction. To execute the input instruction the CPU sends out the port address (07H) on the address bus and sends out an I/O read signal on the control bus. The addressed port device then puts a byte of data on the data bus. The CPU reads in the byte of data and stores it in an internal register called the accumulator. This completes the first instruction.

Having completed the first instruction the CPU must now fetch its next instruction from memory. To do this it sends out the next sequential address (00102H) on the address bus. The CPU then sends out a memory read signal on the control bus. This allows the memory to put the addressed byte (05H) on the data bus. The CPU reads in the instruction byte from the data bus and decodes it. From the instruction byte the CPU determines that it is supposed to add some number to the number stored in the accumulator. The CPU also determines from this instruction byte that it must go to memory again to get the number that it is supposed to add. To get the required byte the CPU will send out the next sequential address (00103H) on the address bus and a memory read signal on the control bus (line 4B). The memory will then put the contents of the addressed byte (in this case the number 09H) on the data bus. The CPU will read in the byte on the data bus and add it to the contents of the accumulator as instructed. Assume the result of the addition is left in the accumulator. This completes the second instruction.

The CPU must now fetch its next instruction. To do this it sends out the next sequential address (00104H) on the address bus, sends out a memory read signal on the control bus, and reads in the addressed byte (A5H) from the data bus. From this byte CPU determines that it is now supposed to do an output operation to a port. The CPU also determines that it must go to memory again to get the address of the port that it is supposed to output to. To do this it sends out the next sequential address (00105H) on the address bus, sends out a memory read signal on the control bus line (6B) and reads in the byte (04H) put on the data bus by the memory. The CPU now has all the information that it needs to execute the instruction. To output a data byte to a port, the CPU first sends out the address of the desired port on the address bus. Next it puts the data byte from the accumulator on to the data bus (line 6E). The CPU then sends out an I/O write signal on the control bus (line 6F). This signal enables the addressed output port device so the data from the data bus lines can pass through it. When the CPU removes the I/O write signal to proceed with the next instruction, the data output will remain latched on the output pins of the port device. Therefore, the computer does not have to keep outputting a value in order for it to remain there.

All of the steps described above may seem like a great deal of work just to input a value from a keyboard, add 9 to it and output the result to a display. Even a simple computer, however, can run through all these steps in a few microseconds.

2.3 THE 8088 MICROPROCESSOR

Most IBM PCs use the intel 8088 CPU as their central processor. The 8088 has 8-bit data bus interface.

It is almost identical to 8086 with respect to arithmetic and logic unit, registers, instruction sets and 20 bit address bus. The only difference being in the data bus, which is 16- bit in case of 8086 processor. To read a 16- bit word from memory, the 8088 will have to do two read operations. The 8088 CPU uses memory segmentation approach to address its 1 MB memory address space. It treats the memory as being divided into segments of 64 KB each. Specific segment registers hold the upper 16 bit starting address of the four memory segments that the 8086 is working with at a particular time. Programs obtain access to code and data in the segments by changing the segment register contents to point to the desired segments.

An 8088 processor can work as either a small uniprocessor system (MN mode) or as a multiprocessor system ($\overline{MX}$ mode). Depending on the selection of MN / $\overline{MX}$ mode pin in the 8088 chip, some of the 8088 pins have dual functions.

2.3.1 INTERNAL ARCHITECTURE OF 8088 - CPU

The 8088 microprocessor is divided internally into two seperate units - the bus interface unit or BIU and the execution unit EU. These two units function independently. the BIU fetches instruction, reads operands and writes results. The EU executes instructions that have already been fetched by the BIU, so that the instruction fetch overlaps the execution. This speeds up processing.

The bus interface unit contains instruction queue, segment registers and instruction pointer. The BIU'S instruction queue is a first - in - first - out group of registers in which upto 6 bytes of instruction codes are prefetched from memory, ahead of time. This is done in order to speed up program execution by overlapping instruction fetch with execution. This mechanism is known as pipelining.

8088 has four 16-bit, segment registers which are intended to store the addresses of various segments. The complete address of a memory location is obtained by identifying the segment with a 16 bit value and specifying a 16 - bit offset address inside the segment. These, segment registers are the code segment (CS), the stack segment (SS), the extra segment (ES) and data segment (DS) register. The code segment register contains the segment address of the code segment containing the program currently being executed. The data segment register contains the segment address of the memory area which is typically addressed for data. Similarly, the stack segment register has the segment address of the memory area which is being currently used as the stack area by the CPU. The extra segment register is an additional segment register provided for convenience. The segments can be contiguous,partially overlapped, fully overlapped, or disjointed

The instruction pointer provides the offset address into the code segment of the program which is currently being executed. This register is incremented to point to the next instruction to be executed in normal sequential program flow. For branch instruction, the contents of this pointer are directly changed as a result of the current instruction.

The **execution unit** decodes and executes instructions. A decoder in the execution unit control system translates instruction. The EU has 16-bit ALU for performing arithmetic and logic operations. A 16-bit flag register in the EU contains 9 active flags. The six conditional flags are - the carry flag (CF), the parity flag (PF), the auxiliary carry flag (AF), the zero flag (ZF), the sign flag (SF) and the overflow flag (OF). The rest three are trap flag (TF), interrupt flag (IF) and the direction flag. The trap flag is used for single stepping through a program. The interrupt flag is used to allow/prohibit the instruction of a program. The direction flag causes string instructions to autodecrement or autoincrement.

The EU has eight, 8 bit general purpose registers. These are - AH, AL, BH, BL, CH, CL, DH, and DL. These registers can be used individually to store 8-bit data or in pairs to store 16-bit data temporarily. The data is accessed much faster if it is in one of these registers than it can be accessed in external memory.

The two pointer registers, SP (stack pointer) and BP (Base Pointer), are used to access data in the stack segment. The SP is used as an offset from the current SS during execution of instructions that involve the stack segment in external memory. The BP contains an offset address in the current SS. The two index registers, source index (SI) and destination index (DI) are used in indexed addressing

2.3.2 THE 8088 INSTRUCTION SET.

The 8088 has approximately 120 different instructions with about 300 op-codes. The 8088 instruction set contains three types of instructions -no operand,one operand and two operand instructions. The 8088 always uses register to register, register to memory or memory to register operations. Except for string instructions that involve array operations, 8088 instructions do not permit memory to memory operations.

The different ways in which a processor can access data are known as its addressing modes. The various addressing modes can be classified in following groups :

1. Register and immediate modes : In register mode, source operands, destination operands or both may be contained in registers.In immediate mode, 8 or 16 bit data can be specified as a part of the instruction.

2. Memory addressing modes : The various memory addressing modes are described below :

(a) Memory direct addressing - In this mode, the effective address is taken directly from the displacement field of the instruction. No registers are involved.

(b) Register indirect addressing - The effective addressing of a memory operand may be taken directly from one of the base or index registers.

(c) Based addressing - In this mode, the effective address is the sum of a displacement value and the contents of register BX or BP.

(d) Indexed addressing - In this mode, the effective address is the sum of a displacement value and the contents of register SI or DI.

(e) Based indexed addressing - In this mode, the effective address is computed from the sum of a base register (BX or BP), an index register (SI or DI), and a displacement.

(f) String addressing - In this mode, SI is assumed to point to the first byte or word of the source string, and DI is assumed to point to first byte or word of the destination, when a string instruction is executed.

2.3.3 Port addressing modes :

There are two types of port addressing modes :

(a) Direct port mode - In this mode, the port number is an 8-bit immediate operand and is able to access 250 models.

(b) Indirect port mode:- In this mode, the port number is taken from DX allowing 64 K- bytes or 32 K-words of ports.

4. Relative addressing mode : Instructions using this mode specify the operand as a signed 8-bit displacement, relative to program counter (PC).

5. Implied addressing mode : Instructions using this mode have no operands. An example is CLS, which clears the carry flag to zero.

The 8088 instruction set contains equivalent instructions found in the 8085 instruction set plus many new instructions, some of the new instructions are for multiplication and division (both signed and unsigned), string operation, bit manipulation instructions and interrupt instructions. The various instructions are described below.

2.4 DATA TRANSFER INSTRUCTIONS

1. MOV INSTRUCTION :

The MOV instructions copies byte or word of data from specified source to specified destination. The source can be a register, a memory location or an immediate number. The destination can only be a register or a memory location. Both of them can't be memory location in an instruction. Both the source and destination must either be of type byte or word. This instruction does not affect any flags.

Example :

MOV BX, CX	:	The contents of register CX is transferred to the register BX.
MOV AH, [416BH]	:	The contents of memory location specified by the offset 416BH in DS is copied to AH.
MOV AX, 3268H	:	The immediate number 3268 H is put into AX.
MOV BL, [CX]	:	The content of memory adress specified by the offset content of CX is transferred to BL.
MOV DS, BX	:	This instruction copies word from BX to data segment register. Only, the contents of a register can be moved into the segment registers.
MOV CS, [BX], DL	:	The content of DL register is copied to the memory location whose effective address is contained in the BX register. CS : indicates that the effective address is added to the CS base in the code segment to produce the physical

address. The CS : is called a segment over-ride prefix. Normally, the offset in BX is added to the data segment base in DS to produce the physical memory address.

2. PUSH INSTRUCTION :

The PUSH instruction copies a word from some source to that location in the stack segment where the stack pointer points after being decremented by two. Hence this instruction copies specified word to the top of the stack. General purpose registers, a segment register or memory could be the source of the word. The stack segment register and the stack pointer need to be initialized before using this instruction. It doesn't affect any flag.

Example :

PUSH CX	: The SP is decremented by two and the contents of CX register are moved onto the stack.
PUSH DS	: It decrements the SP by two and copies the content of DS onto the stack.
PUSH AL	: Illegal because only a word could be transferred to the stack.
PUSH TABLE [DX]	: This instruction decreases SP by two and copies the word from memory at EA = TABLE + [DX] in DS to stack.

3. PC INSTRUCTION :

The POP instruction copies a word from the location pointed at by the stack pointer of the stack to the specified destination. The destination could be a general purpose register, a segment register or a memory location. After this copy operation, the SP is automatically incremented by 2. No flags are affected.

NOTE : POP CS is illegal

Examples :

POP BX :	The stack pointer is incremented by 2 and a word from the top of stack is copied to BX.
POP DS :	A word from the top of the stack is copied to DS.SP is increased by 2.
POP TABLE [BX] :	This instruction copies a word from the top of the stack to memory in DS with EX = TABLE + [BX].

4. XCHG INSTRUCTION (XCHG destination, source) :

This instruction exchanges words or bytes of a register with the contents of another register or the contents of memory location. The source and destination must be both words, or they must be both bytes. The contents of two memory locations can't be exchanged directly. We can't use segment registers in this instruction. It doesn't affect the flags.

Examples :

XCHG BX, CX	: The word in CX is exchanged with the word in BX.
XCHG AL, DX	: The byte content of register AL is exchanged with the byte content of register DH.
XCHG AH, NAME[DX]	: The byte in AH is exchanged with the byte which is at memory location with EA = NAME [DX] in DS.

5. IN INSTRUCTION (IN accumulator, Port) :

The IN instruction copies data from a port in the accumulator. An 8-bit data is transferred in AL and if the data is of 16-bit it gets transferred to AX. It has two possible formats-fixed port and variable port.

In the fixed port type the 8-bit port address is mentioned in the instruction itself.

Examples :

IN AL, C8H : The data content at the port address C8H is input in the AL.

IN AX, F7H : A word from the port F7H is moved into the AX.

NAME EQU 28H

IN AX, NAME : A word is input from port 28H to AX. For the variable-port type IN instruction, first, the DX register is loaded with the port address. DX being a 16-bit register, in this type we can address any of the 0000H to FFFFH (65,536) ports.

Examples :

MOV DX, OFF78H : DX is initialized to point to the port with address OFF78H
IN AL, DX : A byte is input from 8-bit port OFF78H to AL.
IN AX, DX : A word is input from 16 bit port OFF78H to AX.

6. OUT INSTRUCTION : (OUT port, accumulator AL or AX) :

The OUT instruction copies a byte from AL or a word from AX to the specified port. It has two possible forms, fixed port and variable.

In fixed port format the 8-bit port address is specified directly in the instruction.

Examples :

OUT 7FH, AL : A byte from AL is copied to port 7FH.
OUT 36H, AX : A word from AX is moved to port 36H.

In the variable port mode, the address of the port, to which a byte from AL, or a word from AX is to be copied, is moved into the DX register first. Then the actual data transfer proceeds between the two registers.

Examples :

MOV DX, 0777FH : The desired port address is loaded in the DX register.
OUT DX, AL : Contents of AL are copied to port 0777fH.
OUT DX, AX : The word content of AX is transferred to port 0777FH.

NOTE: Both the IN and OUT instruction does not affect any flags.

7. LEA INSTRUCTION :

Load Effective Address (LEA register, source) : This instruction determines the offset of the source (which could be a variable or a memory location) and puts this offset in the indicated 16 bit register. It changes no flags.

Examples :

LEA CX, NAME : The CX register is loaded with the offset of NAME in DS.
LEA BP, SS:STACK TOP : The BP is loaded with the STACK TOP is SS.
LEA BX,[CX][DI] : EA = [CX] + [DI] is moved into the BX register.

8. LDS INSTRUCTION (LDS register, memory address of first word) :

This instruction loads register and DS with words from memory. Firstly, it copies a word from two memory locations into the register specified and the next two memory locations word are then copied into the DS register. It affects no flags.

Example :

LDS CX, [4124H] : The contents of memory at displacement 4124H is DS to BL contents of 4125H to BH. Then the contents at displacement of 4124H and 4127H in DS to DS register.

9. LES INSTRUCTION Load register and ES with words from memory - (LES register, memory address of first word) :

The instruction loads new values into the specified register and into the ES register from four successive memory locations.

Example :

LES BX, [789AH] : Contents of memory at displacements 789AH and 789BH in DS copied to BX. contents of memory at displacements 789CH and 789DH is DS is copied to ES register.

2.5 ARITHMETIC INSTRUCTIONS

ADDITION INSTRUCTIONS

1. ADD INSTRUCTION (ADD destination, source) : The ADD instruction adds specified byte to byte, or specified word to word in the source and destination. The result is placed in the specified destination. The source can be a register, a memory location or an immediate number. The destination can either be a register or a memory location. In the same instruction both can not be memory locations. Both the source and destination must either be of type byte or type word. The flags affected by this instruction are AF, CF, OF, PF, SF, ZF.

Examples :

ADD AH, 53H : The number 53H is added to the contents of AH register.
ADD AX, BX : The contents of register BX are added to register AX.
ADD BX, [SI] : The word from the memory location specified by the offset in SI in data segment is added to BX register.

FLAG RESULTS :

(i) CF = 0 When there is no carry out of bit 7
(ii) PF = 0 When the result has odd parity
(iii) AF = 1 When carry is produced out of bit 3
(iv) ZF = 1 When the result in destination is zero
(v) SF = 1 It copies most significant bit of result, indicates negative result when signed numbers are added.
(vi) OF = 1 This is set to indicate that the result of the addition is too large to bit in the lower 7 bits of the destination used to represent the magnitude of a signed number.

2. ADC INSTRUCTION (ADC destination, source) :

The add with carry instruction ADC, adds the status of the carry flag along with the byte or words specified in the source and destination registers/memory location/immediate number. The destination can not be an immediate number. Also both source and destination can not be memory locations in the same instruction. Both the operands must be of same type. The flags affected are AF, CF, OF, PF, SF, ZF. These flags are affected in the same way as in ADD instruction.

Examples :

ADC AL, DL : The contents of DL and the carry status is added to the contents of register AL.
ADC 54H[SI], AH : The effective address 54H [SI] contains the data to be added to AH.

3. INC INSTRUCTION (Increment destination) :

This instruction adds 1 to the indicated destination. The destination can be a register or memory location. The flags affected are AF, OF, PF, SF and ZF.

Examples :

INC AL : Add 1 to contents of AL register.
INC AH : Add 1 to contents of AH register.
INC ABC : Increment byte or word named ABC in data segment.
INC ABC [AX] : Increment element [AX] in array ABC.

4. AAA INSTRUCTION ASCII (Adjust for Addition) :

The input to a computer is usually a data in ASCII code. In this code the numbers 0-9 are represented by the ASCII codes 30H-39H. With the help of AAA instruction two decimal digits in ASCII code can be added without marking off the "3" in the upper nibble of each. The AAA instruction makes sure that the result is the correct unpacked BCD.

Examples :

ADD AL,DH : AL is adjusted after the addition of two ASCII.
AAA : Coded numbers contained in AL and DH registers.
The AAA instruction only works on AL register.
The flags affected are AF and CF.

5. DAA INSTRUCTION (Decimal adjust accumulator) :

This instruction is used to adjust the result of adding two packed BCD numbers to a legal BCD number DAA only works on AL register. The flags affected are AF, CF, PF, and ZF.

Example :

ADD AL, DL : AL is converted into BCD after the addition of DAA two BCD numbers contained in AL and DL registers

SUBTRACTION INSTRUCTIONS

1. SUB INSTRUCTION (SUB destination, source) :

The SUB instructions subtract byte from byte, or word from word which are specified in source and destination respectively. The source may be an immediate number, a register, or a memory location. The destination may be a register or a memory location. The source and destination cannot both be memory location in the same instruction. Both must be of type byte or type word. The result of subtraction is stored in the indicated destination. The flags affected are AF, CF, OF, PF, SF, and ZF.

CF = 1 if a borrow is required to perform the subtraction.

OF = 1 if the magnitude of the expected result in too large to be bit in 7 bits used for the magnitude in an 8 bit signed number.

The rest of the flags are set in the same manner as in ADD instruction.

Examples :

SUB AX,BX : The contents of BX are subtracted from AX and the result is stored in the AX register.
SUB CX,2467H : The immediate number 2467H is subtracted from CX.
SUB BX,[3576H] : The data specified by the memory location 3576H is subtracted from register BX.

2. SBB INSTRUCTION(SBB destination,source) :

The SBB instructions subtract the source with borrow, from the destination and the result is stored in destination. In all other respects this instruction is similar to SUB instruction.

Examples :

SBB AH,CH : The contents of register CH are subtracted, along with the content of CF, from contents of AH.
SBB AX,48H[BX] : The word from effective address 48H[BX] and status of CF are subtracted from AX.
SBB 53H[CX],BX : The contents of BX and the status of CF are subtracted from the word in memory location specified by effective address 53H [CX].

3. DEC INSTRUCTION (DEC destination) :

The DEC instruction decrements specified byte or word by 1. The destination from which 1 is subtracted, can be a register or a memory location. The flags affected are AF, OF, PF, SF, and ZF.

Examples :

DEC BL : One is subtracted from the contents of BL register.
DEC BP : From the contents of BP register one is subtracted.
DEC XYZ [BX] : A word or byte is decremented (at offset [BX] in array XYZ) by 1
DEC ABC : Subtract 1 from byte or word named ABC.

4. NEG INSTRUCTION(NEG destination) :

The NEG instruction negates (inverts)each bit of a specified byte or word in the destination and add 1 to form 2's complement of the byte or word. The destination can be a register or a memory location. This instruction forms the 2's complement by subtracting the original word or byte in the indicated destination from zero. The flags affected are AF, CF, SF, PF, ZF and OF. The OF will be set to indicate that the operation could not be done.

Examples :

NEG AH : Replace the number in AH with its 2's complement.
NEG CX : The word in CX is replaced with its 2's complement.

5. CMP (INSTRUCTION CMP destination, source) :

The CMP instruction compares two specified bytes or two specified words in source and destination. The source can be an immediate number, a register, or a memory location. The destination can also be an immediate number, a register, or a memory location. Both the source and the destination can not be memory locations in one instruction. The comparison is done by subtracting the source's content from destination's content. The source and destination are not changed. The flags are set to indicate the result of comparison. The flags affected are AF, OF, SF, ZF, PF and CF.

CF = 1 when source > destination.

ZF = 1 when source = destination.

SF = 1 when source > destination.

SF not very reliable, CF = 0, ZF = 0 when source > destination.

Examples :

CMP AH,01H : Compare the immediate number 01H with byte in AH.
CMP BL,CL : Compare the byte in CL with the byte in BL.
CMP CX,[2457H] : Compare the word at the memory location specified by the offset 2457H in DS with the contents of CX. CMP XYZ [BX], 49H : Compare the immediate number 49H with byte at offset [BX] in array XYZ.

6. AAS INSTRUCTION(ASCII Adjust for subtraction) :

The input to a computer is generally a data in ASCII code. In this code the numbers 0-9 are represented by the ASCII codes 30H 39H. Without marking off the "3" in the upper nibble of each number, the numbers can be subtracted using AAS instruction which makes the result the correct unpacked BCD. The AAS only works on AL register. It leaves the correct unpacked BCD result in AL. The AAS instruction updates only two flags - AF and CF. CF is set when the result is a negative number.

Example :

SUB AL,BL : The two ASCII numbers in AL and DL take part in the subtraction operation and their result is adjusted to the correct unpacked BCD.
AAS

7. DAS INSTRUCTION (Decimal Adjust after subtraction) :

This instruction makes the result of the subtraction of two packed BCD numbers correct packed BCD. DAS only works on the AL register. The flags affected are AF, CF, SF, PF, and ZF.

Examples :

SUB AL,BH : The BCD contents of BH are subtracted from the BCD contents of AL register and the result is adjusted to the correct packed BCD in AL.
DAS :

III MULTIPLICATION INSTRUCTIONS

1.MULINSTRUCTION (MUL source) :

This instruction multiplies an unsigned byte from source with the unsigned byte in the AL register, or an unsigned word from some source with an unsigned word in the AX register. The source can be a register or a memory location. When data is of byte type, the product is put in AX. When the data is of type word, the most significant word of the result is put in DX and the least significant word of the result is put in AX. The flags affected are CF and OF. Both are 0 when the most significant byte/word of the product (depending on data type) is 0.

Examples :

MUL BL : The contents of BL are multiplied with the contents of AL and the result is stored in AX.
MUL CX : The contents of CX and AX are multiplied and the upper bits are stored in DX and the lower bits are stored in AX after multiplication

2. IMUL INSTRUCTION (IMUL source) :

This instruction is for multiplication of signed bytes/words. When the data type is byte then the multiplication of the data in the source is done with the contents of AL and the result is stored in AX. When the data is of type word the contents of the source are multiplied with the contents of AX and the result is stored in DX (most significant word) and in AX (least significant word). The flags are affected in the same way as in MUL instruction.

Examples :

IMUL CL : The signed byte in CL is multiplied with the signed byte in AL and the result is in AX.
IMUL AX : The signed word in AX is multiplied with itself and the result is in DX and AX.

3. AAM INSTRUCTION(BCD Adjust after Multiply) :

This instruction is used to adjust the product of two unpacked BCD digits in AX after the two digits have been multiplied. It only works on an operand in AL. The flags affected are PF, SF & ZF.

Example :

MUL BL : After the multiplication of the BCD contents in ALand BL the result stored in AL is adjusted to the correct unpacked BCD digits.
AAM :

IV DIVISION INSTRUCTIONS

1. DIV INSTRUCTION (DIV source) :

This instruction is used to divide an unsigned word by a byte or to divide double word by a word. When dividing a word by a byte, the word must be in the AX register. After the division AL will contain 8-bit result (quotient) and AH will contain an 8-bit remainder. When a double word is divided by a word, the most significant word of the double word must be in DX and the least significant word of the double word must be in AX. After the division AX will contain a 16-bit result (quotient), and DX will contain a 16-bit remainder. The dividend is always in AX or DX and AX. If the quotient is not an integer, it is truncated.

Examples :

DIV CL : The word in AX is divided by the byte in BL. The quotient is in AL and the remainder is in AH

DIV BX : The double word in DX and AX is divided by the word in BX. The quotient is in AX and the remainder is in DX.

2. IDIV INSTRUCTION (IDIV source) :

This instruction is for division performed on signed data. When a signed word is divided by a signed byte, the word must be in the AX register. The quotient is stored in AL and the remainder is stored in AH. When a signed double word is divided by a signed word, the most significant word of the dividend must be in the DX register and the least significant word of the dividend is in AX register. The signed 16-bit remainder is stored in DX and the signed 16-bit quotient is stored in AX. If the divisor does not divide the dividend the quotient will be truncated.

Examples :

IDIV CL : The signed word in AX is divided by the signed byte in BL. The quotient is stored in AL and the remainder in AH.

IDIV BP : The signed double word in DX and AX is divided by signed word in BP. The quotient is stored in AX and the remainder is in BX register.

3. AAD INSTRUCTION (BCD-to-Binary convert before Division) :

The AAD instruction works with unpacked BCD. It converts two unpacked BCD digits in AH and AL to the equivalent binary number in AL. This adjustment is done before dividing the two unpacked BCD digits in AX by an unpacked BCD byte. After the division AL contains the unpacked BCD quotient and AH contains the unpacked BCD remainder. The flags affected are PF, SF and ZF.

Examples :

ADD : The contents of AX are adjusted to binary.

DIV CL : Then AX is divided by unpacked BCD in CL. The remainder is stored in AH and the result is stored in AL. The quotient and remainder are unpacked BCD digits.

2.6 BIT MANIPULATION INSTRUCTIONS

LOGICAL INSTRUCTIONS

1. NOT INSTRUCTION (NOT destination) :

This instruction is for inverting the byte or word at the specified destination. The NOT instruction inverts each bit at the destination which can be a register or a memory location. No flags are affected by this instruction.

Examples :

NOT AX : The contents of 2X register are inverted bitwise.

NOT BL : The content of BL is replace by its 1's complement.

2. AND INSTRUCTION (AND destination, source) :

This instruction performs the bitwise AND operation with the two operands specified by the source and destination. The result is stored in the destination. The source operand can be an immediate number, the contents of a register, or the contents of a memory location. The destination can only be a register or a memory location. Both the source and destination can not be memory locations in the same instruction. The flags affected are CF, OF, PF SF and ZF, CF and OF are both 0 after AND.

Examples :

AND BL,CL : The byte in CL is ANDed with the byte in BL and the result is stored in BL
AND AX, FFFFH : The word in AX is ANDed with FFFFH and the result is stored in AX.
AND BX, [SI] : The word at offset [SI] in data segment is ANDed with the word in BX and the result is stored in BX register.

3. OR INSTRUCTION (OR destination, source) :

This instruction logically OR the corresponding bits of two operands specified in the source and destination. The result is stored in the destination. The source operand can be an immediate number, the contents of a register, or the contents of a memory location. The destination can only be a register or a memory location. The source and the destination can not be memory locations in the same instruction. The flags affected are PF, SF and ZF. The CF and Of are both zero after OR.

Examples :

OR AL, BL : The contents of BL are ORed with that of AL. The result is in AL.
OR SI, BP : The contents of BP are ORed with SI with the result stored in SI.
OR AH, 64H : The contents of AH are ORed with immediate 64H. The result of the OR operation is stored in AH.

4. XOR INSTRUCTION (XOR destination, source) :

This instruction exclusive ORs the corresponding bits of the two operands specified by source and destination. The result replaces the contents of the specified destination. The source can be an immediate number, the contents of a register, or the contents of a memory location. The destination can only be a register or a memory location. Both the source and destination cannot be memory locations in the same instruction. The flags PF, SF and ZF are affected by the OR instruction. CF and OF are set to 0 after XOR.

Examples :

XOR AL, BH : The content of BH is exclusive ORed with the content of AL. The result is put in AL.
XOR BP, SI : The word in SI is exclusive ORed with the word in BP. The result is stored in BP.

ROTATE INSTRUCTIONS

1. ROL/ROR INSTRUCTION (ROL/ROR destination, count) :

The ROL/ROR instructions rotate all bits of operand to the left (ROL) or to the right (ROR) some number of bit positions. The ROL (Rotate to left) instruction rotate bits of byte or word specified by the destination to left, MSB to LSB and to CF. The ROR (Rotate to Right) instruction rotates bits of byte or word specified by the destination to right, LSB to MSB and to CF.

ROL Operation ROR Operation

The destination operand can be in a register or in a memory location. To rotate more than one bit position, load the desired number in the CL register and put "CL" in the CL register and put "CL" in the count position of the instruction ROL/ROR. The flags affected are CF and OF.

Examples :

RCL BX, 1 : The content of BX is rotate one position to the left, MSB to LSB and CF.
MOV CL, 04H : The number of bits to be rotated are loaded in CL.
RCL AL, CL : The content of AL is rotated to left from bit positions.
RCR AX, 1 : All the bits in AX are rotated right one bit position.
MOV CL, 04H : The number of bit position to be rotated are loaded in CL.
RCR BL, CL : The bits in BL are rotated to right form bit positions.

2. RCL/RCR INSTRUCTION (RCL/RCR destination count) :

The RCL/RCR instructions rotate the operand specified by destination around to left (RCL) or right (RCR) through CF some number of bit positions. The operation performed by the RCL/RCR instructions is illustrated below :

CF ←——— MSB ←——— LSB CF ———→ MSB ———→ LSB

RCL Operation RCR Operation

The destination operand can be in a register or in a memory location. To rotate more than one bit position, load the desired number in the CL register and put "CL" in the count position of the instruction. The flags affected are CF and OF.

Examples :

RCL BX,1 : The bits in BX are rotated left 1 bit through carry flag.
MOV CL, 03H : The number of bit positions to be rotated are RCL AX, CL loaded in CL. The bits in AX are rotated left 3 bits through CF.
RCR AX, 1 : The content of AX is rotated 1 bit right through CF.
MOV CL, 03H : The number of bit positions to be rotated are loaded in CL.
RCR DX, CL : The bits in DX are rotated right 3 bits through the carry flag.

III SHIFT INSTRUCTIONS

1. SHL/SAL INSTRUCTION (SHL/SAL distination,count) :

The SHL/SAL instruction shift the operand bits specified in the destination to left and put zero in LSB (S). The operation performed by this instruction is illustrated below.

CF ←——— MSB ←——— LSB ←——— 0

The destination can be in a register or in a memory location. For shifts of more than 1 bit position the desired number of shifts is loaded into the CL register and CL is put in the count position of the instruction

Examples :

SHL BX, 1 : Shift the bits in BX 1 bit position left and put 0 in LSB
MOV CL, 05H : The desired number of shifts is loaded in CL. The SAL BP, CL bits in BP are shifted left five bit positions. 0's are put in the five LSBs.

2. SHR INSTRUCTION (SHR destination,count) :-

The SHR instruction shifts the operand bits specified in the destination to right and puts zero in MSB (s). The operation performed by this instruction is illustrated below.

0 ———→ MSB ———→ MSB ———→ M CF

The destinaton can be in a register or in a memory location. For shifts of more than one bit position the desired number of shifts is loaded into the CL register and CL is put in the count position of the SHR instruction. The flags affected are CF, OF, SF, ZF, and PF.

Examples :

SHR BX, 1 : Shift the contents of BX by one bit position to right and 0 is put in MSB.
MOV CL, OSH : The desired number of shifts is loaded into CL. SHR, BP, CL. The bits in BP are shifted right to five bit positions and 0s are put in five MSBs.

3. SAR INSTRUCTION (SAR destination, count) :-

This instruction shifts operand bits specified by destination to right, new MSB = old MSB as illustrated below :

MSB ———→ MSB ———→ LSB ———→ CF

The destination can be in a register or in a memory location. CL register is used in count position for more than one shifts. The flags affected are CF, OF, SF, ZF, and PF.

Examples :

SAR SI, 1 : The bits in SI are shifted one position to right and new MSB = old MSB

MOV CL, 02H : The bits in AX are shifted right SAR AX, CL [CL] position and two MSBs are now copies of original MSB

2.7 PROGRAM EXECUTION TRANSFER INSTRUCTION

These instruction are used to tell the 8088 to start fetching instructions from some new address, rather than continuing in sequence.

UNCONDITIONAL TRANSFER INSTRUCTIONS :

1. CALL INSTRUCTION (Call a procedure) :-

The CALL instruction is used to transfer execution to a subprogram or procedure. There are two types of CALL, near and far. A near CALL is a call to a procedure which is in the same code segment as the CALL instruction. A CALL is a call to a procedure which is in a different segment from that which contains the CALL instruction.

Examples :

Direct within- segment (near or interasegment)

CALL ABC : ABC is the name of the procedure. The assembler determines displacement of ABC from the instruction after the CALL and codes this displacement in as part of the instruction.

Indirect within- segment near or intrasegment

CALL BX : BX contains the offset of the first instruction of the procedure. Replaces contents of IP with contents of register BX.

2. RET INSTRUCTION :

Return execution from procedure to calling program.

The RET instruction will return execution from a procedure to the next instruction after the CALL instruction in the calling program. In the case of a near procedure, return is done by replacing the instruction pointer with a word from the top of the stack. If the procedure is a far procedure, then the instruction pointer will be replaced.

A RET instruction can be followed by a number, for example RET 6. In this case the stack pointer will be incremented by an additional six addresses after the IP or the IP and CS are popped off the stack.

CONDITIONAL TRANSFER INSTRUCTIONS

These instructions are often used after a compare instruction. Following are the various Jump instructions :

1. JA/JNBE INSTRUCTION :

Jump of above/Jump if not be low or equal.

These two mnemonics represent the same instruction. The terms "above" and "below" are used when refusing to the magnitude of unsigned numbers.

2. JAE/JNB/JNC INSTRUCTIONS :

Jump if above or equal/ jump is not below/jump if no carry.

If after a compare or some other instruction which affects flags, the carry flag is 0, this instruction will cause execution to jump to a label given in the istruction. If CF is 1, the instruction will have no effect on the program execution.

3. JB/JC/JNAE INSTRUCTIONS

Jump if below/jump if carry/jump if not above nor equal.

If, after a compare or some other instruction which affects flags, the carry flag is a 1, this instruction will cause execution to jump to a label given in the instruction. If CF is 0, the instruction will have no effect on program execution.

4. JBE/JNA INSTRUCTIONS

Jump if below or equal/jump if not above. If after a compare or some other instruction which affects flags, either the zero flag or carry flag is 1 this instruction will cause execution to jump to a label given in the instruction. If CF and ZF are both 0, the instruction will have no effect on program execution.

5. JCXZ INSTRUCTION

Jump if the CX register is zero. This instruction will cause a jump to a label given in the instruction if the CX register contains all 0's. If CX does not contain all 0's, execution will simply proceed to the next instruction.

6. JE/JZ INSTRUCTIONS

Jump if equal/jump if zero. If the zero flag is set,then this instruction will cause execution to jump to a label given in the instruction. If the zero flag is not 1, then execution will simply go on to the next instruction after JE or JZ. The destination label for the JE/JZ instruction must be in the range of – 128 to + 128 bytes from the address of the instruction after the JE/JZ instruction.

7. JG/JNLE INSTRUCTION

Jump if greater/jump if not less than nor equal.

The terms "greater" and "less" are used to refer to the relationship of two signed numbers. Greater means more positive. This instruction is usually used after a compare instruction. If the zero flag is 0 and the carry flag is the same as the overflow flag, this instruction will cause a jump to a label given in the instruction.

8. JGE/JNL INSTRUCTION

Jump if greater than or equal/jump if not less than.

This instruction is usually used after a compare instruction. The instruction will cause a jump to a label given in the instruction if the sign flag is equal to the overflow flag.

9. JL/JNGE INSTRUCTION

Jump if less than/jump if not greater than nor equal.

The instruction will cause a jump to a label given in the instruction if the sign flag is not equal to the overflow flag.

10. JLE/JNG INSTRUCTION

Jump if less than or equal/ jump if not greater. The instruction will cause a jump to a label given in the instruction if the zero flag is set, or if the sign flag is not equal to the overflow flag.

11. JMP INSTRUCTION

Unconditional jump to specified destination.

This instruction will always cause the 8088 to fetch its next instruction from the location specified in the instruction rather than from the next location after the JMP instruction.

12. JNC/JNB/JAE INSTRUCTION

Jump if not carry/jump if not below/jump if above or equal.

13. JNE/JNZ INSTRUCTION

Jump if not equal/jump if not zero.

14. JNO INSTRUCTION

Jump if no overflow. This instruction will cause the 8088 to jump to a destination given in the instruction if the overflow flag is not set.

15. JNP/JPO INSTRUCTION

Jump if no parity/ jump if parity odd. This instruction will cause execution to jump to a specified destination address if the parity flag is zero.

16. JNS INSTRUCTION

Jump if not signed (jump if positive). This instruction will cause execution to jump to specified destination if the sign flag is 0. If the sign flag is set, indicating a negative signed result, execution will simply go to the next instruction after JNS.

17. JO INSTRUCTION

Jump if overflow. This instruction will cause the 8088 to jump to a destination given in the instruction if the overflow flag is set. The overflow lag will be set if the result of some signed arithmetic operation is too large a bit in the destination register or memory location.

18. JP/JPE INSTRUCTION

Jump if parity/jump if even parity. If the number of 1's left in a data word after an execution which affects the parity flag is even then the parity flag is set. This instruction will cause execution to jump to a specified destination address if the parity flag is set.

19. JS INSTRUCTION :

Jump if signed(jump if negative).This instruction will cause execution to jump to a specified destination if the sign flag is set. If the sign flag is 0, indicating a positive signed result, execution will simply go on to the next instruction

ITERATION CONTROL SIGNAL :

These instructions can be used to execute a series of instructions some number of times.

1. LOOP INSTRUCTION :

LOOP to specified label until CX = 0.

This instruction is used to repeat a series of instructions a number of times. The no. of times the instruction sequence is to be repeated is loaded into the count register. The content of CX is automatically decremented by one, each time the LOOP instruction executes. If CX is not 0, execution will jump to a destination specified by a label in the instruction. If CX = 0 after the autodecrement, execution will simply go on to the next instruction after LOOP.

2. LOOPE/LOOPZ INSTRUCTION

LOOP while CX = 0 and ZF = 1

This instruction is used to repeat a group of instructions some number of times or until the zero flag becomes 0. If CX is not 0 and the zero flag is set, execution will jump to a destination specified by a label in the instruction. If CX is 0 after the autodecrement or if the zero flag is not set, execution will simply go on to the next instruction after LOOPE/LOOPZ.

3. LOOPNE/LOOPNZ INSTRUCTION

LOOP while CX is not 0 and ZF = 0.

This instruction is used to repeat a group of instructions some number of times or until the zero flag becomes a 1. The number of times the instruction sequence is to be repeated is loaded into the count register, CX. Each time the LOOPNE/LOOPNZ instruction executes, CX is automatically decremented by one. If CX is not 0 and the zero flag is not set, execution will jump to a destination specified by a label in the instruction. If CX is 1 after the autodecrement or if the zero flag is set, execution will simply go on to the next instruction after LOOPNE/LOOPNZ. In other words, the two ways to exit the loop one CX= 0 or ZF = 1.

2.8 INTERRUPT INSTRUCTIONS

1. INT INSTRUCTION :

Interrupt program execution, INT type. This instruction interrupts program execution. There are various types of INT instructions which interrupt the program execution for different purposes. The term type in the instruction refer to a number between 0 and 255 which identifies the interrupt.

Some of the 8088 interrupt types are described as follows :

INT 3H : It is used to insert breakpoints in program for debugging

INT 21H : This instruction provides various functions depending on the value stored in AH register. e.g. if the value loaded in AH is 02H, then the INT 21 instruction interrupts the program execution to display character to standard output device.

INT 20H : It terminates the program execution and returns to DOS.

2.9 PROCESSOR CONTROL INSTRUCTIONS.

FLAG SET/CLEAR INSTRUCTIONS

1. STC INSTRUCTION :

Set the carry flag to a one. This instruction sets the carry flag to a one. STC does not affect any other flags.

2. CLC INSTRUCTION :

Clear the carry flag, CF-CLC . This instruction resets the carry flag to zero. No other flags are affected

3. CMC INSTRUCTION :

Complement the carry flag-CMC. If the carry flag, CF, is a zero before this instruction, it will be set to a one ofter the instruction. If the carry flag is one before this instruction, it will be reset to a zero after the instruction executes. CMC affects no other flags.

4. STD INSTRUCTION :

Set the direction flag to a one STD is used to set the direction flag to a one so that SI and/or DI will automatically be decremented to point to the next string element when one of the string instructions executes. If the direction flag is set, SI and / or DI will be decremented by one for byte strings, and by two for word strings STD affects no other flags.

5. CLD INSTRUCTION :

Clear the direction flag, CLD. This instruction resets the direction flag to zero. No other flags are affected. If the direction flag is reset, SI and DI will automatically be incremented when one of the string instructions such as MOVS, CMPS, or SCAS executes.

6. STI INSTRUCTION :

Set interrupt enable flag to 1. Setting the interrupt flag to a one enables the INTR interrupt of the 8088 after the next instruction after STI. An interrupt signal on this input will then cause the 8088 to interrupt program execution, push the return address and flags or the stack, and execute an interrupt service procedure. An IRET instruction at the end of the interrupt service procedure will restore the flags which were pushed on the stack, and return execution to the interrupted program. STI does not affect any other flag.

7. CLI INSTRUCTION Clear interrupt flag- CLI :

This instruction resets the interrupt flag to zero. No other flags are affected. If the interrupt flag is reset, the 8088 will not respond to an interrupt signal on its INTR. input. The CLI instruction, however, has no effect on the non maskable interrupt input, NMI.

2.10 EXTERNAL HARDWARE SYNCHRONIZATION INSTRUCTIONS :

1. HLT INSTRUCTION (Halt processing - HLT) :

The HLT instruction causes the 8088 to stop yetching and executing instructions. The 8088 enters a halt state. The only ways to get the processor out of the halt state are with an interrupt signal on the NMI pin, or a reset signal on the RESET input.

2. WAIT INSTRUCTION :

Wait for test signal or interrupt signal

When this instruction executes, the 8088 enters an idle condition where it is doing no processing. The 8088 will stay in this idle state until a signal is asserted on the 8088 TEST input pin, or until a valid interrupt signal is received on the INTR or the NMI interrupt input pins. The WAIT instruction is used to synchronise the 8088 with external hardware.

NO OPERATION INSTRUCTION

1. NOP INSTRUCTION (Perform no operation) :

This instruction simply uses up three clock cycles and increments the instruction pointer to point to the next instruction. NOP affects no flags. It can be used to hold a place in a program for instructions that will be added later.

2.11 STRING INSTRUCTIONS

A string is a series of bytes or a series of words in sequential memory location. A string after consists of ASCII character codes. A "W" in the mnemonic is used to indicate that a string of words is to be acted upon.

1. REP/REPE/REPZ/REPNE/REPNZ (Prefix) Repeat string instruction :

Until specified conditions exist REP is a prefix which is written before one of the string instructions. It will cause the CX register to be decremented and the string instruction to be repeated until CX= 0. The instruction is to be repeated until CX= 0.

2. MOVE/MOVSB/MOVSW INSTRUCTION (Move string byte or string word- MOVS destination,source) :

This instruction copies a byte or word from a location in the data segment to a location in the extra segment. The offset of the source byte or word in the data segment must be in the SI register. The offset of the destination in the extra segment must be contained in the DI register. For multiple byte or multiple word moves the number of elements to be moved is put in the CX register so that it can function as a counter. After the byte or word is moved SI and DI are automatically adjusted to point to the next source and the next destination.

3. COMPS/COMPSB/COMPSW (Compare string bytes or string words) :

The CMPS instruction can be used to compare a byte in one string with a byte in another string or to compare a word in one string with a word in another string. SI holds the offset of a byte or word in the source string and DI is used to hold the offset of a byte or a word in the other string. The comparison is done by subtracting the byte or word pointed to by DI from the byte or word pointed to by SI.

The string pointed to by DI must be in the extra segment. The string pointed to by SI is asumed to be in the data segment but a segment override prefix can be used to tell the 8088 to add the offset in SI to CS, SS, or ES.

4. SCAS/SCASB/SCASW (Scan string byte or a string word) :

SCAS compares a string byte with a byte in AL or a string word with word in AX. The instruction affects the flags, but it does not change either the operand in AL (AX) or the operand in the string. The string to be scanned must be in the extra segment and DI must contain the offset of the byte or the word to be compared. SCAS affects the AF, CF, OF, PF, SF and ZF. This instruction is often used with a repeat prefix to find the first occurrence of a specified byte or word in a string.

5. LODS/LODSB/LODSW INSTRUCTION (Load string byte into AL or load string word into AX) :

This instruction copies a byte from a string location pointed to by SI to AL , or a word from a string location pointed to by SI to AX. If the direction flag is cleaned (0), SI will automatically be incremented to point to the next element of the string. For a string of bytes SI is incremented by one and for a string of word SI is incremented by two. If the direction flag, DF, is set (1), SI will be automatically decremented to point to the next string element. For a byte string SI will be decremented by one, and for a word string SI will be decremented by two. LODS affects no flags.

6. STOPS/STOSB/STOSW (Store byte or word in string) :

The STOS instruction copies a byte from AL or word from AX to a memory location in the extra segment. In effect it replaces a string element with a byte from AL or a word from **AX**.

2.12 EXAMPLE PROGRAMS USING i8088 INSTRUCTIONS :

1. Addition of two given hex number (bytes)

```
      MOV  AL, 15H
      MOV  BL, 85H      : This program adds two
      ADD  AL, BL       : 8 bits hex digits 15 and
      JNC  ADD1         : 85 and stores the 16
      MOV  AH, 01H      : bit result in AX register
ADD1  MOV AH, 00H
      INT  20H
```

The above program first moves the two given hex numbers into two registers AL and BL. The contents of AL and BL are added and the result is stored in AL. If the result is more than 8 bits, the carry flag is set. So 1 is moved to AH register. If there is no carry the program skips the above step and 0 is moved to AH. Then the program is interrupted to return to DOS.

2. Swapping of values stored in two memory locations Val 1 and Val 2 in DS

```
MOV  AL, [Val 1]
XCHG [Val 2], AL  : This program exchanges
MOV  [Val 1], AL  : the numbers stored in
INT 20H           : mem.loc. Val 1 and Val 2.
```

This program first moves the content of first memory location to AL register. The content of second memory location and the content of AL register are exchanged. Now AL contains the content of second memory location which is moved to the first memory location. The program is then terminated.

3. Computation of (a + b) * (c + d) Where a, b, c, d, are hex bytes

```
MOV  AL, a
MOV  BL, b     : This program can be
ADD  AL, BL    : Written without PUSH
PUSH AL        : and POP instructions.
MOV  AL, c     : Here PUSH and POP
MOV  BL, d     : instructions are used
ADD  BL, AL    : to illustrate their
POP  AL        : use.
```

MUL BLINT 20H In the program above first the hex digits a and b are moved to registers AL and BL respectively. They are then added. The result stored in AL is pushed into a stack so that AL register can be used again without affecting the previous result. Now the digits c and d are moved to AL and BL and added. The result is stored in BL. The value stored in the stack is poped and moved to AL, BL is multiplied with AL and the product is stored in AX register. The program is then terminated.

4: Read a number from the keyboard and display it on the output device if the number is greater than EEH.

```
MOV  BX, Keyboard port no.
IN   AL, BX                . This program illustrates the
JLE  ADD1                  : use of IN,
MOV  DX,display port no.   : OUT, CMP
OUT  DX, AL                : and JLE instructions.
ADD1 INT 20H
```

This program at first points BX at input port. Then the input is stored in AL register. The content of AL is compared with EEH. If input value is less than or equal to EEH, the program is terminated. If it is not so, then DX is pointed at output port. The content of AL are sent to the output device and the program is terminated.

5. MOVE the bytes stored in an array which starts at memory location X1 to another array which starts at location Y1

```
LEA ST, X1
LEA DI, Y1                  : This program transfer
MOV  OL, 00H                : an array of 10 bytes
ADD1 MOV  BX, CL [SI] : from a location |
MOV  CL [DI], BX            : starting at X 1 to a
INC  CL                     : location starting at
CMP  CL, A                  : Y 1
JNE  ADD1                   :
INT  20H
```

The above program first loads the effective address of operands (X 1 and Y 1) to registers SI and DI respectively. The content at X1 is moved to BX which is again moved to Y 1. Now CL is incrementedwhich acts as an offset displacemnt. CL is compared with A. It both are equal the progam is terminated. If CL is not equal to A, the next byte in the array is moved to BX and then to the new location. Thus the loop is executed till all the 10 bytes in the array are transferred to another location.

6. Addition of all the words in an array of 6 words

```
MOV  BX, 0000H
MOV  CH, 5              : In this program XYZ
MOV  CL,00H             : is the starting address
ADD1 LDS  AX,CL[XYZ]    : of the array.
ADD  AX, DS             : In place of LDS, LES
ADC  BX,AX              : can also be used.
INC CL1
INC  CL1                : It is assumed that
INC  CL1
INC  CL1                : the result of adding
DEC  CH                 : any two words is
JNZ  ADD1               : a word.
INT  20H
```

The above program loads the AX and DS registers with the consecutive words stored in the memory location starting at XYZ. Then the two words are added. The result is stored in AX which is added to BX to store the final result in BX. CL is incremented by 4. CH is decremented. If CH is zero the program is terminated. If CH is not zero the program is executed in a loop. In this way all the six words are added and the final result is in BX.

7. Addition of two ASCII digits

```
MOV  AL, '5'
MOV  BL, '6'  : This program illustrates
MOV  AL, BL     the use of AAA instruction
AAA
INT  20H
```

The above program adds two ASCII digits 5 and 6. The result of the addition stored in AL is adjusted to correct ASCII digit and the program terminates.

8. Addition of two BCD digits

```
MOV  AL, 65
MOVE BL, 25   : This program illustrates
ADD  AL,BL      the use of instruction
DAA             DAA.
INT  20H
```

This program adds two decimal numbers 65 and 25. The result of the addition is not the correct decimal digit, so it is adjusted by using DAA decimal adjust after addition. The result is stored in AL and the program is terminated.

9. Subtraction of a smaller hex digit from a larger hex digit

```
MOV  AL, 15H
MOV  BL, 9H   : This program illustrates
SUB  AL, BL   : the instruction SUB.INT  20H
```

The above program subtracts 9H from 15H and the result is stored in AL. The program is then terminated.

10. Subtraction of two numbers through 2's complement

```
MOV  AL, 10H
MOV  BL, 05H   : This program is for
NEG  BL        : illustrating the use
ADD  AL, BL    : of NEG instruction.
INT  20H
```

The above program loads the two hex digits 10 and 5 to AL and BL respectively. The contents of BL are replaced by its 2's complement which is added to AL, to get the result in AL register. Then the program terminates.

11. Subtraction among two ASCII digits

```
MOV AL '34'
MOV BL '16'  : This program illustrates
SUB AL, BL     the use of AAS instruction.
INT 20H
```

The above program subtracts the content of BL from that of AL, both of which are ASCII digits. The result stored in AL is adjusted to the correct ASCII digit and the program is terminated.

12. Subtraction between two BCD digits

```
MOV AL, 34
MOV DL, 12  : This program is for
SUB AL, DL    illustrating the use
DAS           of DAS instruction.
INT 20H
```

The program above first loads the two decimal digits into AL and DL and subtracts DL from AL. The result stored in AL is adjusted to correct binary coded decimal digit. The program then terminates.

13. Multiplication of two signed numbers

```
MOV AL, -5H
MOV BL, 5H  : Illustration of IMUL
IMUL BL       instruction.
INT 20H
```

The above program multiplies the two signed numbers +5 and -5 and the result is stored in AX register. The program then terminates.

14. Multiplication of ASCII digits

```
MOV AL, '5'
MOV DL, '6'  : To get the result in
MUL DL         ASCII code, the instruction
AAM            AAM is used.
INT 20H
```

The above program loads the two ASCII digits 5 and 6 in AL and DL respecively. The digits are multiplied and the result is stored in AX. The content of AX is adjusted to correct ASCII digit and the program is terminated.

15. Division of an unsigned word by byte

```
MOV AX, 1234H
MOV BL, 04H  : Illustration of DIV
DIV BL         instruction.
INT 20H
```

The above program loads the dividend into AX and divisor into BL. AX is divided by BL and the quotient is in AL and the remainder is in AH. The program is then interrupted.

16. Division of a signed doubleword by word

```
MOV AX 0015H
MOV DX 0134H   : This program illustrates
MOV BX -0AAAH    the use of IDIV
IDIV BX          instruction.
INT 20H
```

The above program loads the double word in AX (LSB) and DX (MSB) as dividend. The divisor is loaded in BX and signed division is performed on the double word. Then the program terminates. The result (quotient) is stored in AX and the remainder is stored in DX.

17. Division among BCD digits

```
MOV AX 0304
MOV BL 02H  : This program illustrates
```

```
ADD                 the use of instruction
DIV  BL             ADD.
INT  20H
```

The above program adjust the unpacked BCD digit in AX to binary before division. Then AX is divided by unpacked BCD digit in BL. The quotient is in AL and the remainder is in AH. Then the program is terminated.

18. Formation of 1's complement of a number

```
MOV  AX, 00FFH
NOT                 :  Illustration of NOT instruction.
INT  20H
```

This program first loads the number whose 1's complement is to be found in AX. Each bit of the number is inverted and the program execution is interrupted. Now AX contains the 1's complement of the given number 00FFH.

19. Separate a word into byte

```
MOV  AX, 1234H
AND  AX, 00FFH  :  Illustration of AND
MOV  BX, 1234H     instruction.
AND  BX, FF00H
INT  20H
```

The above program loads the word into AX and ANDs with 00FF to mask upper byte. The word is again loaded in another register BX and ANDed with FF00H to mask lower byte. Thus AX contains lower byte and BX contains upper byte of the given word.

20. Separate a byte into niffles

```
MOV  AL, 34H
MOV  CL, 04H   :  Illustration of SHL.
SHL  AL, CL       and SHR instructions
SHR  AL, CL
MOV  BL, 34H
SHR  BL, CL
```

The above program first shifts the content of AL to the left 4 bit positions and then to right 4 bit positions. So AL contains 4. The bits in BL are shifted right 4 position, so BL contians 3. The byte is thus separated into nibbles.

21. Find whether parity of a given number is odd or even

```
MOV  AL, EDH
OR   AL, FFH            :  This program illustrates
JPE  Add1                  OR and JPE
MOV  AH, 01H               instructions.
Add1 MOV  AH, 00H
INT  20H
```

The above program ORs the given number with FFH to set the parity flag. If the parity is even 0 is stored in AH. If the parity is odd 1 is stored in AH. Then the program interrupts.

22. Find exclusive OR of a number with FFH

```
MOV  AL, 34H
XOR  AL, FFH
INT  20H
```

The above program illustrates the use of XOR instruction. The given number is moved to AL register. The content of AL is exclusive ORed with FFH. The result of the logical operation is stored in AL. The program is then terminated.

23. Separate a word into bytes through rotate instructions

```
MOV  AX, 345AH
```

```
AND AX, 00FFH   : This program illustrates
MOV BX, 345AH     the use of ROR instruction.
AND BX, FF00H
MOV CL, 08H
ROR BX, CL
INT 20H
```

The above program first ANDs the given number with 00FF to mask the upper byte and stores in AX. It again ANDs the given number with FF00H to mask the lower byte and rotates it right to store in lower 8 bits of BX.

24. Check whether the MSB of the number is 1 or 0

```
MOV AL, 34H
ROL AL,1          : This program illustrates
JC Add1             the use of ROL and JC.
MOV AH, 00H
Add1 MOV AH, 01H
INT 20H
```

The above program stores 1 in AH if the MSB of the given number is 1 and 0 in AH if the MSB of the number is 0.

25. Check whether the seventh bit of the given 8 bit number is 1 or 0

```
MOV AL, 63H
RCL AL, 1         : This program illustrates
RCL AL, 1           the instructions RCL
JNC Add1            and JNC.
MOV AH, 01H
Add1 MOV AH, 00H
INT 20H
```

The above program stores in AH 1 if the seventh bit of the given number is 1 and 0 if the seventh bit is 0.

26. Find whether the third bit of the given 16 bit number is 0 or 1

```
MOV AX, 38ABH
MOV CL, 03H
RCR AX, CL        : This program is
JC Add1             for illustrating RCR
MOV CH, OOH         instruction.
Add1 MOV CH, O1H
INT 20H
```

The above program stores a 1 in CH if the third bit of the given number is 1 and 0 in CH if the third bit of the 16 bit number is 0.

27. Find the greatest number in an array of 10 numbers of type byte

```
MOV AX, XYZ
MOV BL, [AX]      : This program illustrates
MOV BL, [AX]        the use of instructions
MOV CX, A
Add2 INC AX
MOV BH, [AX]        JL (Jump if less than) and LOOP (loop through a sequence of
CMP BH, BL          instruction until CX= 0)
JL Add1
MOV BL, BH
Add1 LOOP Add2
INT 20H
```

The above program loads, the starting address of an array XYZ memory location. The contents of this memory location is moved to BL and the content of the next consecutive memory location is moved to BH. The number of bytes in the array is loaded in CX. The contents of BL and BH register are compared. If the byte in BH is less than that in BL, the content of next memory location is loaded into BH and compared with BL. If the byte in BH is greater than that in BL, its content is moved to BL. Then the content of next memory location is loaded into BH and compared with BL. This loop excutes until CX= 0. LOOP instruction autodecrements CX.

3.0 ASSEMBLY LANGUAGE PROGRAMMING TOOLS

Assembly language programs bring us close to the Computers.

Comparing assembly language programs with other programs we find that the former are the lowest common denominator.

This language was prevalent long before the other languages were developed. It takes us closer to the machine than the high level languages do, as it is at the heart of the computer. All computers have a central processing unit, i.e. CPU, the most important part of any computer system. Learning assembly language also means learning to understand the CPU inside the computer, which may be an 8088, 80286, 80386 etc.

The knowledge of the assembly language programs, by providing a better understanding of the CPU helps in understanding the elements of high level languages in a better way.

It also helps in diagnosing high level language programs.

In computers the speed of execution and the amount of memory space used are critical aspects. Assembly language programs are much faster than the high level language counterparts. Typically assembly language programs are two to three times faster than the equivalent programs in high level languages. Sometimes they also require less memory space. They provide us a full access to the features in the computers. A number of programs such as Sidekick, Prokey and others stay in memory after we run them. Such programs change the way the machine works and they can use all system features available. They are written in assembly language.

To make programming easier many programmers write programs in assembly language. Then the program is translated into its machine code and loaded into memory for execution. Assembly language program uses two, three or four letter mnemonics to represent each instruction type. Mnemonics are names to make assembly language progamming easier. The letters used in the assembly language programs are usually initials or shortened form of the English words, for operation peformed by the instruction. Assembly language statements are usually written in a standard form having four fields.

LABEL FIELD	OPCODE	OPERAND	COMMENTS

The figure above shows the four fields of the assembly language statement. The first field is the label field A label is a symbol used to represent what is not specifically known at the time of writing the program. Labels are not a mandatory requirement, they are used just where required. The opcode of the instruction contain the **mnemonics** for the instruction to be performed. For example the opcode 'ADD' signifies the addition of two numbers. The operand field of the statement contains the data, the memory address, the port address or the register argument.

The fourth field is the comment field, it is only for the understanding of the reader of the program. It is just for making the program much more readable and provides a better understanding of program.

Debug and Macro assembler are two very popular tools for assembly language programming. We will examine each of them in the coming sections.

3.1 DEBUG

DEBUG Command utility enables us to write and modify simple assembly language programs in an easy fashion. It provides a way to run and test any program in a controlled environment i.e. we can change any part of the program and immediately execute the program without having to reassemble it. We can also run machine-language (object) files directly by using debug. Programmers often use this DOS tool to make quick program changes, to test variations and to rapidly isolate errors in assembly-language code.

DEBUG commands may be divided into four categories: Program creation/debugging, memory manipulation, miscellaneous, and input output. Once DEBUG begins if we type a question mark it will display a list of all the debugging commands along with the required command syntax.

3.1.1 DEBUG Commands :

COMMAND	EXPLANATION
A	Assembles the instructions at a particular address.
C	Compares two memory ranges.
D	Display contents of memory.
E	Enters new or modifies old memory contents.
F	Fills in a range of memory.
G	Executes a program in memory.
H	Adds and subtracts two hex values
I	Inputs and displays a byte from a port.
L	Loads disk data into memory
M	Copies a range of memory values.
N	Names a file to load or create.
O	Outputs a byte to a port
P	Proceeds with execution to the next memory instruction
Q	Quits from DEBUG back to DOS.
R	Displays (and changes) contents of registers and flags.
S	Searches for characters.
T	Traces execution of memory code.
U	Unassembles hex bytes into assembler instructions
W	Writes memory data to disk
XA	Allocates expanded memory
XD	Deallocates expanded memory
XM	Maps logical pages onto physical ones.
XS	Displays expanded memory status.

3.1.2 Debugging Functions :

Some of the most elementary functions that a debugger can perform are the following :

1> Assemble short programs
2> View a program's source code, along with its machine code
3> View the CPU registers and flags.
4> Trace or execute a progam, watching variables for changes
5> Enter new values into memory
6> Search for binary or ASCII values in memory.
7> Move a block of memory from one location to another.
8> Fill a block of memory.
9> Load and write disk files.

The following is a sample register display :

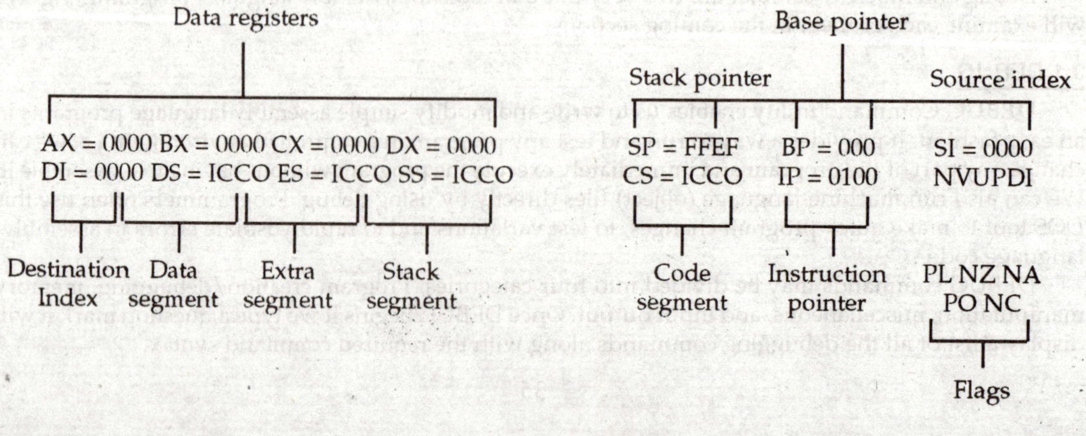

Assemble and Test the Program :

If we have DEBUG available, we can assemble and test our program. We will find a debugger to be the perfect tool for learning how assembly language instructions work. It prompts for commands using the hyphen (-) character. The DEBUG commands to assemble and test a sample program are as follows :

DEBUG	(Load the DEBUG. COM program)
-A 100	(begin assembly at location 100)
	(enter rest of the program)
MOV AX,5	(Put 5 in AX register)
ADD AX,10	(add 10 to AX register)
ADD AX,20	(add 20 to AX register)
MOV [0120], AX	(sum is at location 0120)
INT 20	(end prog)
-	(press ENTER to end program)
-R	(display register)
-T	(Trace each instruction)
-T	
-T	
-G	(execute the rest of the program)
-Q	(Quit DEBUG, and return to DOS).

DEBUG commands used above are A (Assemble) command which allows to input a program and have it assembled into machine instruction. After typing A command, we will be prompted for each assembler instruction.

The T (Trace) command executes a single instruction, displays the registers and stops. The R (Register) command displays the registers. The G (Go) command executes all remaining instructions in the program, and the Q (quit) command returns to DOS.

As we assemble each line of the program, we will see a computer address appear at the left side of the screen. The address show the location of each instruction. For example :

```
- A       100
5511 :    0100 MOV  AX, 7
5511 :    0103 ADD  AX, 12
```

After the last MOV instruction press ENTER to return to DEBUG'S command mode. If we would like to see the machine instructions that make up our program, type U for Unassemble (this is often called disassembling a program). A modified listing of the statements is as follows :

Machine Instruction	Assembly Instruction
B8 07 00	MOV AX,0007
07 12 00	ADD AX,0012
07 20 00	ADD AX,0020
A3 20 01	MOV AX,0120
CD 20	INT 20

DEBUG always displays numbers in hexadecimal.The number [0120] in brackets is DEGUG's way of reffering to the contents of a memory location. The variable SUM is located at address 0120H.

Trace the program :

Use DEBUG's T (Trace) command to execute each program statement. After each instruction is executed, DEBUG stops and displays the CPU registers and the next instructions. One advantage of using this procedure is that we can halt the program and return to DOS at any time. We can also change the contents of registers and variables before going on. A trace of our sample program appears in the given figure below :

Fig : Sample program trace, using DEBUG :

```
-R
AX = 0000     BX = 0000   CX = 0000   DX = 0000
SP  = DF12    BP = 0000   SI  = 0000   DI  = 0000
```

```
DS = 1FDD    ES = 1FDD  SS = 1FDD  CS = 1FDD
IP  = 0100   NV  UP EI PL NZ NA PO NC 1FDD : 0100   B80500   MOV  AX,0007
-T
AX = 0007    BX = 0000   CX= 0000   DX = 0000
SP  = DF12   BP = 0000   SI  = 0000   DI  = 0000
DS  = 1FDD   ES = 1FDD  SS = 1FDD  CS = 1FDD
IP  = 0103   NV  UP EI  PL  NZ  NA   PO  NC
1FDD : 0103   051000   ADD  AX,0012
-T
AX = 0019    BX = 0000   CX= 0000   DX = 0000
SP  = DF12   BP = 0000   SI  = 0000   DI  = 0000
DS  = 1FDD   ES = 1FDD  SS = 1FDD  CS = 1FDD
IP  = 0106   NV   UP  EI  PL  NZ  NA  PO  NC
1FDD : 0106    052000    ADD   AX,0020
-T
AX = 0039    BX = 0000   CX= 0000   DX = 0000
SP  = DF12   BP = 0000   SI  = 0000   DI  = 0000
DS  = 1FDD   ES = 1FDD  SS = 1FDD  CS = 1FDD
IP  = 0109   NV   UP  EI  PL   NA  PE  IC
1FDD : 0109    A32001     MOV [0120],AX
-G
-D 120,121  (dump memory locations 120 through 121)
1FDD : 0120   39 00 (byte are reversed).
```

In the above example figure we see that the value of AX register is changed by each instruction. Now taking another example with DEBUG :

```
DEBUG
-A 100
MOV ah,1
INT 21          (input character will be in AL)
MOV ah,2
MOV dl,al       (move the character to DL)
INT 21
INT 20          (end the program press ENTER on the blank line)
-U              (unassembled the program)
-G              (Go-execute the program)
-Q              (Quit-return to DOS)
```

To trace a program containing INT instructions, we have to use the P (procedure trace) command instead of the T command. Example : using DEBUG

```
-R
AX = 0000    BX = 0000   CX= 0000   DX = 0000
SP  = FFEE   BP = 0000   SI  = 0000   DI  = 0000
DS  = 3D7D   ES = 3D7D  SS = 3D7D  CS = 3D7D
IP  = 0100   NV  UP  EI  PL  NZ  NA  PO  NC
3D7D : 0100   B401    MOV  AH,01
-P
AX = 0100    BX = 0000   CX= 0000   DX = 0000
SP  = FFEE   BP = 0000   SI  = 0000   DI  = 0000
DS  = 3D7D   ES = 3D7D  SS = 3D7D  CS = 3D7D
IP  = 0102   NV UP  EI  PL  NZ  NA  PO  NC
3D7D : 0102    CD21    INT 21
```

```
-P
AX = 012A    BX = 0000  CX= 000C  DX = 0000
SP = FFEE    BP = 0000  SI = 0000  DI = 0000
DS = 3D7D    ES = 3D7D SS = 3D7D CS = 3D7D
IP = 0104    NV  UP EI PL  NZ  NA  PO  NC
3D7D : 0104  B402      MOV AH,02
-P
AX = 022A    BX = 0000  CX= 000C  DX = 0000
SP = FFEE    BP = 0000  SI = 0000  DI = 0000
DS = 3D7D    ES = 3D7D SS = 3D7D CS = 3D7D
IP = 0106    NV  UP EI PL  NZ  NA  PO  NC
3D7D : 0106  88C2      MOV DL,AL
-P
AX = 022A    BX = 0000  CX= 000C  DX = 002A
SP = FFEE    BP = 0000  SI = 0000  DI = 0000
DS = 3D7D    ES = 3D7D SS = 3D7D CS = 3D7D
IP = 0108    NV  UP EI PL  NZ  NA  PO  NC
3D7D:0108    CD21   INT 21
-P
AX = 022A    BX = 0000  CX= 000F  DX = 002A
SP = FFEE    BP = 0000  SI = 0000  DI = 0000
DS = 3D7D    ES = 3D7D SS = 3D7D CS = 3D7D
IP = 010A    NV  UP EI PL  NZ  NA  PO  NC
3D7D:010A    CD20   INT 20
-P
```

3.1.3 Example of Assembly Language programming on the IBM - PC using a debugger :

```
1> DEBUG
- A 100
MOV ax,7          ; move 7 into the AX register
MOV bx,13         ; move 13 into the BX register
ADD ax,bx         ; add content of bx to the content of ax and result stored in ax.
INT 20            ; end the program.

2> DEBUG
-A 100
MOV ax,5          ; move 5 into the AX register
ADD ax,15         ; add 15h to the AX register
ADD ax,25         ; add 25h to the AX register
MOV [0120], ax    ; SUM is at location 0120.
INT 20            ; end the program.
3> DEBUG
-A 100
MOV ah,5F         ; move 5F into the Ah register
MOV ax, 1234      ; move 1234 into the AX register
MOV bh,al         ; move the content of al to bh register
MOV bl,ah         ; move the content of ah to the bl register
INT 20            ; end the program.
4> DEBUG
- A 100
MOV aX, FFFE      ; move FFFE to the AX register
SUB al,2          ; subtract 2 from al
MOV bl,8C         ; move 8C to the bl
```

```
MOV bh, 2D          ; move 2D to bh
ADD bx, ax          ; addition of contents of AX & BX.
INT 20              ; end the program.
```

```
5> DEBUG
- A 100
MOV bl, FE          ; FE to the BL register
NOT bl              ; reverses all bit in number
ADD bl,1            ; addition of 1 to the register BL.
INT 20              ; end the program.
```

```
6> DEBUG
- 100    MOV ax, 0  ; move 0 to AX register.
DEC ax              ; decrease AX by 1.
DEC ax              ; decrease again of AX.
ADD ax,2            ; add 2 to AX register
INC ax              ; increase AX by 1.
INT 20              ; end the program
```

```
7> DEBUG
- A 100
MOV ax, 1234        ; move 1234 to AX register
MOV bx,ax           ; move AX to BX.
MOV cx,ax           ; move AX to CX.
ADD ch,al           ; add al with ch register
ADD bl,ah           ; add ah with bl register
ADD ax,FFFF         ; add FFFF to AX register
DEC bx              ; Decrease Bx by 1.
INC ax              ; Increase Ax by 1.
INT 20              ; end the program.
```

```
8> DEBUG
- A 100
MOV ax, 7FFF        ; move 7FFF to AX register
INC ax              ; increase AX by 1.
MOV bx,8000         ; move 8000 to BX register
DEC bx              ; decrease BX by 1.
INT 20              ; end the program.
```

```
9> DEBUG
-A 100
MOV ax,2B10         ; move 2B10 to AX register
MOV bx,ax           ; AX to BX register
MOV dl,ah           ; move ah to dl.
MOV cl,bl           ; move bl to cl.
INT 20              ; end the program.
```

```
10> DEBUG
- A 100
MOV ax, FFFF        ; move FFFF to AX register
INC al              ; increase al.
SUB al,2            ; subtracts 2 from al.
MOV dl,al           ; move al to dl.
ADD dx,2            ; add 2 with dx register
INT 20              ; end the program.
```

3.2 MASM

The MASM is the short form for Macro Assembler. The Microsoft Macro Assembler is used for assembling i.e. converting the assembly level programs written for the 8088 microprocessor. The merits of using MASM are two fold. It produces the binary code of our programs and it also provides us with the facility of refering the data items by their names rather than by their addresses.

This makes the programs easier to write and also makes it (program) more readable.

3.2.1 8088/8086 PROCESSOR INSTRUCTIONS

AAA	IN	JNLE		
AAD	INC	JNO		
AAM	INT	JNP		
AAS	INTO	JNS		
ADS	IRET	JNZ		
ADD	JA	JO		
AND	JAE	JP		
CALL	JB	JPE		
CBW	JBE	JPO		
CLC	JC	JS		
CLD	JCXZ	JZ		
CLI	JE	LAHF		
CMC	JG	LDS		
CMP	JGE	LEA		
CMPS	JL	LES		
CMPSB	JLE	LODS		
CMPSW	JMP	LODSB		
CWD	JNA	LODSW		
DAA	JNAE	LOOP		
DAS	JNB	LOOPE		
DEC	JNBE	LOOPFW		
DIV	JNC	LOOPNE		
ESC	JNE	LOOPNEW		
HLT	JNG	LOOPNZ		
IDIV	JNGE	LOOPNZW		
IMUL	JNL	LOOPW	LOOPZ	SCASW
LOOPZW	SHL			
MOV	SHR	MOVS	STC	
MOVSB	STD			
MOVSW	STI			
MUL	STOS			
NEG	STOSB			
NOP	STOSW			
NOT	SUB			
OR	TEST			
OUT	WAIT			
POP	XCHG			
POPF	XLAT			
PUSH	XLATB			
PUSHF	XOR			
RCL				
RCR				
RET				
RETF				
RETN				
ROL				

SAHF
SAL
SAR
SBB
SCAS
SCASB

80186 PROCESSOR INSTRUCTIONS

BOUND	INSW	OUTSW
INTER	LEAVE	POPA
INS	OUTS	JPUSHA
INSB	OUTSB	PUSHW

3.2.2 80286 PROCESSOR INSTRUCTIONS

ARPL	SIDT	VERR
LAR	SLDT	VERW
LSL	SMST	
SGDT	STR	

3.2.3 80286/386 PRIVILEGED MODE INSTRUCTIONS

CLTS	LIDT	LMSW
LGDT	LLDT	LTR

3.2.4 80386 PROCESSOR INSTRUCTIONS

BSF	CMPSD	LFS			
BSR	CWDBE	LGS			
BT	INSD	LODSD			
BTC	IRETD	LOOPD			
BTR	IRETDF	LOOPED			
BTS	IRETF	LOONED			
CDQ	JECXZ	LOOPNZD			
LOOPZD	SETBE	SETNLE			
LSS	SETC	SETNO			
MOVSD	SETE	SETNP			
MOVSX	SETG	SETNS			
MOVZX	SETGE	SETNZ			
OUTSD	STEL	SETO			
POPAD	SETLE	SETP			
POPFD	SETNA	SEFPE			
PUSHAD	SETNAE	SETES			
PUSHD	SETNB	SETS			
PUSHFD	SETNBE	SETEZ			
SCASD	SETNC	SETZ			
SETTA	SETNE	SHLD			
SETAE	SETNG	SHRD	SETB	SETNGE	STOSD

3.2.5 80486 COPROCESSOR INSTRUCTIONS

BSWAP INVD WBINVD

CMMPXCHG INVLPG XADD(Following are the few assembly language programs that have been tested on MASM 6.1)

3.2.6 ASSEMBLY LANGUAGE PROGRAMS

```
DATA_SEG SEGMENT PUBLIC
DS-VAR   DW      1
DATA_SEG ENDS
```

```
EXTRA_SEG SEGMENT   PUBLIC
ES_VAR    DW      2
EXTRA_SEG ENDS
STACK_SEG SEGMENT  STACK
DB  10 DUP ('STACK  ')   ; 'STACK' followed by 3 spaces
STACK_SEG
CODE_SEG SEGMENT  PUBLIC    ASSUME  CS : CODE_SEG, DS : DATA_SEG,ES : EXTRA_SEG,
SS :         STACK_SEG
TEST          PROC      FAR
PUSH ES                           ; Save return address for long RET below
XOR  AX,     AX                   ; There is an INT soh inst. at ES:0
PUSH AX
MOV  AX,   DATA_SEG               ; Segment address for DATA_SEG
MOV  DS,   AX                     ; Set up DS register for DATA_SEG
MOV  AX,   EXTRA_SEG              ; Segment address for EXTRA_SEG
MOV  ES,   AX                     ; Set up ES register for EXTRA_SEG
MOV  AX,   DS_VAR                 ; Read a variable from data segment
MOV  BX,   ES: ES_VAR             ; Read variable from extra segment
RET                               ; Return to DOS
TEST         ENDP
CODE_SEG ENDS      END  TEST
```

The above program shows how we can write to two different segment, using the DS and ES register to point to the two segments, so segment override instructions are used in this program.

```
HEX_TO_DIGIT      PROC      NEAR
CMP          AL,'O'                ; Is it a legal digit?
JB           ILLEGAL               ; Nope
CMP          AL,'9'                ; Not sure yet
JA           SEE_HEX               ; Is decimal digit, convert to nibble
SUB          AL, '0'               ; Convert to nibble
CLC                                ; Clear carry
RET
SEE_HEX:
CMP          AL,'A'                ; Not sure yet
JB           ILLEGAL               ; Not hex
CMP          AL,'F'                ; Not sure yet
JA           ILLEGAL               ; Not hex
SUB          AL,'A'-10             ; Is hex, convert to nibble
RET                                ; Clear the carry, no error
ILLEGAL
STC                                ; Set the carry, error     RET
HEX_TO_DIGIT        ENDDP
```

The above procedure a converts a character from SCII (hex) to a nibble (4 bits).

```
PUBLIC       HEX_TO_BYTE
HEX_TO_BYTE   PROC      NEAR
PUSH          BX
PUSH          CX  MOV  BX,DX ;Put address in BX for indirect addr
MOV           AL, [BX]           ; Get first digit
CALL          HEX_TO_DIGIT
JC            BAD_HEX            ; Bad hex digit if carry set
MOV           CX,4
SHL           AL,CL
MOV           AH,AL
INC           BX
MOV           AL,[BX]
```

```
CALL      HEX_TO_DIGIT
JC        BAD_HEX
OR        AL,AH
CLC
DONE :
POP       CX
POP       BX
RET
BAD_HEX :
STC
JMP       DONE
HEX_TO_BYTE   ENDP
```

The above procedure converts the two characters at DS:DX from hex to one byte.

```
PUBLIC    READ_BYTE
READ_BYTE   PROC    NEAR
[ISJ      DX
MOV       CHAR_NUM_LIMIT, 3
LEA       DX,KEYBOARD_INPUT
CALL      READ_STRING        CMP     NUM_CHARS_READ,1
JE        ASCII_INPUT
JB        NO-CHARACTERS
CMP       BYTE PTR NUM_CHARS_READ<OFFh
JE        SPECIAL_KEY
CALL      STRING_TO_UPPER
LEA       DX, CHARS
CALL      HEX_TO_BYTE
JC        NO-CHARACTERS
MOV       AH,1
DONE_READ :
POP       DX
RET
NO_CHARACTERS :
XOR       AH,AH
JMP       DONE_READ
ASCII_INPUT :
MOV       AL, CHARS
MOV       AH,1
JMP       DONE_READ
SPECIAL_KEY :
MOV       AL, CHARS         MOV
JMP
READ_BYTE    END
```

The above procedure reads either a single ASCII character or two_digithex number.

```
PUBLIC    GET_DECIMAL
GET_DECIMAL  PROC     NEAR
PUSH      BX   PUSH     CX
PUSH      DX
MOV       CHAR_NUM_LIMIT,6         ; MAX number is 5 digit (65535)
LEA       DX,KEYBOARD_INPUT
CALL      READ_STRING
MOV       CL,NUM_CHARS_READ   ; Get number of characters
READ
XOR       CH,CH                    ; Set upper type of  count to 0
CMP       CL,0                     ; Returns error if no characters read
```

```
JLE          BAD_DECIMAL_DIGIT        ; No chars read, signal error
XOR          AX,AX                    ; Start with number set to 0
XOR          BX,BX                    ; ; Start at beginning of string
CONVERT_DIGIT :
MOV          DX,10                    ; Multiply number by 10
MUL          DX                       ; Multiply AX by 10    JC
BAD_DECIMAL_DIGIT                     ; If set if MUL over-flowed are word
MOV          DL,CHARS [BX]            ; Get the next digit
SUB          DL,'0'                   ; And convert to a nibble (4 bits) JS
BAD_DECIMAL_DIGIT                     ; Bad digit if < 0
CMP          DL, 9                    ; Is this a bad digit ? JA
BAD_DECIMAL_DIGIT                     ; Yes
ADD          AX,DX                    ; No, so add it to number
INC          BX                       ; Point to next character
LOOP         CONVERT_DIGIT            ; Get the next digit
DONE_DECIMAL :
POP          DX
POP          CX
POP          BX
RET
BAD_DECIMAL_DIGIT :
STC                                   ; Set carry to signal error
GET_DECIMAL
```

The above procedure takes the output buffer of READ-STRING and converts the string of decimal digits to a word.

```
GROUP        GROUP    CODE_SEG,    DATA_SEG
ASSUME       CS:CGROUP,DS:CGROUP
BS           EQU 8
CR           EQU 13
ESC          KQU 27
CODE_SEG  SEGMENT PUBLIC
PUBLIC       STRING_TO UPPER
STRING_TO_UPPER     PROC      NEAR
PUSH         AX
PUSH         BX
PUSH         CX
MOV          BX,DX
INC          BX
MOV          CL,[BX]
XOR          CH,CH
TO_LOOP :
INC          BX
MOV          AL,[BX]
CMP          AL,'a'
JB           NOT_LOWER
CMP          AL,'Z'
JA           NOT_LOWER
ADD          AL, 'A'- 'a'
MOV          [BX], AL
NOT_LOWER :
LOOP TO_UPPER
POP          CX
POP          BX
POP          AX
```

```
STRING_TO_UPPER ENDP
```

The above procedure converts the string, using the DOS format for strings to all uppercase letters.

```
PUBLIC      BACK_SPACE
EXTRN       PUT_CHAR:NEAR
BACK_SPACE  PROC    NEAR    PUSH    AX
PUSH        DX
CMP         BX,2                    ; Is buffer empty ?
JE          GETC                    ; Yes, read the next character
DEC         BX                      ; Remove one character from buffer
MOV         AH,2                    ; Remove character from screen
MOV         DL,BS
INT         21h
MOV         DL,20h
CALL        PUT_CHAR
MOV         DL,BS                   ; Back up again
INT         21h
ETC:POP     DX
POP         AX
RET

BACK_SPACE      ENDP
CODE_SEG        ENDS
DATA_SEG        SEGMENT  PUBLIC
KEYBOARD_INPUT LABEL     BYTE
CHAR_NUM-LIMIT DB    0              ; length of input buffer
NUM_CHARS_READ  DB    0             ; Numbers of characters read
CHARS       DB     80 DUP (0)       ; A buffer for keyboard input
DATA_SEG        ENDS
```

The above procedure deletes characters, one at a time, from the buffer and the screen when the buffer is not empty.

3.3 More on The Macro Assembler

MASM can be divided into three levels

(a) The module level

(b) The segment level

(c) The procedure level.

By modules we refer to the parts of the program which have their independent identity. These modules can be independently maintained and assembled.

Segments are the physical grouping of like items within a program like the code segment, the data segment and the stack segment. Procedures are the functional subdivision of an executable program.

3.3.1 PROGRAM MODULES

The source code of individual routines are placed in the files contained in the module-level structure. The programs have a top-down structure and in this structure a large programming problem is broken up into small modules. The source file is translated by the assembler into a relocatable object module. These object modules are grouped together and kept in a file. The assembler links the object modules with other additional library modules into an executable program file.

The use of modules and object module libraries reduces the size of the application source files, because these files are not required to contain the source code for the routines they have in common with other programs. This also helps in the easier modification of the programs as we have to alter any one copy of the source code stored in one place.

3.3.2 PROGRAM SEGMENTS :

The programs segments can be divided into two wide groups

(a) Physical segment

(b) Logical segment.

The physical segments are 64KB blocks of memory. There are basically four segment registers which act as pointers and point specifically to these memory blocks. Each segment register can point to the bottom of the a different 64KB area of memory. A program can address to any location in the memory space by the proper manipulation of the segments.

Logical segments are the program compoments. A minimum of three logical segment must be defined for any program i.e. the data segment, the code segment and the stack segment. Programs having more than 64KB, of code or data, have more than one code or data segment.

The segment is declared with the directive SEGMENTS and ENDS. Additional térms are often added to a SEGMENT directive statement to indicate some special case in which we want the assembler to treat the segment. There are a few segment attributes which are align type, combine type, and class type. These attributes are of use in the linkers with which it combines the logical segment to create physical segment.

The programs are classified into different memory modules on the basis of their code and data segments. The most commonly used memory model for assembly language programs is the small model. These have one code and one data segment. We can also use medium, compact and large models.

MODEL	CODE SEGMENTS	DATASEGMEN
Small	One	One
Medium	Multiple	One
Compact	One	Multiple
Large	Multiple	Multiple

For each model, Microsoft has established certain segment and class names that are used by its HLL compilers. Because segment names are arbitrary, one may as well adopt Microsoft conventions.

Another important Microsoft high-level language convention is to use the GROUP directive to name the near data segment and the stack segment as members of DGROUP (the automatic data group), a special name recognised by the linker and also by the program loader in Microsoft Windows and Microsoft OS/2. The GROUP directive causes logical segments with different names to be combined into a single physical segment so that they can be addressed using the same segment base address.

Segments, group, and classes for the standard memory models :

MEMORY MODEL	SEGMENT NAME	ALIGN TYPE	COMBINE TYPE	CLASS TYPE	GROUP
SMALL	- TEXT	WORD	PUBLIC	CODE	
	- DATA	WORD	PUBLIC	DATA	DGROUP
	- STACK	PARA	STACK	STACK	DGROUP
MEDIUM	MODULE-TEXT	WORD	PUBLIC	CODE	
	:				
	:				
	- DATA	WORD	PUBLIC	DATA	DGROUP
	- STACK	PARA	STACK	STACK	DGROUP
COMPACT	- TEXT	WORD	PUBLIC	CODE	
	- DATA				
	:				
	:				
	- DATA	WORD	PUBLIC	DATA	DGROUP
	STACK	PARA	STACK	STACK	DGROUP

One can ignore DGROUP for pure assembly language programs running under MS-DOS. One will want to follow the Microsoft DGROUP convention if one wants to integrate assembly language routines and programs written in high-level languages. If one plans to link routines from C library into assembly language program, one should include the line DGROUP group - DATA, STACK at the beginning of the program.

3.3.3 PROGRAM PROCEDURES

Procedure level of program structure is purly real and partly conceptual. Procedures within a program are declared with PROC and ENDP directives.

name PROC attributes : : RET

name ENDP The atribute in the procedure decleration statements, which is either NEAR or FAR, tells the assembler what type of call one expects to with the procedure - that is, whether the procedure will be called by routines in the same segment or from routines in other segment. When the assembler encounters a RET instruction within a procedure, it uses the attribute information to generate the correct opcode for either a near (intra segment) or far (inter segment) return.

Each program should have a main procedure that receives control from MS-DOS. One specifies the entry point for the program by including name of the main procedure in theEND statement in one of the program's source files. The main procedure's attribute (NEAR or FAR) is not important because program returns control to **MS-DOS** with a function call rather than RET instruction.

One should break the remainder of the program into procedures in an orderly way, with each procedure performing a well defined single function returning its result to its caller, and avoiding action that has global effect within the program. The effort invested in making the procedures compact, clean, flexible and well documented will be repaid many times over when we reuse the procedure in other programs.

3.3.5 MASM-MACRO ASSEMBLER VER 6.X

INTRODUCTION

The Microsoft Macro Assembler programmer's guide provides the information one needs to write and debug assembly-language programs with the Microsoft Macro Assembler (MASM), version 6.1. This book, documents enhanced features of the language and the programming environment for MASM 6.1.

NEW AND EXTENDED FEATURES IN MASM 6.1

MASM 6.1 breaks the tradition established by version 6.0. It incorporates conveniences of high level language while offering all the traditional advantages of assembly- language programming.

MASM 6.1 includes the Programmer's Work Bench, which provides the same integrated software development environment enjoyed by programmers of Microsoft high level languages such as C and "Basic". From within PWB one can edit, build, debug or run a program. One can perform most of these operations with either menu selection or keyboard commands. One can customise PWB to suit one's individual programming and editing requirements & preferences.

COMPATIBILITY BETWEEN MASM 5.1 AND MASM 6.1

MASM 6.1 provides a "compatibility mode", making it easy for us to transfer existing MASM 5.1 code to the new version. We can invoke the compatibility mode through the OPTION M510 directive or the /zm command line switch.

REWRITING CODE FOR COMPATIBILITY

In some cases, MASM 6.1 with OPTION M510 does not support MASM 5.1 behaviour. In several cases, this is because bugs in MASM 5.1 were corrected. This usually requires minor changes.

NEW FEATURES SINCE VERSION 5.1

MASM 6.1 includes several features designed to make the programming more efficient and productive. The following list briefly discribes how MASM 6.1 improves on the language features of the popular version 5.1

MASM 6.1 has many enhancements related to types. One can now use the same type specified in initializations as in other contexts. One can also define ones own types, including pointer types, with a new TYPEDEF directive.

The syntax for defining and using structures and records has been enhanced since version 5.1. One can also define unions with new UNION directives.MASM now generates the complete code view information for all types.

New control-flow directives lets one use high level-language constructs such as loops and if then else blocks defined with .REPEAT and .UNTIL or .UNTIL CXZ;

.WHILE and .ENDW .IF and .ELSE and .ELSEIF.

The assembler generates the appropiate code to implement the control structure.

MASM now has more powerful features for defining and calling procedures. The extended PROC syntax for generating stack frames has been enhanced since version 5.1. One can also use the PROTO directive to prototype a procedure which one can then call with the INVOKE directive. INVOKE automatically generates code to pass arguments and makes the call according to the specified calling convention.

MASM optimizes jumps by automatically determining the most efficient coding for a jump and then generating the appropiate code.

Maintaining multiple-module programs is easier in MASM 6.1 than in version 5.1. The EXTERNDEF and PROTO directives make it easy to maintain all global definitions in include files shown by all the source modules of a project.

The assembler has many new macro features that make complex macro clearer and easier to write. One can specify default values for macro arguments or mark arguments as required. And with the VARARG key word, one parameter can accept a variable number of arguments.

One can implement loops inside macros in various ways. For example the new WHILE directive expands the statements in a macro body while expression in not zero.

One can define macro functions, which return text macros. Several predefined text macro are also provided for processing strengh. Macro operations and other features related to processing text macro and macro arguments have been enhanced.

Other Improved Capabilities :

- The .STARTUP and EXIT directives automatically generates appropriate start up and exit code for the assembly language programs.

- MASM 6.1 supports flat memory model available with the new Microsoft Windows NT. Operating system. Flat model allows segments as large as four gigabytes instead of 64K. Offsets are 32 bits instead of 16 bits.

- The program H2INC.EXE converts C include files to MASM include files and translates data structures and declarations.

MASM 6.1 produces a library of assembly routines that enables one to create a terminate-and-stay resident program (TSR).

MASM 6.1 includes many other minor new features as well as extensive support for features of earlier versions of MASM. - ML now runs in 32 -bit protected mode under MS-DOS, giving it direct access to extended memory for assembling very large source files.

- A collection of tools lets one write a dynamic link library (DLL) for the Microsoft Windows operating system without the Windows software development kit. The LIBW.LIB library provides access to all functions in the windows application programming interface (API). So our DLL can display menus, dialog boxes,and scroll bars.

- Program listing now shows instruction timing. The number of required processor cycles appears adjacent to each instruction in the listing, based on the selected processor.

- All utilities have been updated for version 6.1. Documentation is clearer and better arranged, with a new Environment & tools reference books.

- Version 6.1 generates debugging information for code view of version 4.0 and later.

MASM 6.1 provides even greater compatibility with version 5.1 than does MASM 6.0. Many programs written with version 5.1 will assemble unchanged under MASM 6.1

ML AND MASM COMMAND LINES

MASM 6.1 provides an updated version of the command line driver, ML, introduced in version 6.0. ML in more powerful and.flexible than the MASM driver of version 5.1. ML assembles and links with one command. It recognizes all the old MASM driver command syntax, however, to support existing batch files and makefiles that use MASM command lines.

COMPATIBILITY WITH EARLIER VERSIONS OF MASM

MASM 6.1 is fully compatible with version 6.0 and, in many cases, with version 5.1. Code written for MASM 5.1 will often assemble correctly without modification under MASM 6.1. However, NASM 6.1 provides the OPTION directive to let one selectively modify the assembly process. In particular, one can use the M510 argument with OPTION to set most features to be compatible with version 5.1 code.

THE ASSEMBLER ENVIRONMENT, AND UTILITIES

Most of the executable files provided with MASM 6.1 are new or revised. For a complete list of these files, there is PACKING.TXT file on the distribution disk.

THE ASSEMBLER

The macro assembler, named ML.EXE, can assemble and link in one step. Its new 32 bit operation gives ML.EXE the ability to handle much large source files than MASM 5.1. The command line options are new and are case sensitive and must be separated by spaces.

H2INC

H2INC converts C include files to MASM include files. It translates data structures and declaration but does nottranslate executable codes.

INTEGRATED ENVIRONMENT

PWB is an integrated development environment for writing, developing anc debugging programs.

ONLINE HELP

MASM 6.1 incorporates the Microsoft Advisor Help System. Help provides vast database of on line help about all aspects of MASM, including the syntax and timings for processors and co-processor instructions, directives, command line options, and support programs such as LINK and PWB.

HELPMAKE

One can use, the HELPMAKE utility to create additional help files from ASCII text files, allowing one to customize the on-line help system.

OTHER PROGRAMS

MASM 6.1 contains the most recent versions of LINK, LIB, BIND, CODEVIEW and mouse driver. The CREF program is not included in MASM 6.1. The source Browser provides the information that CREF provided under MASM 5.1.

SEGMENT MANAGEMENT

This section lists the changes and additions to memory-model support and directive that relate to memory model.

PREDEFINED SYMBOLS

The following predefined symbols provide information about the segments

PREDEFINED SYMBOL	VALUE
@ STACK	DGROUP for near stacks,"STACK" for far stacks
@ INTERFACE	Information about language parameters
@ MODEL	Information about the current memory model
@ LINE	The source line in the current file
@ DATE	The current date
@ FILECUR	The current time
@ ENVIRON	The current environment variables

ENHANCEMENTS TO THE ASSUME DIRECTIVE

MASM automatically generates ASSUME values for the code segment register (CS) It is no longer necessary to include lines such as "ASSUME CS": statement in one's program. In addition, the ASSUME directive can include ERROR, FLAT, or REGISTER: type. MASM 6.1 issues a warning when some body specifies ASSUME values for CS other than the current segment or group.

RELOCATABLE OFFSETS

For compatibility with applications for windows, the LROFFSET operator can calculate a relocatable offset, which is resolved by the loader at the run time .

FLAT MODEL

MASM 6.1 supports the flat memory model of Windows NT, which allows a segment as large as 4 gigabytes. All other memory models limit segment size to 64k for MS DOS, and Windows.

DATA TYPES

MASM 6.1 supports an improved data typing. This section summarizes. the improved forms of data declaration in MASM 6.1.

DEFINING TYPED VARIABLES

One can use the type names as directives to define variables. Initializers are unsigned by default.

SIGNED TYPES

One can use the SBYTE, SWORD & SDWORD directives to declare signed data.

FLOATING-POINT TYPES

MASM 6.1 provides the REAL 4, REAL 8, and REAL 10 directives for declaring floating point variables.

QUALIFIED TYPES

Type definition can now include distance and language type attributes, procedures, procedure prototypes and external declarations. It lets one specify the type as a qualified type.

STRUCTURES

Changes to structure since MASM 5.1 include :

Structures can be nested.

The name of structure fields need not to be unique.

Initialization structure variables can continue over multiple lines provided the last character in the line before the comment field is a comma.

Curly braces and angle brackets are equivalent.

UNIONS

MASM 6.1 allows the definition of unions with the UNION directive. Unions differ from structures in that all fields within the union occupy the same data space.

TYPE DEFINED WITH TYPEDEF

The TYPEDEF directive defines a type for use in the later program It is most useful for defining pointer types.

NAME OF INDETIFIERS

MASM 6.1 accepts identifier names upto 247 characters long. All characters are significant, whereas under MASM 5.1, names are significant to 31 characters only

MULTIPLE-LINE INITIALIZERS

In MASM 6.1 a comma at and of a line implies that the line is continuous.

DETERMINING SIZE AND LENGTH OF DATA LABELS

The LENGTHOF operator returns the number of data items allocated for a data label. MASM 6.1 also provides the SIZEOF operator. When applied to a type, SIZEOF returns the size attribute of the expression. When applied to a data label, SIZEOF returns the no. of types used by the initializer in the label definition. In this case SIZEOF for a variable equals the no. of bytes in the type multiplied by LENGTHOF for the variable.

MASM 6.1 recognizes the LENGTH and SIZE operators for backward compatibility.

HIGHWORD AND LOWWORD OPERATORS

These operators return the high and low words for a given 32 bit operand. They are similar to the

HIGH & LOW operators of MASM 5.1 except that HIGHWORD and LOWWORD can take only constants as operands.

PROCEDURES, LOOPS, AND JUMPS

With its significant improvements for procedures and jump handling, MASM 6.1 closely resembles high-level-language implementation of procedure calls. MASM 6.1 generates the code to correctly handle argument passing, check type compatibility between parameters and arguments, and process variables and arguments, it also do automatically recast jumps to correct for insufficient jump distance.

FUNCTION PROTOTYPES AND CALLS

The PROTO directive tells us prototype procedures, it enables type checking and type conversion of arguments when calling procedures with INVOKE.

The INVOKE directive sets up code to call a procedure and correctly pass arguments according to the prototype. MASM 6.1 also provides the VARARG keyword to pass variable number of arguments to procedure with INVOKE

NEW PROCESSOR INSTRUCTIONS

MASM 6.1 supports these instructions for the 80486 processor.

80486 INSTRUCTIONS	DESCRIPTION
BSWAP	Byte swap
CMPXCHG	compare and exchange
INVD	Invalidate translation lookaside Buffer entry
INVLPG	Write back and invalidate data cache
WBIND	Write back
XADD	Exchange and add.

RENAMED DIRECTIVES

Although MASM 6.1 still supports the old names in MASM 5.1, the following directives have been renamed for language consistency.

MASM 6.1	MASM 5.1
.LISTIF	.FLCOND
.LISTMACRO	.XALL
.LISTMACROALL	.LALL
.NOCREF	.XCREF
.NOLIST	.XLIST
.NOLISTIF	.SFCOND
.NOLISTMACRO	.SALL
ECHO	% OUT
EXTERN	EXTRN
FOR	IRP
FORC	IRPC
REPEAT	REPT
STRUCT	STRUC
SUBTITLE	SUBTTL

SPECIFYING 16-BIT AND 32 BIT INSTRUCTIONS

MASM 6.1 supports all instructions that work with the 32-bit registers of 80386/486. For certain instructions, one can override the default operand size with the W and the D suffixes.

MACRO ENHANCEMENTS

There are significant enhancements to Macro functions in MASM 6.1. Directives provide for a variable number of arguments, loop constructions, definition of text equates, and macro functions

VARIABLE AGRUMENTS

MASM 5.1 ignores extra arguments to passed to macros.InMASM 6.1 one can pass variable no. of arguments a macro by appending the VARAGR keyword to the last macro parameter in the macro definition. Hence macros can be referenced by additional arguments relative to the last declared parameter.

DEFAULT MACRO ARGUMENTS

With MASM 6.1, we can use REQ or the := operator to specify required or default arguments

NEW DIRECTIVES FOR MACRO LOOPS

Within a macro definition, WHILE repeats assembly as long as conditions remain true. Other macro directives IRP, IRPC, and REPT, have been renamed FOR, FORC, and REPEAT.

TEXT MACROS

The EQU directive retains its old functionality, but MASM 6.1 also incorporates TEXTEQU directive for defining text macros, it allows greater flexibility than EQU.

THE GOTO DIRECTIVE FOR MACROS

Within a macro definition, GOTO transfers assembly to a line labeled with a leading colon (:)

MACRO FUNCTIONS

At assembly time, macro functions can determine and return a text value using EXITM. Predefined macro string functions concatenates strings, returns the size, and returns the position of a sub string within a string.

PREDEFINED MACRO FUNCTIONS

Here is a set of instructions with the type of repeat prefix it uses, and indicates whether the instruction works on a source or destination or both.

Requirements for string Instructions :

Repeat	prefix	source/dest.	Register pair
MOVS	REP	Both	DS:SI,ES:DI
SCAS	REPE/REPENE	Destination	ES:DI
CMPS	REPE/REPENE	Both	DS:SI,ES:DI
LODS	-	Source	DS:SI
STOS	REP	Destination	ES:DI
INS	REP	Destination	ES:DI
OUTS	REP	Source	DS:SI

NO CLOSING VIOLATION MARKS IN MACRO AGRUMENTS

In MASM 5.1, one can use both single & double quotation marks ('and") to begin strings in macro arguments. The assembler does not generate an error or warning if the string does not end with quotation marks on a macro call. To correct such error in MASM 6.1 either end the string with a closing quotation mark or use the macro escape character (!)to treat the quotation mark.

MAKING A SCOPED LABEL PUBLIC

MASM 5.1 considers code labels defined with a single colon inside a procedure to be local to that procedure if the module contains a. MODEL directive with a language type.

BYTE FORM OF BT, BTS,BTC & BTR INSTRUCTIONS

MASM 5.1 allows a byte argument for the 80384 bit test instructions, but encodes it as a word argument. The byte form is not supported by the processor.

DEFAULT VALUE FOR A RECORD FIELD

In MASM 5.1 default values for record fields can range down n to -2 where n is no. of bits in a field. This results in the loss of sign bit.

DESIGN CHANGE ISSUES

MASM 6.1 includes design changes that make the language more consistent. These changes are not affected by the OPTION. therefore the changes require necessary revisions.

In MASM 5.1 even if the operands for the instructions do not match in size, yet the instruction assembles correctly. A warning informs that a size mismatch has occurred. But its not so in MASM 6.1

CONFLICTING STRUCTURE STAEMENTS

MASM 5.1 allows to declare two or more structures with the same name. Each declaration replaces the previous declaration. However the field names from previous declaration still remain in the assembler list of declared values.

MASM 6.1 does not allow conflicting declarations of a structure. The error note contains conflicting no. of fields, conflicting name of fields or conflicting initializers.

FORWARD REFRENCES TO MACROS OUTSIDE OF EXPRESSION

MASM 5.1 allows forward references to text macros in specialized cases.

MASM 6.1 with (OPTION M510) also permit forward reference, but only when the text macro is referenced in an expression.

SIGNED COMPARISON OF HEXADECIMAL VALUES USING GT,GE,T,LE

The values for 2's complement comparision have changes. In MASM 5.1 the expression,

OFFFh GT - 1

Is false because the 2's complement values are equal. However, because hexadecimal numbers are now treated as an unsigned, the expression is true in MASM 6.1. To update, rewrite the affected code.

RET USED WITH A CONSTANT IN PROCEDURES

By default in MASM 6.1, the, RET instruction followed by a constant is generation of epilogue code. MASM 5.1 ignores the operand and creates the epilogue

USE OF % AS AN INDENTIFIER CHARACTER

MASM 5.1 allows % as an identifier character. This behaviour leads to ambiguities when % is used as the expansion operator in macros. Since % is not allowed as a character in MASM 6.1 we must change the names of any identifier contaning the % character.

ASSUME CS SET TO WRONG VALUE

With MASM 6.1 we do not need to use the ASSUME statement for CS instead it generates an automatic assume statement for the code segment register to the current segment or group.

CODE REQUIRING TWO-PASS ASSEMBLY

Unlike version 5.1 MASM 6.1 does most of its work on its first pass, then performs as many subsegment passes as necessary. In contrast, MASM 5.1 always assembles in two source passes, as a result we require some pass-dependent constructs under MASM 6.1. To assure compatibility MASM 6.1 supports 5.1 directives refering to two passes.

IFDEF AND IFNDEF WITH FORWARD-REFERENCED IDENTIFIERS

If we use names that has yet not been defined in IFDEF or IFNDF expression, MASM 6.1 gives False for the IFDEF expression and TRUE for IFNDEF expression. When OPTION M510 IS enabled the assembler generates a warning.

ADDRESS SPACE AS A CONSTANT

The value of off sets calculated in the first assembly pass may not be the same as those calculated on latter passes, therefore we should avoid comparisions with an address span. However DUP operator allows such an expression as its count value.

.TYPE WITH FORWARD REFERENCE

MASM 5.1 evaluates .TYPE on both assembly passes. It means it yields zero on the first pass and non zero on the second pass, if applied to an expression that forward references as symbol. Whereas MASM 6.1 evaluates .TYPE only on the first pass. It yields a value zero if operand references a symbol that has not been yet defined. It means. TYPE yields different results in MASM 6.1 OF & 5.1 if used in conditional assembly construction.

THE ESC INSTRUCTION

MASM 6.1 no longer supports the ESC instruction which was used to send handcoded commands to the co-processor MASM 6.1 recognizes and assembles full set of co-processor mnemonics and ESC instruction is not necessary.

USING OPTION DIRECTIVE

The OPTION directive lets us control compatability with MASM 5.1 code. This section explains the differences in MASM 5.1 and 6.1 behaviour that the OPTION directive can influence.

The OPTION M510 (directive) (or / zm command-line option) initiates all aspects of 5.1 compatability mode. We can select from among specific characteristics of MASM 5.1 behaviour with the OPTION arguments. All these arguments are discussed in the following sections.

OPTION M510

This section discusses the M510 argument to the OPTION directive, which selects the MASM 5.1 compatability mode. In this mode, MASM 6.1 implements MASM 5.1 behaviour relating to macros, offsets, scope of code labels, structures, identifier names, identifiers case, and other behaviours. The OPTION M510 directive automatically sets the following :

```
OPTION   OLDSTRUCTS  ; MASM        5.1   Structures
OPTION   OLDMACROS   ; MASM        5.1   macros
OPTION   DOTNAME     ; Identifiers may   begin with a dot (.)
OPTION   SETIF2:TRUE ; Two-pass activates on every pass
```

If one does not have a .386, 386P,.486, 486P directive in ones module then option M510 adds :

OPTION EXPR16 ; 16 bit expression precision

If one wants to remove option M510 from ones code or / zm from the command line add the OPTION directive argument.

There may be compatibility issues affecting ones code that are supported under the OPTION M510, but are not covered by the other OPTION directive arguments.

Once we have modified our source code so it no longer requires behaviour supported by OPTION M510 then we should replace OPTION M510 with other OPTION directive argument. By doing this our code works correctly.

RESERVED KEYWORDS DEPENDENT ON CPU MODE WITH OPTION M510

With OPTION M510, keywords and instructions not available in the current CPU mode (such as INTER under.8086) are not treated as key words. It means the USE 32,FLAT,FAR32, and NEAR 32segment types and the 80386/486 registers are not keywords with the processor selection less than .386.

INVALID USE OF INSTRUCTION PREFIXES WITH OPTION M510

Code without OPTION M510 generates errors for all invalid uses of the instruction prefixes, OPTION M510 supresses some of these errors to match MASM 5.1 behaviour. MASM 5.1 does not check for illegal uses of instruction prefixes LOCK, REP, REPE, REPZ, REPNE,and REPNZ. This generates error as instruction prefix are not allowed.

SIZE OF CONSTANT OPERANDS WITH OPTION M510

In MASM 5.1, a large constant value that can fit only in the processor's default word (4 bytes for .386 and .486, 2 bytes otherwise) is assigned a size attribute of the default word size, the value of constant effects the no. of bytes changed by the instruction. For example,

; Legal only with OPTION M510 MOV [6x],0100h is legal in OPTION M510 mode since 0100h cannot fit in a byte, the assembler interprets the value as word.

Without OPTION M510, the assembler never assigns a size automatically. One must state it explicitly with the PTR operator, as shown in following example :

```
;Without  OPTION M510
mov [6x], WORD PTR 0100h
```

CODE LABELS WHEN DEFINING DATA WITH OPTION M510

MASM 5.1 allows a code label definition in a data definition statement if that statement does not also define a data label. MASM 6.1 allows such definitions if OPTION M510 is enabled; otherwise it is illegal.

SEG OPERATOR WITH OPTION M510

In MASM 5.1, the SEG operator returns a label's segment address unless the frame is explicitly specified, in which case it returns the segment address of the field. A statment such as SEGDGROUP: Var always returns DGROUP, where as SEG var:always returns the segment address of Var. OPTION M510 forces the same behaviour in MASM 6.1.

If we do not use OPTION M510, the behaviour of the SEG operator is determined by the OPTION OFFSET directive, as described in "OPTIONOFFSET".

In MASM 6.1, the value returned by the SEG operator applied to a non-external variable depends on compatibility mode.

Without OPTION M510, SEG returns the address of the frame if one has been explicitly set.

With option M510, SEG returns the group if one has been explicitly defined. In the absence of a defined group, SEG returns the segment where the variable is defined.

EXPRESSION EVALUATION WITH OPTION M510

By default, MASM 6.1 changes the way expressions are evaluated. In MASM 5.1,

Var - 4[bx]

is passed as

(var-4) [bx]

Without OPTION 510, one must rewrite the statement, since the assembler passes it as

Var - (4[bx])

Which generates an error.

LENGTH AND SIZE OF LABEL WITH OPTION M510

With OPTION M510, one can apply the length and size operators to any label. For a code label, SIZE returns a value of OFFFFh for NEAR and OFFFEh for FAR.LENGTH always returns the constant count. For arrays initialized with DUP, SIZE returns the length multiplied by the size of the type. The LENGTH of, and SIZE of operators in MASM 6.1 handle arrays much most consistently. These operators return the number of data items and the number of bytes in an initializer.

COMPARING TYPES USING EQ AND NE WITH OPTION M510

With OPTION M510, the assembler converts type to a constant value before comparisions with EQ, and NE. Code types are converted to values of OFFFFh (near) or (OFFFEH) (far). If OPTION M510 is not enabled, the assembler converts only when comparing them with constants, thus MASM 6.1 recognizes only equivalent qualified types as equal expressions.

For existing MASM 5.1 Code, these distinctions affect only the use of the TYPE operator in conjunction with Ed and NE.

BUG FIXES SINCE MASM 5.1

This section list the differences between MASM 5.1 and MASM 6.1 due to bug corrections since MASM 5.1.

INVALID USE OF BOCK,REPNE AND REPNZ

Except in compatability mode, MASM 6.1 flags illegal uses of instruction prefixes LOCK, REPNE, and REPNZ.

The table summarizes the correct use of instruction prefixes. It lists each string

```
MYSTRUCT                      STRUC
F1                            DB 0
F2                            D3 0
MYSTRUCT                      ENDS                : WITH OPTION M510
VAL = (TYPE MYSTRUCT) EQ WORD                     : TRUE : 2EQ2
VAL = 2 EQ WORD                                   : TRUE : 2EQ2
VAL = WORD EQ WORD                                : TRUE : 2EQ2
VAL = SWORD EQ WORD                               : TRUE : 2EQ2
                                                  : WITHOUT OPTION M510
VAL = (TYPE MYSTRUCT) EQ WORD                     : TRUE : 2EQ2
VAL = 2EQ WORD                                    : TRUE : 2EQ2
VAL = WORD EQ WORD                                : TRUE : WORD EQ WORD
VAL = SWORD EQ WORD                               : FALSE.SWORD NE WORD.
```

USE OF CONSTANT AND PTR AS A TYPE WITH OPTION M510

One can use a constant as the left operand to PTR in compatibility mode. otherwise one must use type expression. With OPTION M510, a constant must have a value of 1 (BYTE), 2(WORD), 4(DWORD), 6(FWORD), 8(QWORD) or 10(TBYTE). The assembler treats the constant as the parenthesized type. Note that the TYPE operator yields a type expression, but the SIZE operator yields a constant.

STRUCTURE TYPE-CAST OF EXPRESSIONS WITH OPTION M510

In compatability mode, use of PTR operator is to type-cast a structure type. This is done in data initializers to affect the CODE View information of the data label. Without OPTION M510, the assembler generates an error

```
MYSTRC          STRUC
F1              DB   (1)
MYSTRC          ENDS
Myptr DW MYSTRC PTR 0; Illegal without OPTION M510.
```

SPECIFYING RADIXES WITH OPTION M510

If the current radix of our code is greater than 10 decimal, MASM 6.1 allows the radix specifiers B (binary) and D (decimal) only in compatibility mode. We must change B to Y for binary, and D to T for decimal, since both B and D are legitimate hexadecimal values for making numbers such as 12 D.

NAMING CONVENTIONS WITH OPTION M510

By default, MASM 5.1 does not write the names of public variables in upper case to the object file, even when a language-type of PASCAL, FORTRAN, or BASIC is specified. Unless we use OPTION M510 , these language types in MASM 6.1 write identifier names in upper case even with the /cp or /cx command line options. When we link with /NOI , case must match in the object files to resolve externals.

LENGTH SIGNIFICANCE OF SYMBOLS WITH OPTION M510

With MASM 5.1, only the first 31 characters of a symbol name are considered significant, and only first 31 characters of a public or external symbol name are placed in the object file.

Without OPTION M510, the entire name is considered significant and the maximum no. of characters placed in the object file is controlled with the /H number command-line option, with a default of 247 (the maximum length of an identifier in MASM 6.1).

STRING DEFAULTS AND STRUCTURE VARIABLES WITH OPTION M510

In compatibility mode, a constant initializer can overwrite a structure field initialized with a string value. Without OPTION M510, only under string or a list can overwrite a string initializer. To update our code, surround the constant value with angle brackets or curly braces to indicate a list with one element.

CURRENT ADDRESS OPERATOR WITH OPTION M510

In compatibility mode, the current address operator ($) applied to a structure returns the offset of the first byte of a structure. When OPTION M510 is not enabled $ returns the offset of the current field in the structure.

SEGMENT ASSOCIATION FOR FAR EXTERNAL WITH OPTION M510

In MASM 5.1, One must place an EXTRN directive for a variable in the same segment that holds the variable. For far data, this information entails opening and closing a segment just to place the EXTRN statement.

MASM 6.1 offers much greater flexibility as where EXTRN and EXTRNDEF statement can appear.

DIFFERENCE IN TEXT MACROS WITH OPTION M510

MASM 6.1 recursively expands text Macros used as values, whereas MASM 5.1 simply replaces the text Macro with its value the following example illustrates the differences :

```
; WITH OPTION M510
im1 EQU <contains im2>
im2 EQU <value>
im3 CASTER im1 : ==< contains im2>
; WITHOUT OPTION M510
im3 CATSTR im1 : == < contains value>
```

CONDITIONAL DIRECTIVES AND MISSING OPERAND WITH OPTION M510

MASM 5.1 considers a missing argument to be a zero. MASM 6.1 requires an argument unless option M510 is enabled.

OPTION DOTNAME

MASM 5.1 allows names of identifiers to begin with a period. The MASM 6.1 default is OPTION NO DOT NAME. Adding OPTION DOTNAME to ones code enables MASM 5.1 behaviour.

If one doesn't want to use this directive in souce code, rename the identifiers whose names begin with a period.

OPTION EXPR16

MASM 5.1 treats expressions as 16 bit words if one does not specify .386 or .386P directive MASM 6.1 by default treats expressions as 32 bit words, regardless of the CPU type. We can use smaller expression size in MASM 6.1 by using OPTIONEXPR16 statement.

Unless MASM 5.1 code specifies .386 or .386P, OPTION M510 also sets 16 bit expression size. One can selectively disable this by following OPTION M510 with the OPTION EXPR 32 directive which sets the size back to 32 bits.

OPTION NOKEYWORD

MASM 6.1 has several new keywords that MASM 5.1 does not recogonise as reserved. To resolve any conflict we can :

Rename any offending symbols in ourcode.

Selectively disable keyword with OPTION NOKEYWORD directive.

The second option lets us retain the offending symbol names in our code by forcing MASM 6.1 to not recogonize them as keywords. For example,

OPTION NOKEYWORD: <INVOKE STRUCT>

Removes the keywords INVOKE and STRUCT from the assemblers list of reserved words, however one can not use the key words in their intended function, since the assembler no longer recognizes them. The following list shows MASM 6.1 reserved words new since MASM 5.1 :

.BREAK	.UNTILCXZ	FRSTOCD
.CONTINUE	.WHILE	FRSTORW
.DOSSEG	ADDR	FSAVED
.ELSE	ALIAS	FSAVEW
.ELSEIF	BSWAP	FSTENVB
.ENDIF	CARRY?	FSTENVW
.ENDW	CMPXCHG	GOTO
.EXIT	ECHO	HIGHWORD
.IF	EXTERN	INVD
.LISTALL	EXTERNDEF	INVLPG
.LISTIF	FAR16	INVOKE
.LIST MACRO	FAR32	IRETDF
.LISTMACRO	ALL FLAT	IRETF
.NO87	FLDENVD	LENGTHOF
.NOCREF	FLDENWD	LOOPD
.NOLIST	FNSAVED	LOOPED
.NOLISTIF	FNSAVEW	LOOPEW
.NOLISTMACRO	CNSTENVD	LOOPNED
.REPEAT	FNSTENVW	LOOPNEW
.STARTUP	FOR	LOOPNZD
.UNTIL	FORC	LOOPNZW
LOOPW	PUSHCONTEXT	SWORD
LOOPZW	PUSHD	SYSCALL
LOWWORD	PUSHW	TEXTEQU

LROFFSET	REAL 10	TR3
NEAR16	PUSHCONTEXT	TR4
NEAR32	REAL8	TR5
OPATTR	REPEAT	TYPDEF
OPTION	SBYTE	UNION
OVERFLOW?	SOWORD	VARAGR
PARITY?	SIGN	WBINVD
POPAW	SIZEOF	WHILE
POPCONTEXT	STDCALL	XAOD
PROTO	STRUCT	ZERO?
PUSHAW	SUBTITLE	

OPTION SETIF2

By default MASM 6.1 does not recognize pass dependent constructs. Both the OPTION M510, and OPTION SETIF2 statements force MASM 6.1, **to handle MASM** 5.1 **constructs that activate on the second** assembly pass, such as .ERR2, IF2 and **ELSEIF2.**

Invoke the option like this:

OPTION SETIF 2: [TRUE/FALSE]

When set to TRUE, OPTION SETIF2 forces all second pass constructs to activate on every assembly pass. OPTION where set to FALSE, second pass constructs do not activate on any pass. OPTION M510 implies OPTION SETIF2: TRUE.

CHANGES TO INSTRUCTIONS AND ENCODING

MASM 6.1 contains changes to the encodings for several instructions. In some cases the changes help optimize the code size.

CO-PROCESSOR INSTRUCTIONS

For the 80287 coprocessor, MASM 5.1 adds on extra NOP before the no-wait version of coprocessor instructions. MASM 6.1 does not. In the rare case if the missing NOP affects timing, insert NOP.

For the 8087 co-processor or higher, MASM 5.1 inserts FWAIT before certain instruction & MASM 6.1 does not prefix any 80287, 80387, co-processor instruction with FWAIT except for wait forms of instructions that have no wait form.

RET INSTRUCTION

MASM 5.1 generates a 3 byte encoding for RET, RETN, or RETIF instructions with an operand value of zero unless the operand is an external absolute. In this case the, MASM 5.1 ignores the parameter and generates a 1 byte encoding.

MASM 6.1 does the opposite. It ignores a zero operand for the return instructions and generates a one byte encoding, unless the operand is an external absolute. In this case MASM 6.1 generates 3 byte encoding.

ARTHEMATIC INSTRUCTIONS

Versions 5.1 and 6.1 differ in the way they encode the **arithmetic** instruction ADC, ADD, AND, CMP, OR, SUB, SBB, and XOR under the following conditions.

The first operand is either AX or EAX.

The second operand is a constant value between 0 and 127.

Chapter Four

DOS & BIOS INTERRUPTS

4.0 INTRODUCTION TO DOS INTERRUPTS :

An operating system is a program which acts as an interface between a user of a computer and the computer hardware. DISK OPERATING SYSTEM (DOS) is the most popular operating system used on the PC.

A major class of events which an operating system must handle is a class of I/O interrupts. Interrupts are signals that cause the computer's central processing unit to suspend it's current activities and transfer to a program called an interrupt handler.

Interrupts can be broadly classified into categories :

(i) Hardware Interrupts

(ii) Software Interrupts

(i) Hardware Interrupts : There can be either

(a) Internal Hardware Interrupts : These are generated by internal hardware events encountered during program execution.

(b) External Hardware Interrupts : These interrupt signals are directly sent to the interrupt lines (pins) of the microprocessor by peripheral device controllers or by coprocessors. The microprocessor halts its operation temporarily, services the device that interrupted it and resumes its operation afterwards.

(ii) Software Interrupts : A program can generate a

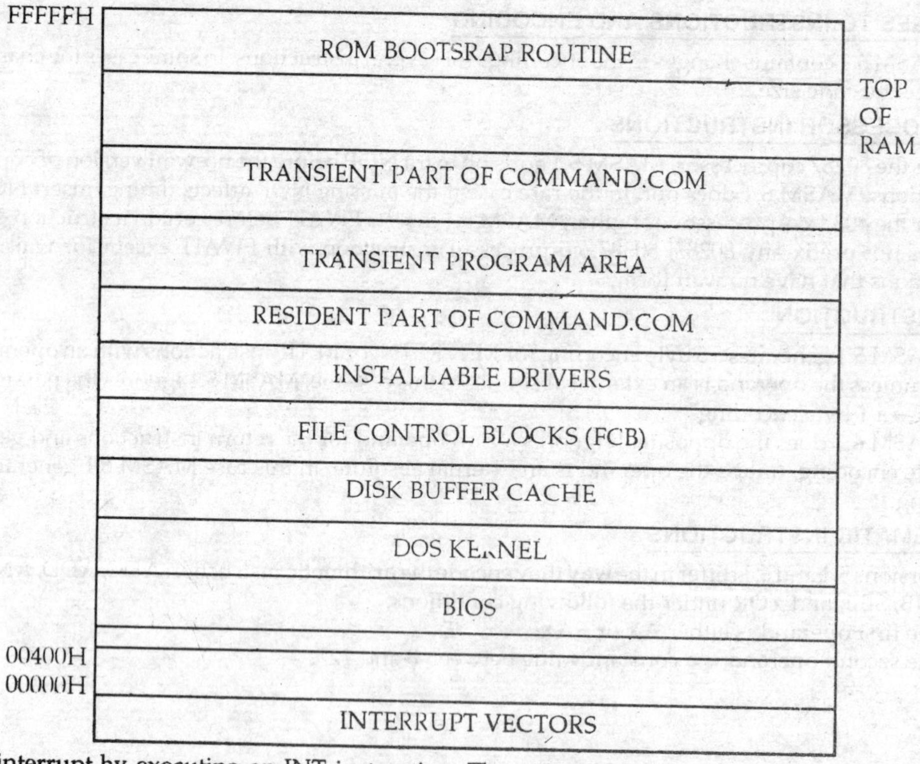

software interrupt by executing an INT instruction. The services rendered by the DOS are grouped together and there are two classes.

(i) A number of services are grouped together because they are invoked by the same interrupt 21H. The services in this group are differentiated by putting different values in the AH register.

(ii) The second class of services have an individual interrupt number for each service. Thus the individual services are characterized by their own interrupt value i.e. INT.

The different interrupt handlers have reserved locations in memory. The bottom 1KB of system memory is called the interrupt vector table (IVT). The table contains the interrupt type and the address of the interrupt handler for that interrupt. Thus whenever there is an interrupt request, the CPU looks for that interrupt in the IVT and gets the address of the interrupt service routine. It can then access the routine and perform the interrupt request.

The interrupts are handled by the interrupt handlers which are programs.

When there is an interrupt request for an interrupt, the following actions are taken.

(i) The other interrupts are disabled, so that they do not occur while the present interrrupt is being serviced.

(ii) The IVT is searched for the interrupt of interest and the control is moved to the interrrupt handler to perform the specific task.

(iii) After performing the particular task, the other interrupts which were disabled earlier, are enabled.

4.1 SERVICING AN INTERRUPT :

When the CPU senses an interrupt, it places the program status word (PSW), the code segment (CS) register and the instruction printer (IP) onto the stack and disables the interrupt system. After the interrupt has been serviced, the execution of program resumes from the address where it had been interrupted. The interrupt handler sends a special code called END of INTERRUPT (EOI) to tell that interrupt processing has been completed. The handler then executes the special INTERRUPT RETURN instruction that restores the original state of the CPU flags, the CS register and the instruction printer (IP).

4.1.1 PROGRAM SEGMENT PREFIX :

Whenever a program runs, the DOS first reserves an area of memory for the program called the program segment. It is the space where the program will reside after being loaded from disk. Before DOS loads the program, it sets up the first 100H bytes of the program segment with a control block called the program segment prefix (PSP). It contains two types of information : one that concerns the newly loaded program and information that DOS needs to restore the entire DOS environment to its previous state when the new program exits.

The first 2 bytes of the PSP contain interrupt 20H instruction that terminates the current program on calling.

O5H - 09H This part of the PSP contains a long call to the DOS function request that processes the interrupt 21H.

LAYOUT OF PSP (PROGRAM SEGMENT PREFIX)

Byte offset		
00H	Interrupt 20H instruction	O-P Offset portion
02H	Top of available memory (above value)	B-P Base portion
04	Reserved byte	
	Long call to DOS (location 06 contains the number of bytes available for program use in the segment)	
0A	Termination address (offset portion)	
0C	Termination address (Base)	
0E	Ctrl Break Exit address (B.P)	
10	Critical error quit address (offset) (Base)	
16	Reserved area (6 bytes)	
2C	Base address of environment	
2E	Reserved area (34 decimal bytes)	
50	Call to DOS	
52	Reserved area (10 decimal bytes)	
5c	First unopered standard FCB 16 bytes	
6c	Second unopered standard FCB	

0A - 0DH - TERMINATION ADDRESS : These four bytes contain the segmented address where control returns when this program exits.

12H - 15H Critical error exit address : The DOS interrupt 24H can change this address.

4.2 INVOKING THE DOS INTERRUPTS :

As described earlier the DOS interrupts can be broadly classified into two categories — (i) that are called directly by individual DOS interrupt requests and (ii) a set of interrupts with same interrupt request INT 21H which fall under the category DOS function requests. The individual functions are distinguished by moving a particular value corresponding to the desired function request into AH register. To invoke the services, certain registers are set up first. After setting up the registers, the interrupt routine is invoked by issuing the INT instruction with the corresponding interrupt number.

4.2.1 DOS FUNCTION REQUESTS :

The function requests like the interrupts are services that DOS provides to enable programs to directly access the capabilities of the operating system or hardware modules. The way the programs invoke function requests is similar to the way they invoke DOS interrupts. But unlike interrupts which have individual interrupt numbers for different services, all the DOS functions are invoked via the same software interrupt i.e. 21H. The individual services are distinguished by the value in the AH register.

DOS function requests can be divided into several categories based on the services they perform. These services are :

(i) Execution and termination of program.
(ii) I/O functions for character devices.
(iii) File management functions such as choosing a disk drive, creating or deleting files, opening or closing files and reading and writing file information.
(iv) Memory management functions (such as allocating and freeing memory).
(v) Time and date functions.
(vi) Network functions such as locking or unlocking files, getting the name of the local computer, and setting up the return printer.

4.2.2 FILE MANAGEMENT :

The file management involves function requests with numbers 0FH through 24H. These function requests, allow to create and delete files, open and close them, read and write etc. The key to using this set of function requests is a data.

FILE CONTROL BLOCK

BYTE									
-7H	OFFH								FCB EXT
-6H	RESERVED (Set these 5 bytes to 0)								
	Attribute byte								
0H	Drive number								
1H	Filename or reserved device name (8 bytes)								Std FCB
	Filename extension (3 bytes) current block (2 bytes)								
	File size (2 bytes)								
	Y	Y	Y date	Y	Y	Y	Y	M	
	m	m	m	d	d	d	d	d	
	Reserved (10 bytes)								
	Current relative record								
	Relative random record (2 bytes)								
	Relative random record (high portion)								
24H									

Structure called the file control Block (FCB).

This FCB is a 44-byte area which is used to pass information to DOS, concerning the file that is manipulated, the same FCB is then used by DOS to send back information.

The major disadvantage of this system is that it does not allow a subdirectory.

In this management system, to open a file, one has to create a data structure that matches the structure of the FCB. Then the fields of FCB, that specify the drive number, filename, and extension of the file are filled. Then the OPEN FILE function request (OFH) is placed in AH register and a pointer to the FCB in the DS: DX is moved.

4.2.3 DISK TRANSER ADDRESS (DTA) :

The DTA is the starting location of a buffer of memory that these function requests use when reading information from a file or when writing to a file. eg. to write information to a file, the information is first placed in memory beginning at the DTA and then the FUNCTION REQUEST (15H) is invoked for the write operation.

When a program starts running, the DTA, is not set by the programmer, it automatically takes the value 80H (offset) in the program segment prefix (PSP) of that program. With this value, there are 128 bytes for the transfer and if the information is longer than this, the program will be overwritten. To prevent this, we can change the DTA by invoking the set Disk transfer Address function request (1AH).

4.3 IMPLEMENTATION OF DOS INTERRUPTS USING ASSEMBLY LANGUAGE PROGRAMS :

DOS FUNCTION REQUESTS :

Here a number of programs which invoke a DOS function via interrupt 21H are given. The programs were run and tested on PC/AT using MASM6 assembler. The editor used was the Wordstar.

In assembly language, invoking DOS function requests is straightforward. For each function request, we set up the AH register with the corresponding number for that function and set up a few other registers as described for each function request.

The methods for invoking the DOS functions are :

(i) The "number"of the function request is placed in the AH register and the interrupt 21H is issued.

(ii) The "number" of the function request is placed in the AH register and a long call to offset 50H in Program Segment Prefix (PSP) is executed.

(iii) This method applies only to function 00H through 24H. It is provided for compatibility with DOS 1.X programs. To make use of this method, place the "number" of the function request in the CL register, and make an intrasegment call to offset 5 in the current code segment which contains a long call to the DOS function dispatcher.

The functions are described next :

(i) DOS Function Request 01H

Used to read a character from the keyboard and echo it to the screen. The function request accepts a character from the standard input device and echoes it to the standard output device i.e. the display screen. The standard input and output devices can also be redirected. This redirection enables programs that use this function request to read from data files. The output can also be redirected to other devices, such as a data file or a printer.

This function request checks the entered character to see if it is a Ctrl-Break, and if it is, the function request invokes an iterrupt 23H to start the Ctrl-Break handler.

If no input character is available when this function request is invoked, it waits until they become available.

Registers invoked :

AH register : This contains 01H, indicating the number of this function request.

AL : The character retrieved from the keyboard.

This program will display the character (A) on the screen.

```
. model small
. stack 100h    . code
main proc
mov ah, 01h
Int 21
```

```
mov Al,61
Int 21
Int 20
main endp
end main.
```

Let us study the program step by step.

.model small	:	The model is assigned small when either code or data may not be greater than 64K.
Stack 100h	:	A stack of 100h i.e. 256 bytes are reserved.
Mov ah,01h	:	The function number 01H is to display a character.
int 21	:	This invokes the function request.
Mov AL, 61 h	:	The ASCII value of the character to be displayed is stored in this register.
Int 20	:	This will return the program to DOS
Main endp	:	This ends procedure main.
Endmain	:	This ends the main program.

(II) DOS Function Request 02H :

Display a character at the standard output devices.

This function request displays a character at the standard output device. It displays the character at the current location of the cursor and then advances the cursor by one position.

If the character displayed is a backspace, the function request moves the cursor one position to the left. However it does not erase the character.

When the function displays a character at the end of the line, the cursor moves to the left edge of the next line. If the cursor is at the location right corner of the screen, the screen scrolls up one line when the cursor moves.

If Ctrl-Break is entered, the function request invokes an interrupt 23H to start the Ctrl-Break handler.

Registers affected :

AH : This register contains 02H, i.e. the number of the function request invoked.

DL : ASCII code for the character to be displayed.

An Assembly Language Program for invoking the function request 02H to display a character -

```
dosseg
. model small
. stack 100h
. code
. main proc
mov AH, 02h
mov SI, offset char
mov dl, [SI]
int 21
int 20
char db 'character to be displayed'
main endp
end main
```

Explanation :

MOV SI, offset Char - SI is the source index and the offset char has the ASCII value of the character that is to be displayed. This is moved to the offset given by [SI]. It is then transfered to Dl which contains the ASCII value of the character that is to be displayed by function request 02h. The rest of the explanation is as given for the previous function request.

(III) DOS Function Request 09H :

It displays a character string at the standard output device.

This function request displays a string of characters at the standard output device. It displays the characters starting at the current location of the cursor and then advances the cursor by one position.

To determine the end of the string, it assumes that the last character of the string is a $ character

(ASCII code 24H). It does not display the $ If any character in the string is a backspace character, it causes the cursor to move one position to the left.

When the function request displays a character at the end of the line, the cursor moves to the left edge of the next line.

If the cursor is at the bottom right corner of the screen, the screen scrolls up one line when the cursor moves.

The function checks for a control-Break after displaying the character, and if found, invokes an interrupt 23H to start the handler.

REGISTERS AFFECTED :

AH : - This register contains the function request number 09H.

DS : DX This register pair must point to the start of the character string in memory. The function request displays characters until it encounters a $ character (ASCII code 24H). Assembly language program to invoke function 09H.

```
dosseg
. model small
. stack 100h
. code
main proc
mov ah, 09
mov dx, offset string
int 21h
mov ah,00h
int 21h
string db 'This is a byte string.' '$"
end mainp
main end
```

Explanation :

MOV, dx, offset string - The string which is defined at the end of the program by statement string db, is moved into the DX register. The end of the string is indicated by $. The entire string which is moved into the DX register is displayed on the screen by invoking the function request 09H followed by interrupt 21h.

(iv) DOS Function Request 39H

MKDIR - Create a subdirectory.

Description : This function request creates a new subdirectory, just like the MKDIR command does. If any part of the specified pathname, except for the new subdirectory does not exist, the function request does not create the directory.

INPUT : Before invoking this function request, these registers must be set.

AH : This register must contain 39H, indicating the number of this function request.

DS:DX : This register pair must point to an ASCII string containing the drive and directory pathnames. As an ASCII string,it must be terminated with a byteof 0.

OUTPUT : None.

ERROR CONDITIONS : If an error occurs, the carry flag will be set and the AX register will contain one of the following values.

03 H The pathname specified does not exist.

05 H This value can indicate a number of conditions: if there is no proper access to at least one of the directories; there is no room in the parent directory; the subdirectory name already exists; if the path specifies a device.

Assembly language Program To invoke the DOS function Request 39H- MKDIR_create a subdirectory : dosseg

```
. model small
. stack 100h
. code
main proc
```

```
mov ax, cs
mov ds, ax
mov dx, offset newdir
mov ah,39h
int 21
jc  error
mov dx, offset msg1
mov ah, 09h
int 21
jump done
error: mov dx, offset msg2
mov ah, 09h
int 21
done: move ah, 4ch
int 21
code ends
data-hex    segment
newdir      db 'temp',0
msg1     db 'DirectoryTEMP created in current directory','$'
msg2       db 'ERROR', DIRECTORY NOT CREATED', '$'
end mainp
main end.
```

The above ALP creates a subdirectory named TEMP in the current directory by invoking the DOS function request 39h.

(v) DOS Function Request 4EH Find the first matching file.

Description : This function request searches a given directory for the first file that matches the name supplied. The name can contain the global characters "?" and "*" indicating that several files might match this name. The function request 4Eh accepts a full pathname as input, enabling of any directory. It returns enough information to form a complete directory entry for the file.

By using an attribute byte in the CX register this function request can be used to search for files according to their attributes, as follows :

(i) If the attribute byte is set to 0, the function request searches only for normal files. It does not find volume labels, subdirectories, hidden files, or system files.

(ii) If the attribute byte is set for hidden files, system files, and/or subdirectories, the function request searches through the normal files and through the special files selected to obtain a matching file. Setting all three bits enables the function request to search through normal files, hidden files, system files and directories.

(iii) If the attribute byte is set for the volume label, the function request searches only for the volume label, not for normal files.

The read- only bits have no offset on searches.

When the function request finds the first matching file, it supplies information about that file in memory starting at the disk transfer address (DTA), and this information can be used to open the file. Function request 4EH also uses the information starting at the DTA when searching for the next file that matches your specifications.

Input :

AH : This register contains 4EH, indicating the number of this function request.

DS : DX This register pair must identify the file which is searched by pointing to an ASCII string containing the drive, directory path, and filename. As an ASCII string, it must, be terminated with a byte of 0.The filename portion can contain global filename character "?" and "*"

CX : The low-order byte of this register is encoded with the file attributes to use in the search, as follows :

Bits

7	6	5	4	3	2	1	0

To use the attribute in the search, the coresponding bit is set to 1.

Bit	Description
0	Read only file
1	Hidden file
2	System file
3	Volume label
4	Subdirectory
5	Archive
6-7	Unused.

Output : The following is set after control returns. DTA - The disk transfer address is the starting location of 43 decimal bytes of information that describe the first matching file. It has the following fields :

(i) Reserved : The first 21 bytes are reserved for DOS use. It stores information here that allows it to find the next matching file if the function request 4EH is invoked.

(ii) File attribute : This byte is the file's attribute byte. It is encoded in the same way that the CX register was encoded.

(iii) File's time stamp : This two-byte value indicates the time when the file was last created or modified.

(iv) File's date stamp:- This two-byte value indicates the date that the file was last created or modified.

File Size : This four-byte value indicates the size of the file in bytes.

File name and extension : These 13 bytes contain an ASCIIZ string identifying the first matching file. This filename contains no leading blanks or separators.If the filename includes an extension, a period appears between the name and extension. As an ASCIIZ string, a byte of 0 terminates the name.

ERROR CONDITIONS :

If an error occurs, the carry flag will be set and the AX register will contain one of the following values.

02H : The function request could not find the file specified.

03H : At least one of the directory pathnames specified does not exist.

12H : There is no matching file in the directory.

Assembly language program to invoke DOS function Request 4EH.

```
dosseg
. model small
. stack 100h
. code
main proc
code segment public
assume CS:code, ds: code
mov ax, cs
mov ds, ax
mov dx, offset msg1
mov ah, 09h
int 21h
mov dx, offset file
mov cx, 0
mov ah, 4eh
int 21h
jnc found
mov dx, offset msg2
mov ah, 09h
```

```
int 21h
jmp done
found mov dx, offset msg3
mov ah, 09h
int 21h
done:
Data_Hex      segment
file        db  'testfile.asc', 0
msg1            db  'searching for testfile.asc.', 0dh, 0ah, '$'
msg2            db  'testfile.asc NOT FOUND!', 0dh, oah, '$'
msg3            db  'testfile.asc FOUND', odh, oah, '$'

mov ah, 4ch
int 21h
code ends
main endp
endmain
```

In the above program, we are searching for the file testfile. If it is found a message "Testfile Found" is given else the message "Testfile NOT found" is given. The $ is given to indicate the end of the string.

DOS Function Request 56H

Rename a file

Description : This function request changes the name of a file. It can change the name of any file in any subdirectory.

This function request is similar to the DOS RENAME command, but adds an extra feature i.e. it can also move the file from one subdirectory to another. The function request does this not by moving the file's data, but rather by moving the directory entry. Any movement between directories is restricted to directories on the same drive.

This function request applies to single files only. Therefore global filename characters are not allowed in the filenames.

This function should not be used to rename open files, hidden files, system files, or subdirectories as there is a risk of corrupting the disk when renaming these files.

REGISTERS AFFECTED :

AH : This register must contain 56H, indicating the number of this function request.

DS : DX This register pair must contain a pointer to an ASCII2 string that identifies the file to be renamed. This string can contain the drive, path and filename. The global filename characters "?" and "*" are not allowed.

ES : DI : This register pair must contain a pointer to an ASCII2 string that identifies the new name of the file. Although the path and file name can be different than those of the original file, the drive, if present, must be the same.

ERROR CONDITIONS :

If an error occurs, the carry flag will be set and the AX register will contain one of the following values.

02H The function request could not find the specified file.

03H One of the specified pathnames does not exist.

05H Access denied. The first pathname (pointed to by DS:DX) specifies a directory, the second pathname (pointed to by ES=D1) specifies an existing file, or the file could not be opened.

11H It is used to rename the file to a different drive.

ASSEMBLY LANGUAGE PROGRAM to invoke DOS Function Request 56H → Rename a file.

Suppose in this example program, we rename a file ABC to XYZ

```
dosseg
. model small
. stack 100h
```

```
data_here       segment
old       db    'ABC' , 0
new       db    'ZYZ' , 0
msg1      db    'ABC' renamed to 'XYZ, 0dh,  0ah, '$'.
msg2      db    ' File not renamed', 0dh, 0ah, '$'
data-here end
 code     segment
assume    CS: code,  ds: code
main      proc      comments:
mov       ax, cs    set up ds to
mov       ds, ax    same as cs
mov       dx, offset old     address of old file
mov       es, ax    set up es same as ds
mov       di, offset new     address of new file
mov       ah, 56h   rename file function request
int       21h
jc        error
mov       dx, offset msg1 (address of the message)
mov       ah, 09h   (display string)
int       21h
jmp       done
error:    mov       dx, offset msg2
mov       ah, 09h
int       21h
done:     mov       ah, 4ch
int       21h
code  ends
end mainp
main end.
```

(vii) DOS Function Request 57H : Get or set a file's date and time.

Description : This function request allows to retrieve or set the date and time information that is maintained as part of a file's directory entry. This date and time information indicates when the file was created or when it was last changed.

REGISTERS AFFECTED

AH : This register must contain the DOS function request number 57H

AL : This register is set to indicate the kind of operation to perform, as follows :

00 Get the date and time information

01 Set the date and time information

BX : This register must contain a file handle returned by the create a file (3CH), create a new file (5BH), or open a file (3DH) function request.

CX : If we have to set the file's date and time (set AL to 1), this request must contain the new time. The bits in this register are set as follows :

h	h	h	h	s	s	s	s	s	m	m	m	m	m

16 15   11 10   54   0

DX : If the file's date and time is set, this register must contain the new date

OUTPUT :

CX : If the output is file's date and time, this register contains information about the time. It is formatted as described for the input registers

DX : This register contains information about the date.

OTHER REQUIREMENTS :

Before a file's date is set, we must obtain a handle for the file, either by creating it (function request 3CH) or by opening it; before the date and time change take place, the file must be closed.

Error conditions :

If an error occurs, the carry flag will be set and the AX register will contain one of the following values:
01H If there is any other value in the AL register (other than 0 and 1)
06H The file handle supplied was not valid

Assembly Language Program to invoke DOS Function request 57H :

```
Get or set a file's Date and Time
dosseg (comments)
. model small
. stack 100h
. code
. main proc
mov ax, cs
mov ds, ax
mov dx, offset file
mov al, 0 attributes
mov ah, 3dh open file
int 21
jc error
mov handle, ax
mov bx, handle
mov al,0 get date and time
mov ah, 57h et/set file/time
int 21
jc error
mov time, cx
mov date, dx
mov dx, offset msg1
mov ah, 09h
int bx, handle
move ah, 3eh
int 21
jmp done
error: mov dx,  offset msg2
mov  ah,  09h
int      21
done:move  ah,  4ch
int      21
data-here:     segment
file    db  'tstfile.asc', 0
handle   dw  ?   date    dw  ?
time    dw  ?
msg1     db  'Get date and time'., '$'
msg2     db  'unable to get date and time', '$'
main endp
end main.
```

(viii) Function Request 5AH Create a unique file.

Description : This function request examines a directory specified and creates a new file in that directory one whose name is different from any file currently in that directory. This function request is useful for programs that use temporary files. Instead of checking every file name itself or using an unusual name without checking (and possibly destroying an existing file), a program can invoke this function request to create a temporary file and be assured that the resulting file will not have the same name as an existing file.

To use this function request, the calling program must have create occurs rights to the directory that will contain the new file.

INPUT:

Before invoking this function request, these registers are set.

AH : This register must contain 5AH, indicating the number of the function request.

DS:DX This register pair must identify the directory in which the new file should reside by pointing to an ASCIIZ string containing the drive and path of the directory. The last character of the path must be a backslash. As an ASCII2 string, it must be terminated with a byte of 0.

CX: The low order byte of this register is encoded with the file attributes that the new file has

Bits

7	6	5	4	3	2	1	0

To indicate the attribute, the corresponding bit is set to 1.

BIT	Description
0	Read-only file
1	Hidden file
2	System file
3	Volume label
4	Subdirectory
5	Archive
6-7	Unused.

OUTPUT : After control returns, the following is set:

DS : DX This register pair identifies the new file by pointing to an ASCIIZ string containing its drive, directory path, and filename. As an ASCII2 string, it is terminated with a byte of 0.

OTHER REQUIREMENTS : This function call creates a new file but does not open it. Before using the file, the program must invoke function request 3DH to open the file. The program should close the file when it finishes using it. If the program uses the new file as a temporary file, it must delete the file when it finishes using the file. DOS does not delete the files when the program exits.

ERROR CONDITION :

If an error occurs, the carry flag will be set and the AX register will contain one of the following values.

03H : At least one of the directory pathnames specified does not exist.

04H : There are no file handles available

05H : There is no space for a new entry in the directory.

ASSEMBLY LANGUAGE PROGRAM TO INVOKE DOS FUNCTION REQUEST 5AH (Create a unique file)

```
dosseg
. model small
. stack 100h
. code
main proc
mov ax, cs
mov ds, ax
mov dx, offset path
mov cx, 0
mov ah, sah
int 21
jc error
```

```
mov handle, ax
mov dx, offset msg1
mov ah, 09h
int 21
mov bx, handle
mov ah, 3eh
mov 21
jmp done
error:   mov dx, offset msg2
mov ah, 09h
int 21
done :   mov ah, 4ch
int 21h
code     ends
data-here segment
handle   dw  ?
msg1 db  'File created', 0dh, 0ah,
path db  '\', 0
file     db  '     ', '$'
msg2     db  'File not created', oah, '$'
data-here end
main     endp
end main
```

Thus if the file is created, then it is displayed using function request 09H "File created" and there wil be an entry in the directory abe the message "file not created" is displayed.

(ix) DOS Function Request 5BH : Create a New file.

Description : This function request, is identical to function request 3CH (create a file)except that it only creates new files. If the file you intend to create already exists, it returns an error.

To use this function request, the calling program must have create access to the directory that is to contain the new file. The file created will be open for reading and writing in compatibility mode.

INPUT : These registers must be set before invoking the function request.

AH : This register must contian 5BH, indicating the number of this function request.

DS:DX : The register pair must identify the new file by pointing to an ASCII string containing drive, directory path, and filename. As an ASCII byte of 0.

CX : The low-order byte of this register is set to contain the encoded file attributes of the new file

7	6	5	4	3	2	1	0

Bit	Description
0	Read only file
1	Hidden file
2	System file
3	Volume label
4	Subdirectory
5	Archive
6-7	Unused.

OUTPUT: After control returns, the following is set.

AX : If no error has occured, this register contains the file handle of the new file. If an error has occured, the register contains an error code.

OTHER REQUIREMENTS : To use this function request in a network environment, we must have occurs right to the directory that will contain the file.

ERROR CONDITIONS : If an error occurs, the carry flag will be set and the AX register will contain one of the following values.

03H : At least one of the directory pathnames specified does not exit.
04H : There are no file handlers available.
05H : There is no space for a new entry in the directory.
50H : The file already exists.

ASSEMBLY LANGUAGE PROGRAM TO CREATE A NEW FILE (Function Request 5BH). The name of the new file is suppose xxx.

```
dosseg
. model small
. stack 100h
. code
main proc
mov ax, cs
mov ds, ax
mov dx, offset new file
mov cx, 0
mov ah, 5bh
int 21
jc error
mov handle, ax
mov dx, offset msg1
mov ah, 09h
int 21
mov bx, handle
mov ah, 3eh
int 21
jmp done
error: mov dx, offset msg2
mov ah, 09h
int 21
done : mov ah, 4ch
int 21h
code ends
Data-here segment    newfile db  '1xxx', 0 (new file name)
handle  dh  ?
msg1    db  'File created.', odh, oah, '$'
msg2    db  'File not created' odh, oa, '$'      Data-here end
end     main
main    end.
```

(x) DOS FUNCTION REQUEST 5CH

To Lock or Unlock File Access.

Description : This function request is useful in file-string environments where several programs want to access the same file.It lets a program lock a range of bytes in a file there by pressenting any other program from reading or writing those bytes until the first program unlocks the bytes. This range of bytes is called a region. The starting location and the length of the region is specified in the function request.

Locking and unlocking are useful when one program needs to update a file of information and ıst guarantee that no other program accesses the information until the entire update is complete.

If this function is used to lock a portion of a file, and another program attempts to access the locked portion, its DOS I/O operation is retrieved a certain number of times. If the lock is still in place after the retries tape place, the other program's DOS function request returns with a general failure error. That program should invoke function request 59 H to receive additional error information.

It is not recommended to determine whether a lock is in place by attempting the I/O operation and checking the error status. Rather one should attempt to set up a lock, and if an error occurs, we come to the conclusion that the specified region is already locked.

If a region of a file is locked and the file handle is duplicated, any program that accesses the file using the duplicated handle also has access to the locked region. However if a process is started using the EXEC function request (4BH), that subprocess does not have access to the locked region.

INPUT : Before invoking the function request, the following registers are set.

AH : This register must contain 5CH, indicating the number of this function request.

AL : This register is set to indicate whether to lock or unlock the region of the file, as follows :

00H Lock the region

01H Unlock the region

BX : This register must contain a file handle returned by create a file (3ch), create a New File (5Bh) or Open a File (3Dh) function request. The file handle indentifies the file to lock or unlock.

Cx,DX: These two registers combine to form a four byte integer that identifies the start of the locked portion of the file. The four-byte integer is an offset from the start of the file. The low-order bytes are placed in the DX register and the high-order byte in the CX register.

When unlocking a region this four-byte integer must be the same as the one you used when locking the region.

SI, DI: These two registers combine to form a four byte integer that identifies the length of the locked region in bytes. The low-order two bytes are placed in the DI register and the high-order two bytes in the SI register. While unlocking, this four-byte integer must be the same as the one used when locking the region.

OUTPUT : None

OTHER REQUIRMENTS : Closing a file does not automatically remove any locks that are in place Rather, closing a file that contains locked regions produces undefined results. Therefore any locked region must be first unlocked before closing a file.

ERROR CONDITIONS :

If an error occurs, the carry flag will be set and the AX register will contain one of the following error codes. The function request 59H is invoked to receive additional information about the error class, suggested action and laws of the error.

01H : file sharing must be loaded to use this function request.

06H : The value in BX is not a valid, open handle.

21H : All or part of the region specified is already locked, or the region that is tried to unlock is not identical to the one which is locked.

24H : The buffer that DOS uses to keep track of locked regions is full.

4.4 THE BIOS

INTRODUCTION:

The BIOS is short form for Basic Input/Output system. It is actually a set of programs or software services which act as a layer between the hardware of computer and other software that we run on the computer. It is engraved in the ROM (read only memory) and although it is a set of programs it is considered as a keyword between the hardware and the software. The main function of the BIOS is to enable the programs to access the hardware, and to directly control the hardware.

The hardware of personal computer can be controlled in four ways :

i) through application programs. (Limited control)
ii) through high level languages. (Limited control)
iii) through DOS services
iv) through BIOS.

The BIOS routines themselves directly communicate with the hardware which is very complicated. Thus the programmer is relieved from the hassles of accessing the hardware through long complicated programs. Also in the ROM, are a set of routines which start working as soon as we switch on our computers. These routines are generally for testing the proper working of hardware of computer. They also load the operating system of the PC from the disk to the RAM. The BIOS is available as soon as we turn on computer.

As the BIOS shields the user program from the hardware. Hence any program running on a PC can also run on a PC - AT, which is its advanced version. Another advantage of the use of BIOS is that though it takes considerable amount of code to control a device, with the presence of BIOS we can control the devices by accessing the required BIOS routine with only a few instruction. Because the BIOS performs low level services, programs can improve their performance by calling them instead of the equivalent DOS routine. The disadvantage of using the BIOS services in the programs is the portability of the programs. BIOS in IBM PC is a proprietary piece of software and hence it is not legally transferable to PC compatibles from other manufactures.

4.4.1 Different Services of BIOS

The Services provided by the ROM-BIOS are :

a> Print services
b> Video Services
c> Equipment Services
d> Memory Services
e> Diskette Services
f> Serial Port Services
g> Cassette Services
h> Keyboard Services
i> Printer
j> Reset
k> Clock & time-of day.

4.4.2 VIDEO SCREEN SERVICES

There are 16 separate video screen services in the basic catalogue of the PC family's ROM-BIOS services.

These services are numbered from zero. The first service, (number 0), is used to change the video mode. For PC'S with just monochrome adapter there is no option. For PCs with color Graphics Adapter or its equivalent, there is a choice of seven modes, four text modes and three graphics modes.

Video service 1 is used to control the size and shape of cursor. It sets the scan lines on which cursor appears. Video services 2 sets the cursor location on the screen. Video service 3 reports to our program where cursor is located and also the shape of the cursor. It allows our programs to use the current state of the cursor so that it can be restored after the program is done. Video service 4 is the sole service supporting the PC'S little-used ligh-pen feature, the BIOS reports if the pen is "triggered" and where it is touching the screen. Video service 5 selects which display page is active for the video mode where more than one display page is available in memory. By display page we mean the page which is currently shown on the screen.

Services 6 and 7 do window scrolling. These two services allow us to define a rectangular "window" on the screen and scroll the data inside the window up from the bottom or down from top.The up from bottom scrolling in done by service 6 and down from top is done by service 7. When a window is scrolled blank lines are inserted at the bottom on top, ready for our programs to write new information.

The next three video services are used to work with text characters on the screen. Video service 8 reads the current character off the screen. Video service 9 writes a character on the screen with display attributes that we specify.

Service 10 also writes a character, but uses whatever display attribute is presently in place for that screen location.

The next three services provide operations for the graphics modes.

Video service 11 sets the colour palette to be used. Service 12 writes a single dot on screen. Service 13 reads a dot off the screen.

Video service 14 is another variety of service 8. This service writes a character to the screen, and advances the cursor to next position on the screen, so that it is in place for the next character. This service makes it possible to use the display service like a printer. For this reason this service is called "write teletype".

The service no 15 reports the current video state so that our programs can adjust their operation to the video mode or record the current mode to be able to go back to it after changing the mode.

The video services give a way for our programs to put information on the screen. They have the advantage that output for the screen is handled in a standard way.

4.4.3 PRINT SCREEN SERVICE

The print screen service is designed to read from the screen the information that is displayed and write it to the printer. This particular service is comlelety built from other ROM-BIOS services.

Print screen service begins work by using video service 3 to save the current cursor position and service 15 to learn the dimensions of the screen. It saves the cursor position so that it can later restore it to its original position, and then proceeds to move the cursor through every location on the screen, from top to bottom. At each location it uses video service 8 to read a character off the screen, and then uses a printer output service, to copy the character to the printer. When this service is finished, it restores the cursor to where it was, and then returns control to program that evoked it.

4.4.4 DISK SERVICES

The disk services are invoked with interrupt number 19. There are six basic services, numbered 0-5.

The first service number 0, is used to reset the disk device and its controller. This is an initialization and error recovery service that prepares the disks for a fresh start before subsequent disk operations.

Disk service 1, reports the status of the disk drive which is useful for the error handling.

Disk service 2, reads disk sectors into the memory. This service reads as many consecutive sectors as specified by the programmer.

Disk service 3 writes sectors into the memory. The no of sectors to be read in this case also is defined by the programmer.

Disk service 4 tests whether data written on the disk is properly recorded or not. It there is wrong data but it is properly recorded this service will report that it is correct.

Disk service 5 is used to format a track of a disk. This formatting service specifies for each track how many sectors will be there, how the sectors will be identified by sector number, the order the sectors will appear in and the size of each sector. Normally all the sectors on a track are of the same size, and are numbered sequentially. On floppy diskettes there sectors physically appear in numeric order.

4.4.5 SERIAL PORT SERVICES

The serial port services are invoked by interrupt 20. There are altogether 4 services, numbered 0-3.

Service number 0 initializes the communication port, the baudrate and other basic parameters.

Service 1 is used to write a byte to the port.

Service 2 reads a byte.

Service 3 is used to get a status report which indicates things like whether the data is ready or not.

4.4.6 CASSETTE TAPE INTERFACE SERVICES

PC's cassette tape interface is no more in use in advanced systems of today. There are four services, in two symmetrical pairs, invoked with interrupt 21.

Services 0 and 1 turn the cassette tape motor on and off.

Services 2 and 3 read and write 256 byte blocks of data.

4.4.7 KEYBOARD SERVICES

The keyboard services are invoked with interrrupt 21. There are three key board services.

Service 0 reads the next character from the keyboard input buffer. These characters are recognised and a report is given in two-bytes.Whatever character is read is removed from the keyboard input buffer.

Service 1 reports if there is any keyboard input ready. If there is one this service reads the character and puts it into the keyboard buffer in two byte form.

Service no 2 gives the keyboard status bits which tell us the status of the shift keys etc.

4.4.8 PARALLEL PRINTER PORT SERVICES

Parallel printer port services use interrupt 23. There are three services. Service 0 gives out a single byte to the printer. Service 1, initialises the printer. Service 2 reports the printer status in which it reports things like whether there is paper in printer or not.

4.4.9 EQUIPMENT LIST SERVICES

Interrupt 17 is used to get equipment list information. The equipment list reports how many diskette drives the machine has. It reports the number of parallel ports and serial ports. It also reports if there is a game adapter. A companion service to the equipment list reports the amount of memory the computer has.

4.4.10 CLOCK & TIME OF DAY SERVICES

Interrupt 26 is used for clock and time-of-day services. There are two services.
Service 0 reads clock, and
Service 1 is used to set the clock. The BIOS time-of-day clock is kept in the form of a long 4-byte integer, with each count representing one clock-tick.

The PC's hardware clock "ticks" by generating a clock interrrupt 18.2 times a second, and the interrupt handler for the clock adds one to the clock count each time. The clock count is supposed to represent the number of ticks since last midnight. It only shows the right time if it has been set properly.

DOS converts the clock tick count into the time-of-day in hours, minutes, seconds and hundredth of second by simple arithmatic.

4.4.11 ROM BASIC

ROM BASIC is reached by booting our computers without a disk in machine. They can also be activate by simply invoking its interrupt.

4.4.12 BOOT-STRAP

The boot-strap start up routine can be reached by pressing Ctrl-Alt-Del Keys. One thing special abourt the ROM -BASIC and Bootsrap services are that they take full charge of the machine and control never returns to the program that invoked them.

In the following pages we have given some assembly language programs to use the different BIOS services.

Following are important main BIOS interrupts and their function requests

Bios Interrupt Hex	Dec	Function Request Hex	Dec	Function
O5H	05			Print Screen
10 H	16			Video I/O
		00H	0	Set video mode
		01H	1	Set cursor shape
		02H	2	Set cursor position
		0AH	10	Write character and attribute
		0CH	12	Write dot
		0DH	13	Read dot
12H	18			Memory-size determination
13H	19			Disk I/O
		00H	0	Reset disk
		01H	1	Get disk status
14H	20			Rs-232 serial I/O
		00H	0	Initialize serial port
		01H	1	Send one character
15H	21			Joystick
		83H	131	Event wait
		84H	132	Joystick support
16H	22			Keyboard
		00H	0	Read Next key board charcter
		01h	1	Determinewhether character in available
17H	23			Printer I/O
		00H	0	Print a character

Bios Interrupt Hex | Dec	Function Request Hex | Dec	Function
	01H 1	Initialize the Printer print
	01H 2	Get printer status
18H 24		ROM BASIC
19H 25		Bootstrap loader (Reboot the system)
1AH 26		Time_of-day
	00H 0	Read the current clock value.
	01H 1	Set the current clock value.
1BH 27		Keyboard break Address
1CH 28		timer tick
1EH 30		Diskette parameters

4.5 EXAMPLES OF USING BIOS FUNCTIONS

BIOS Function : Intialize or scroll window up.

Interrupt used : 10H ; function - 06H
Call with : AH = 06H
AL = No of lines scroll if zero, entire window is blank
BH = Attribute to be used.
CH = Y co-ordinate, upper left corner of window
CL = X co-ordinate, upper left corner of window
DL = X Coordinate, lower right corner of window.
Returns ; Nothing

```
CLEAR. SCREEN        Proc
        PUSH         AX
        PUSH         BX
        PUSH         CX
        PUSH         DX
        XOR          AL,AL
        XOR          CX,CX
        MOV          DX,24
        MOV          DL,79
        MOV          BH,7
        MOV          AH6
        INT          10H
        POP          DX
        POP          CX
        POP          BX
        POP          AX
        RET
CLEAR-SCREEN         ENDP
```

BIOS Function : Set cursor

Interrupt used :- 10H ; Function Request ; 02H
Call with : AH = O24
BH = Page
DH = row (y co-ordinate)
DL = Column (x co-ordinate) Returns : nothing

```
GOTO -  XY PROC
PUSH    AX
PUSH    BX
MOV     BH,0
MOV     AH,2
INT     10H
POP     BX
POP     AX
RET
GOTO -  XY ENDP
```

SET DISPLAY PAGE

Call with ; FOR CGA, EGA, MCGA, VGA
AH = 05H
AL = PAGE
RETURNS : NOTHING

```
Program: Main Proc
MOV  ax, @date
MOV  ds, ax
MOV  ah, 9
MOV  dx, OFFSET PAGE 0
INT  21h
MOV  AH,1
INT  21H
to- page - 1:
MOV  ah,5
MOV  al,1
INT  10H
MOV  AH,a
MOV  DX, OFFSET PAGE 1
INT  21H
MOV  AH,1
INT  21H
to- page - 0
MOV  AH,5
MOV  AL,0
INT  10H
MOV  AX,4COOH
INT  21H
Main ENDP
```

Initialize Printer Port

Call with : AH = 01H
DX = Printer number (0=lpt,1=lpt2, 2= LPT3)
Returns : AH = Status
This program sends string of characters to a printer port

```
MOV     AX, STACK - HERE
MOV     SS, AX
MOV     SP, OFFSET STRACK-TOP
MOV     AX, DATA-HERE
MOV     DS,AX
MOV     AH,O1
```

```
MOV         DX,0
INT         17H
LEA         BX,MESSAGE
MOV         CX, CHAR-COUNT    AGAIN:
MOV         AH,0
MOV         AL, [BX]
INT         17H
CMP         AH,01H
JNE         NEXT
NOT-RDV: STC
JMP         EXIT
NEXT : CLC
INC         BX
LOOP        AGAIN
EXIT : NOP
CODE_HERE ENDS
END
```

SET CURSOR TYPE

Call with : AH = 01H

CH bits 0-4 = starting line for cursor

CL bits 0-4 = Binding line for cursor

Returns : NOTHING

```
MOV         ah,1
MOV         ex, 0007h
INT         10h
MOV         ax, 4cooh
INT         21h
```

Set Video Mode

Call with : AH = 00H

AL = Video Mode

Returns : NOTHING

```
MOV         ah,0
MOV         AL,6
INT         10H
MOV         AH,1
INT         21H
MOV         AH,0
MOV         AL,3
INT         10H
```

GET CURSOR POSITION

CALL WITH : AH = 03H

BH = Page

Returns : CH = Starting line for cursor

CL = Binding line for cursor

DH = row (y coordinate)

DL = Column (x coordinate)

```
MOV      AH,3
MOV      BH,0
INT      10H
```

```
MOV     SAVECURSOR,CX
MOV     AH,1
OR      CH,00100000B
INT     10H.
```

READ CHARACTER AND ATTRIBUTE AT CURSOR

Call with : AH = 08H
BH = Page
Returns AH = attribute
AL = character

```
MOV     AH,2
MOV     BH,0
MOV     DX,0501H
INT     10H
MOV     AH,8
MOV     BH,0
INT     10H
MOV     CHAR, AL
MOV     ATTRIB, AH
INT     11H
```

GET Equipment Configuration

Call with : Nothing
Return: AX = Equipment list code word. Bit(s) significance
0 = 1 if floppy disk drive (s) installed
1 = 1 if math coprocessor installed
2 = 1 if point device installed (PS/2)
2-3 System row size
00 = 16KB
01 = 32KB
10 = 48KB
11 = 64 KB,

This procedure determines how many logical floppy disk drives in the system. The next drive letter will be used for hard disk drives.

```
GET - NUM - FLOPPIES    PROC    NEAR
ASSUME   CS: CODE_SEG, DS: CODE_SEG
INT     11h
MOV     CL,6
SHR     AX,CL
AND     AL,3
INC     AL
CMP     AL,1
JA  DONE_GET_FLOPPIES
MOV     AL,2
DONE_GET_FLOPPIES:
MOV  NUM_FLOPPIES, AL
RET
GET_NUM_FLOPPIES   ENDP
CODE_SEG          ENDS
END         BEGIN
```

Read character from Keyboard

Call with : AH = 00H

Return : AH = Keyboard scan code
AL = ASCII character

```
Read-key PROC
XOR      AH, AH
INT      16H
OR       AL,AL
JZ  EXTENDED_CODE
XOR      AH, AH
DONE-READING:
RET
EXTENTED-CODE:
MOV      AL,AH
MOV      AH,1
JMP  DONE-READING
READ_KEY  ENDP
INT      14H
FUNCTION  01H
```

Write character to Communication port

INT 14H
Function 02H
Read character from communications port
INT 16H
Function 01H
Get Keyboard status

This program sends characters entered on the IBP/PC to the COM 1. Serial port at 1600 Band, and displays recieved from the COM1 serial port on the CRT.

```
MOV      AX, STACK-HERE
MOV      SS,AX
MOV      SP,OFFSETSTACK- TOP
MOV      AH, 00
MOV      DX, 0000
MOV      AL, 0100111B
INT      14H
ST1
CHKAGN:  MOV  DX, 0000
MOV      AH, 03
INT      14H
TEST     AH,01H
JNZ      RDCHAR
JAM      KEYBD
RDCHAR:  MOV  AH,02
INT      14H
MOV      DL,AC
MOV      AH,DH
INT      21H
KYBD:
MOV      AH,1
INT      16H
JNZ      RDKY
JMP      CHKAGN
RDKY:    MOV  AH,0
```

```
        INT     16H
        MOV     DX,0000H
        MOV     AH,01
        INT     14H
        JMP     CHKAGN
```

4.6 FEATURES OF .COM & .EXE PROGRAMS

The Command Processor :

The command processor, or shell, is the user's interface to the operating system. and it is responsible for passing and carrying out user's command. This includes the loading and execution of other programs from disk or any other storage device.

The default shell that is provided with MS-DOS is called COMMAND.COM Although COMMAND.COM prompts and responds to the ordinary user's perception of MS-DOS, it is important to know that COMMAND.COM is not an operating system, but simply aspecial class of program running under the control of MS-DOS.

The user commands accepted by COMMAND.COM falls into three catagories :

- Internal Commands
- External Commands
- Batch files

In order to interpret a user's command, COMMAND.COM locks to see if the user typed the name of a built-in (intrinsic) command that it can carry out directly, if not, it searches for an external command (executuble program file) or batch file by the same name. It searches the current directory of the current disk drive and then in each of the directories specified.

Functionally, both EXE or COM types may be chosen for the purpose of writing programs respectively. The significant difference between them is that. COM programs are stored in their files as memory image whereas .EXE programs are stored in a more complicated fashion. The latter format is however more versatile in terms of memory allocation and loading and it is a preferred format today.

Both .COM and .EXE are loaded from disk files through the EXEC functions (function 4BH,INT 21H) which is provided by DOS. The loader function of DOS is used by COMMAND.COM or any other (parent) program to load and execute another (small) program. EXEC may also be used to load overlays of the same program. This is rarely in use. If Transient program Area (TPA) is there in RAM - and memory has enough space, then the EXEC function does the following:

* Allocates memory for new program
* Builds the program segment prefix (PSP) at the lowest area of this memory
* Loads the program above the PSP
* Sets up appropriate registers, i.e., segment registers and the stack and transfers control to the new program.

For .EXE programs, the EXEC function may also do some additional processing, like passing parameters from parent to child through the environment block. Both the .EXE and .COM programs are referred to as Transient programs. When transient programs are brought into memory, they are executed and subsequently discarded after the job has been completed. They only own the memory allocated to them and they have full control over all system resources while they are executing. On exit, both these types of programs would release the memory allocated, which are already allocated to them on loading. The memory released may be subsequently used to load other programs.

Introduction to .COM Programs :

Programs of .COM are stored on disk files that hold the absolute image of the machine instruction to be executed. Because these files contain no relocation information, .COM file is very much compact and loaded for execution little faster than that of .EXE files, .COM files are directly loaded by DOS, without any relocation or error checking. DOS directly transfers control to the location in the current segment for its execution. This current segment location corresponds to the location immediatly after the 256-byte PSP (Program segment prefix). DOS creates the PSP from location 0000H to location OOFFH, It loads the actual program from location 0100H, and sets up the segment registers at appropriate place. After this, control is transfered to the instruction at 0100H. That's why .COM programs are always with origin specified as 010H by the ORG 010H assembler directive. It was kept in mind that program should be written such that all the code and data lie in one 64K segment. The program should not define stack segment and the programmer should ignore the corresponding warning from the linker. (warning are of type : no stack segment).

When control is transfered from DOS to .COM program, all the segment registers point to the PSP. (PSP-program segment profix).

By loading .COM programs DOS initializes all segment registers - i.e. CS, DS, ES, & SS - to point to the base of the PSP and also loads the IP registers with 0100H to point to the first instruction of the .COM program. The stack pointer register SP is inilialized to the top of the segment, i.e., offset OFFEH. In case this setting is not allowed because of lack of memory, it is instead set as high as the available memory will allow.

If a .COM program is being built from separate object modules, the programmer should note that:
* All procedures must be near since the .COM program cannot exceed 64k in any case.
* Only one of than have the ORG 0100 statement. This is the module which will get control from DOS and must be linked first.
* All modules must specify the code-segment name and the same class name.

Actually a .COM program can use at most 65278 bytes of memory -(Plus-256 bytes of PSP-2 mandatory bytes of stack). This not only includes all its code and data but it can also maximize the stack area it may use. For longer programs, the programmer has no choice but to go for .EXE program format. It was noted that this instruction comes from the fact mentioned earlier that the total volume of a .COM cannot have memory more than 64K bytes.

DOS provides a number of different techniques to terminate a .COM program. The Recommended methods are to use INT 21H, 31H functions. In addition, one can end a .COM program with a NEAR RETURN instruction. This is possible because the 0000H word is pushed on the stack before control is **given to the .COM program and the fact that the location 0C00H in the current segment has the INT 20H** instruction for terminating a program.

Terminations which provide a return code (i.e. functions 4CH or 31H, INT 21H) are preferred since the return code may be monitored by the parent program being returned to. This execution of the transient program is invoked from a batch file, then on termination the next instruction (if any) of the batch file will be done. The return code set by above functions may also be examined by the batch file through its conditional instructions.

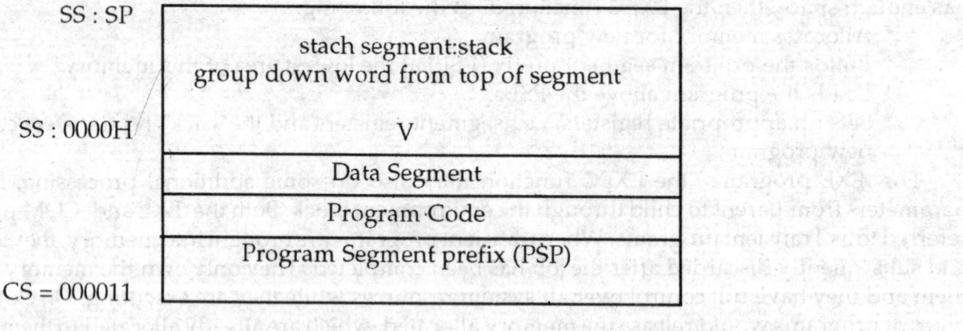

Fig. A memory image of typical .EXE program immidiatly after loading.

Features of .EXE Program :

While writing a program (assembly language program) it is essentially determined whether it will run as .EXE or .COM Program. This is evident if one compares the .EXE and .COM programs. Both **programs can achieve same function but do it in different ways. This is elaborated in greater detail in this** section. d

Unlike .COM programs, .EXE programs can be of any size, upto whatever memory is available in the TPA (Tramsvent program area). The corresponding assembly language program (with ASM extension) must specify its code, data and stack segments. Also the program should not have an ORG statement. This is because the exact load location of the .EXE program is derived by DOS when the program is loaded. The program should end with a statement of the type 'end xxxxx'. The loader ensures that after the .EXE program is loaded control is transferred to the statement labeled xxxxx. This should be the first executable instruction of the .EXE program. If the .EXE program is larger than 64K bytes, it is the user's responsibility to ensure that the various procedures of the program are appropriately declared to be either NEAR or FAR in nature.

One can also generate a .EXE program by linking together several modules. As before procedure should be NEAR OR FAR depending upon their naming conventions and the size of the program. Note that in this case, only one module must define the stack segment and only one module should have the 'end xxxxx' type of statement. Here too, after loading, DOS will transfer control to the statement labelled xxxxx.

A typical loading pattern of the .EXE program is -

LOW Memory - PSP

- Code

- Data

High Memory - Stack (stack grows towards low memory) After loading a .EXE program, DOS will initialize

CS :IP to the progam's entry point specified by the end statement and DS & BS to begining (base) of the PSP.

SS: SP to point to the top of the stack area. The register SS is initialized to the segment with the stack attribute and SP to the size of this segment.

The .EXE program should always terminate with either function 4CH, INT 21H (terminate with return code) or FUNCTION 31H, INT 21H (terminate with return code but stay resident). No other type of termination should be used.

Chapter Five

MICROPROCESSORS AND MOTHERBOARD

5.0 INTRODUCTION

The horizontally mounted, slightly large printed circuit board which contains many tiny components mounted or fixed on it, and is placed on the base of the system unit is called the system board or the mother board. It determines almost every characteristic of the system, from its speed to the number of peripheral units connected.

A large number of motherboards are available and we classify them into the following there categories:

(i) **Microprocessor Based :** This classification is made on the basis of the microprocessor mounted on the motherboard.

Thus motherboards can be of PC 286, PC 386 and PC486 types, depending on the type of microprocessor used. PC 286 uses the Intel 80286 chip, PC 386 uses the Intel 80386 chip while the PC 486 based motherboards use the Intel 80486 microprocessor chip.

(ii) **Functionality Based :** On the basis of functionality motherbóards are classified as normal or integrated.

Normal motherboards donot have the input-output sections built into the motherboard. Thus seperate boards are used for the floppy drive controller, hard disk drive controller, ports controller, and display controller. In the integrated type of motherboards, all these are built on to the motherboard itself Hence the name integrated.

(iii) **Input/Output Bus Architecture Based :** Two types of architectures are popularly used for implementing the bus. These are Industry Standard Architecture **(ISA)** and Enhanced Industry Standard Architecture **(EISA)**.

IBM uses another type of Bus architecture for its PS/2 line of personal computer, called Micro Channel Architecture **(MCA)**. The MCA is an enhancement of the AT's ISA Standard, but has not gained much appreciation with the clone manufacturers.

The point to be noted is that every system board can be classified on the basis of the microprocessor used, functionality and bus architecture. Therefore you can have a 386 based, normal ISA motherboard as well as a 386 based, integrated ISA motherboard also. Many different types of permutations and combinations are possible. ISA uses 8/16 bit I/O bus while EISA uses 32 bit I/O bus with down ward compatibility provisions.

5.1 IBM PC MOTHERBOARD

Many tiny black chips can be seen mounted on the motherboard. Among them, the most important one is the microprocessor, which actually is the think tank of the computer. The original PC motherboard used the 8088 microprocessor chip. A slot known as the co-processor slot is present in every motherboard. A co-processor enables the computer to process certain math instructions faster, and works as an adjunct to the microprocessor. The 8087 co-processor was present in the original IBM PC motherboard. The co-processors for the various micropro-cessor chips used in the AT's are given below (Table 5.1) :

Processor	C0-Processor
80286	80287
80386	80387
80486	Inbuilt 80387 chip present
80586	80387

Table 5.1 : Processor and Their Co-processors

The other chips present on the motherboard carry out certain specialized functions. We mention the chips and their functions next.

8259 - Interrupt controller
8284 - Clock Generator
8253 - Programmable Interval Timer
8237 - Direct Memory Access
8255 - Programmable peripheral Interface
8288 - Bus controller
8250 - Serial port controller
2764 - Rom - BIOS. This is an EPROM.

In some earlier systems, four empty slots next to the ROM BIOS will be noticed. These slots were meant to hold the ROM chips containing the BASIC language interpreter. This is easily recognized bythe paper stack on the chips,to cover the window on the chip. The ROM of the original PC had **POST** (Power On Self Test) routines, a boot strap loader, and BIOS (Basic Input Output System) routines loaded in it. Nowadays, the AT motherboard ROM has in addition to the above there routines, a CMOS RAM modifier routine and also a board and pheripherals diagonistics routine.

Next RAM banks are considered. These are slots for RAM chips and RAM SIMMs. The original IBM PC motherboard had four banks, each having nine chip Sockets. These were numbered from 0-3. Bank 0 and 1 were having the 41256 chips, while banks 2 and 3 had the 4164 chips. The AT-286 motherboards have two banks each with two SIMM slots. The AT-386 motherboards have four banks each having two SIMM slots. The 386DX and 486 motherboards have two banks each with four SIMM slots. Apart from this, all motherboards have sockets for ROM ICs. The PC motherboard has a minimum of 8KB ROM. The AT motherboards have a minimum of 32KB ROM. AT motherboards have a seperate keyboard BIOS chip. Only ATs have CMOS RAM chips to store the AT's configaration.

Looking towards the rear of the chasis, certain connector slots can be noticed. These are known as the **expansion slots**. The PC was designed with an open mind architecture. This enabled the user to buy units to expand the capability of the PC. PCs have 8 bit slots in the motherboard, while ATs have 16 bit slots in the motherboard. ATs also provide some 8 bit slots to accomodate old 8 bit cards.

A crystal can be located on the motherboard. It acts as a source of clock pulse. The speed of the system is generally 1/3 the speed of the crystal. If the crystal is 14MHZ, then the computer's speed will be 4.77 MHZ.

Motherboard jumpers are provided to set various hardware parameters. When shorted they are in ON position and when open, they are in OFF position. The various setting possible are colour/ monochrome display, RESET active speaker active, and keylock active etc.

5.2 MOTHERBOARD COMPONENT RECOGNIZATION

This section deals with component recognization and starts right away with the chips. Chips are the black-cased rectangular objects scattered over the motherboard. Chips are found with pins of various numbers i.e. 8 pin, 14 pin, 16 pin, 18 pin, 20 pin, 24 pin, 28 pin and 40 pin. Some chips are mounted on sockets, facilitating their possible change when damaged. Others are soldered on the PCB. Every chip has a notch or groove at one end of the chip as shown belows. The notch marks the end of the chip where pin 1 can be found. Pin 1 is always towards the left side of the groove, as seen when looked from the top with the chip pointing away from the viewer.

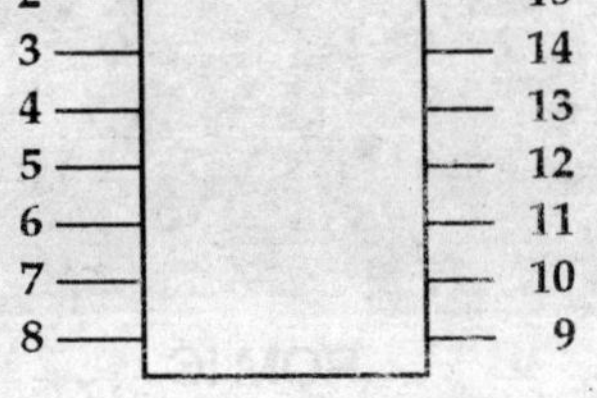

Fig. 5.1: Locating and Understanding Pin Numbering on an IC

The next most informative part of the chip is the chips top surface. On the chips top, special markings are made by the manufacturers. The method of decoding these markings is explained next. As an example consider the following code marked on the chip (Fig. 5.2). The prefix DM is usually used to **identify the manufacturer**. Sometimes the Prefix is omitted. In this example DM represents the National Semiconductor company.

DM	74LS214	AN
SP8505		

Fig. 5.2: A Manufacturer's Code On A Chip.

The next block indicates the **basic logic family** to which the clip belongs. The number 74 denotes that the chip belongs to the **74xx** series.74xx chips belong to the TTL Logic family. The letters in the middle of the block describe the particulars of the chip. In this case LS stands for Low Power Schotty, which is a specific type of Low power Consumption TTL Logic based chip.

The last block describes the **package type** and/or the temperature range. In this case AN denotes Dual-In line package (DIP).

The inscription below this denotes the **date and week of manufacture**. In this case 8507 means that the chip was produced in 1985, on the 7th week of the year.

Basically two types of resistors can be located on the motherboard PCB. These are the **wire wound resistors** and **network resistors**. Every one of you must have worked with the wire wound resistors during the electronics and physics laboratories. The network resistors are actually a group of resitors built into a Single In-line Package (SIP) or a Dual In-line Package (DIP). **These resistors are designated RNxx** or RMxx.

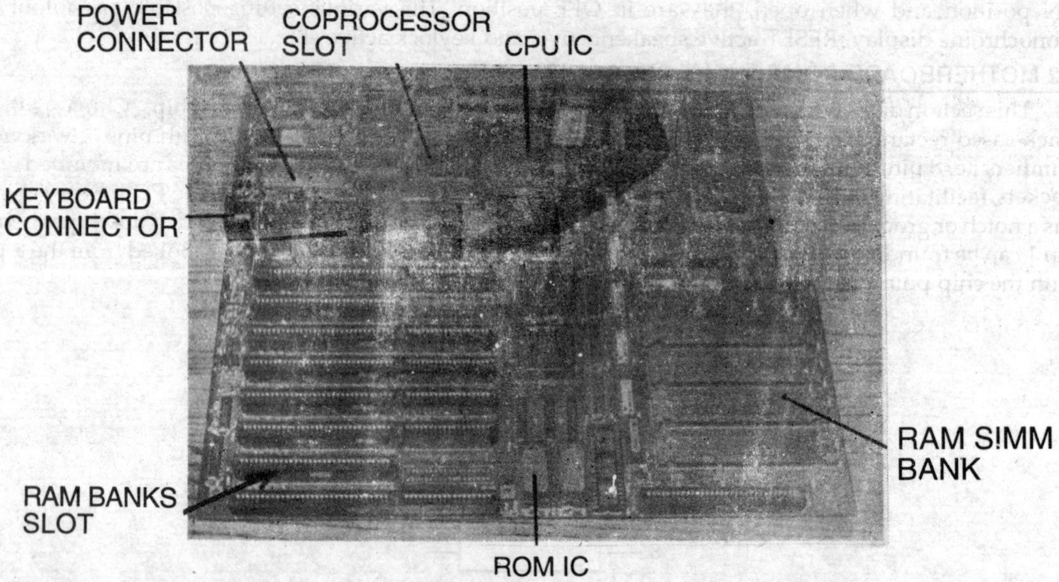

PLATE 3 : "THE MOTHER BOARD"

Many capacitors and diodes can also be seen scattered over the motherboard.

Another moticable component is the crystal. A crystal is a device that vibrates or oscillates when a voltage is applied across two of its input terminals. It is characterised by a shinny metal can, and is located on the right edge of the motherboard.

Transistors, diodes, relays and capacitors are also found on the motherboard. But we donot go into the details of their recognization. From this point onwards the emphasis is onthe microprocessor-the brain of the motherboard. Refer plate 3.

5.3 THE MICROPROCESSOR

Microprocessor is the computers brain. It is this small chips responsibility to process instructions and produce outputs. It determines the speed and power of your system. Just pause and think for a while. You will surely agree that it a a fabulous piece of work by science.

We choose to define the microprocessor as a large scale integration (LSI) component which implements the functions of the arithmetic and logical units of your computer, along with its associated control units in a single silicon chip. Most microprocessors come in a packing called DIP (Dual-In line Package)and have as maximum of 40 to 48 pins. The threeessential advantages of the microprocessor are that they require fewer components, represent a low cost solution, and offer the flexibility of programming. It is because of these advantages, microprocessors have gained immmense popularity.

In the subsequent discussions microprocessor's evolution, its family tree, motherboards internals and support ICs are considered in sufficient detail.

5.4 HISTORICAL BACKGROUND

Foundation of the Silicon Valley can be traced to the famous Bell Laboratories at New Jersey. Bell Laboratory worked like a farmer who first grows the paddy in a marshy area, and then transplants them to a more fertile field. Bell shifted all the promising companies to the Santa Clara Valley, keeping in view the traditional intellectual nature of this region. Within a span of few years, many semiconductor companies came up in this region, which is popularly described as the Silicon Valley. William Shockley, the noble prize winner for developing the transistor, left Bell Laboratories in late 1955 to establish a company of his own. Christened Shockley Semiconductor Laboratories, this company never faired well in business. Tired of failure, some enterprising engineers left Schockley to start a company of their own. After securing support from the Fairchild group, they started the now famous Fairchild Semiconductor company in the early sixties. But the habit of breaking away from their parent organization had become an inherent part of the semiconductor industry. In 1968, Robert Noyce and Gordon Moorse broke away from the Fairchild company to start their own company, the Intel Corporation, which stands for **INT**egated **EL**ectronics.

Integrated Circuits (IC's) were available since 1981. Small scale Integration (SSI) was realized in 1961, followed by Medium Scale Integration (MSI) in 1968. Large Scale Integration (LSI) was already available by 1971 in the form of 1K bit memory and UART (Unversal Asynchronous Receiver Transmitter). Dr.Ted Hoff of Intel Corporation developed the first microprocessor after Busicon, a now extint Japanese Calculator Company approached Intel for a microprocessor to be used in its calculator. This microprocessor was called the Intel 4004 chip, and marked the advent of microprocessors.

5.5 GENEALOGY OF INTEL MICROPROCESSORS

FAMILY	LIFE TIME
4004	1971-1974
8080	1974-1978
X86	1978-1993
Pentium	1993-

Table 5.2 : Microprocessor Famities.

A quick glance through table 5.2 gives you an idea of the various microprocessor families that came, lived, and passed away, paving way for newer ones. The longest living microprocessor family is the X86, also known as the 8086 family. Even today it cannot be said to be exitint. Most desktops in use are of the X86 group and slowly Pentium is trying to phase out the X86 chips. But still Pentium is very much in a developing stage, and has got a long way to go. It is with the Pentium family that Intel tries to deviate from its age old **CISC** architecture, which came into existance when CISC was implemented on the 8086 chip way back in 1978. But in a $150 billion silicon industry you have to maintain compatibility to succeed. So Intel has promised to ensure full compatibility with the X86 forever, a voe made taking into account the rich resource of X86 based softwares. Already a lot has been said about Pentium's successors - code named P6, which is slated to touch the market by late 1995. We go through the Intel family of microprocessor, and for the thirsty readers we have collected some official and unofficial stuff on P6, blended and pasted them in the Appendix Three.

5.5.1 The 4004 Family

The 4004 was the first general purpose microprocessor of the world. It worked both internally and externally with four bits. Hence it was code named 4004. Widely used in calculaters, it was the first move towards microcomputing, which was realized in 1975 with MITS Altair.

To facilitate use of microprocessors in computers, Intel revised its 4004 design. In 1972 it came out with the first eight bit microprocessor, called 8008. It had a clock speed of 0.75 MHZ and used a fourteen bit wide address bus, making the total amount of directly addressable memory 16KB. But the 8008 was essentially a 4004 at heart. With the arrival of the 8080 family, 4004 type of chips were completely washed out.

In 1974, Intel introduced the 8080 chip. It was the first chip designed with the microcomputer in mind. It work both externally and internally with eight bit. The directly addressable memory was increased to 64K, by making use of a sixteen bit wide address bus. Intel brought out an improved version of 8080 called 8085, which for many reasons did not find much favour with the microcomputer manufacturers. In 1978, Intel introduced the 8086 chip, which ushered in a new era of chips, now popularly known as the X86 chips. The X86 chips have been the dominating force in the micro market for the past fifteen years, and are going strong even today.

The X86 family is by far the largest group of microprocessor. It ranges from the old 8086 chip to the young 80486 chip. We briefly understand each member of this family, which finds itself in the bulk of desktops used in the world.

1. The 8086 Chip :

The first member of the X86 family, the 8086 came into the market in 1978. It worked both externally and internally on 16 bits, and had a 20 bit wide address bus. This wider address bus increased the directly addressable memory to 2^{20}, or 1 MB.

For the first time, the concept of **segmented memory** was introduced. The 1MB of memory was divided into sixteen segments of 64KB each. The only hasle associated with this segmented memory was that a single large data structure was not allowed to span across segments. This was possible only when some complex routines were used.

Originally the 8086 was to operate at a frequency of 5 MHZ. Later versions enhanced its speed to 8 MHZ.

But this substantial increase in memory and speed did not catch the attention of micro manufacturers immediately. By that time most micro manufacturers had settled down to an eight bit architecture and for them this transition would have turned out to be very costly. Secondly DRAM prices were very high in those days. No micro manufacturers could even think of implementing 1 MB of RAM. When the 8086 didn't fare well in the micro market, Intel came out with a scale down version called the 8088, to make the transition smoother.

2. The 8088 Chip :

Introduced in 1979, the 8088 chip implemented the 8086 design, with the data bus slashed down to eight bits. This eight bit communication with the outside world enabled it to use all the existing eight bit hardware.

IBM,while introducing its IBM PC, decided to cash on by using the 8088 chip. 8088 used eight bit architecture, but internally worked with 16 bits, giving IBM the oppurtunity of advertising its product as a 16 bit machine.

Most of the remaining features of the 8088 were just a replica of its predecessor. Had IBM not used the 8088 chip,it might have meet the same fate as the 8085 Chip.

3. The 80286 Chip :

Introduced in 1982, it was actually noticed in 1984 when IBM brought out the AT/286 model. It was a true 16 bit processor, just like the 8086, but used a wider data bus of 24 bits. Thus the 80286, popularly called 286, allowed 2^{24} or 16 MB of physical memory.

For the first time the concept of **virtual memory** was introduced. As the name itself spells out, this is not a physical memory. Virtual memory is information stored in some mass storage medium, which is converted into physical memory when called for. This conversion was implemented in both hardware and software, and allowed 1 GB of virtual memory.

To ensure compatibility with all previous X86 members, 286 implemented two modes of usage, known as the **protected** and **real mode**. in real mode the chip works exactly like the 8086 and thus inherently adheres to its 1 MB limit. In protected mode 16 MB of physical and 1 GB of virtual memory is allowed. But the real problem was switching between these modes. The chip always boots up in the real mode. It allows you to go from real to protected mode, but prohibits back tracking. This essentially one-way traffic was the 286 chip's serious drawback. It was corected to two-way movement in the 386 group of chips. Another drawback was the protected mode memory management. In this mode, it allowed memory segments of 64KB, instead of a full stretch of 1 GB of memory.

4. The 80386 Chip :

The 80386 chip was introduced in 1985. Intel's 386 was a true 32 bit microprocessor, that worked both externally and internally with 32 bits. The number of address lines went upto 32, thus increasing the physically addressable memory to 4 GB.

The major thrust of the 386 was to ensure enhanced memory management and organization. Along with the 4 GB physical memory, provision was made for another 16 terabytes of virtual memory. Segmentation was made optional. You were given free hand in using the entire memory as one big segment. When using segments, the 64KB segment size limitation was removed. New segments could be of any size, provided they were less than 4GB in size. Two way switching was established between real and protected mode. Real and protected mode have to be there to ensure compatibility with the earlier 286 chips. Another new mode known as the **virtual 8086** mode was implemented. In this mode, the 386 microprocessor mimics several 8086 processors. This concept brought for the first time hardware-based implementation of multitasking.

A 16 byte cache was incorporated in the 386 chip. The cache is used to store the next few instructions to be used by the microprocessor. This reduces wait states (wait state are discussed in chapter 3) and enhances chip performance. Seeing that the market will take some time in absorbing the 386 chips 32 bit design, it introduced a downgraded version called **386SX**. The original 386 was code named **386DX**, where DX stands for DelUX, an etymology that is now lost in history. The 386SX kept all the features of the original 386 except for reducing the data bus width to 16 bits.

The first 386 Worked at 16 MHZ, but now 50 HZ 386 machines are common.

5. The 80486 Chip :

The 80486 chip was introduced in 1989 and was supposed to be Intel's ultimate chip. But in any arena where speed and power measure success, the greatest and the strongest are for ever challenged and replaced. So as this piece is being penned, 486 has started meeting its final requiem. But is it right to consider the 486 dead in our Indian Context ? Not at all is the answer.The 486 based machines have a dominant share in our markets, and have the potential of being upgraded. The ability of upgrading is a must for a developing country like ours, where the canopy of financial crisis is always hovering over us. Overall, a very modest estimate suggests that 486 based machines will be found in the work places for at least another five years. So we look upon 486 as a very much alive chip and continue our discussion.

When introduced in 1989, the 486 retained all principal features of the 386, that were essential for compatibility. After all compatibility is the backbone for a chip's success. The 486 implements a streamlined hardware design, tighter silicon placement rules and an integrated co-processor. The internal cache was increased to 8K. This larger internal cache caused substantial decrease in wait states. The internal co-processor causes no input/output cycles to be wasted due to math instruction. It also incorporates built-in self-test and hardware debugging and a new floating point error reporting module. The streamlined design of a 486 makes it quite faster than any 386 processor-based machine of the same clock speed. The original 486 was called the **486 DX** when the curtailed version of 486 was introduced.

The trimmed 486 was called **486SX**, and was devoid of the internal math co-processor. For people who are not going to use intensive maths, this was the ideal choice.

In mainstream market, and increasingly in the low end market, 486 chips that run at the same speed internally and externally are fading away. Nowadays, chips that run at twice and even thrice their internal speeds are very common. This is implemented using a technology called **clock-doubling** and was introduced to enable CPU upgrading. These upgrading processors are called **OverDrive** processors. Intel was the first to introduce this with its 486 processors.

Intel ships two types of OverDrive procesors : one for PCs which have an OverDrive socket and the other for PCs which do not have the OverDrive Socket. But what is an OverDrive socket ? It is a **Zero In Force (ZIF)** socket into which the upgrade processor can be slipped in. Once fixed it automatically disables the original processor. It has all the hardware to disable the original processor built into it. The other type of OverDrive processor is used for those PC motherboards which do not have an OverDrive socket. In these motherboards we have to determine whether the present 486 chip is placed in a ZIF socket. If yes, you have to simply remove this 486 chip and put the OverDrive processor in its place. And what happens if the microprocessor is fixed directly to the motherboard ? Then all that can be done is to replace the PC to get a new one ! Intel sells its OverDrive with a chip extractor and demonstrative and diagnostic floppy. Needless to mention, all these are packed attractively. After all you would not buy a biscuit, however good it may be, if it is badly packed, leave aside an OverDrive.

The OverDrives available are basically of three types: DX2, DX4 and Pentium. If your system is 486SX or DX based, you can use any of the above mentioned OverDrives. If you already have DX2, you go for DX4 or Pentium.

To understand how to choose/select OverDrives we go into their speed details. Whatever be your present 486 processor, you opt for a DX2 twice its speed, or a DX4 thrice its speed or a pentium two-and-a-half times the originals speed. As an example let us consider that you have a 486 DX-33 based machine. This 486 DX processor works both externally and internally at 33 MHZ. So when you upgrade, you go for a processor that essentially works at 33 MHZ externally, while increasing speed of operations internally. The options that can be offered are DX2/66, DX4/100 and Pentium /75. A DX2/66 internally runs at 66 MHZ, a DX4/100 internally runs at 100 MHZ while a Pentium internally runs at 75 MHZ while all these chips externally run at 33 MHZ. Similarly for upgrading a 486 DX-25, the available OverDrives are DX2/50, DX4/75 and Pentium/63.

While going through this section you might get the feeling that it is more like an eulcgy of the 486 chips. If you think so it is correct, and 486 deserves it, as it has played its part very well. After all it was the 486 chip, with its 32-bit architecture, that made the graphical operating systems like OS/2 and windows dominant in the desktop market. And may be Intel was correct in calling 486, the ultimate X86.

6. Pentium Chip :

This high-end processor family came into existance when Intel launched its first Pentium chip in 1993. Though fully compatible with all its X86 predecessors, it breaks away from the X86 nomenclature. We have thus placed the Pentium chip under its own baton as a new family of chips.

The Pentium chip works internally with 64 bits, while externally it operates with 32 bits. It implements many RISC features like the **super scaler design**. In this design scheme the multiprocessor has multiple execution units, called **pipelines**. Each of these pipelines can independently process instructions led to them from the different processor parts. This capability of handling more than one instruction per clock cycle enhances the Pentium chip's performance. The transistors are placed using **micro-architecture** concept, which is also borrowed from RISC. But the Pentium chip is essentially RISC at heart.

The internal cache size of the Pentium chip is 16KB, made up of two 8KB caches. This two cache implementation reduces bus conflicts. A concept known as **Branch prediction** is used to fill the cache. In this technique, a set of most likely instructions are predicted and prefetched into the internal cache. This facilitates immediate instruction availability to the pipelines, when a request for an instruction is made. The Branch Prediction technique is reported to have over-all cache hit of 95 percent. This dramatically increases the Pentium chip's performance.

The floating point unit **(FPU)** of the Pentium is now optimized, after it suffered its biggest drawback due to some error in the FPU. We see this FPU bug later. The Pentium FPU operates five times faster than the 486DX2 FPU. This is acheived by using twin parallel pipelines for integer instructions. Two integer instructions can be executed in parallel if they are not interdependent. Also addition, substraction, division and multiplication is implemented in hardware. These features put together account for its five times faster FPU.

In late 1993, it was observed that the Pentium chip gave serious calculation errors while performing double precision calculations. Intel claimed that an average spread-sheet user will detect the flaw once in about 27,000 years of use, but decided to replace any flawed chip without questioning to keep its reputation. Problems were also reported in multithreading capability of the 100MHZ Pentium chips. To illustrate, consider the following calculation. You declare two double precision variables and assign them the values 4195835 and 3145727 respectively. First we divide 4195835 with 3145727 and store the result in one of the double precision variables. Then the result is multiplied with 3145727, but the answer obtained was 4195579. The difference in the last three digits is due to the FPU error.

e.g. (4195835 / 3145727) * 3145727 = 4195579

This FPU error has now been fixed by Intel. Initially Pentium was released with an operating frequency of 60MHZ. Now Pentium chips are available in 100 MHZ version also.

Characteristics	8008	8080	8086	80286	80386	80486	Pentium
Year of Introduction	1972	1973	1978	1982	1985	1989	1993
Width of data bus	8	8	16	16	32	32	32
Width of internal register	8	8	16	16	32	32	32
Width of address bus	14	16	20	24	32	32	64
Directly addressable memory	16K	64K	1M	16M	4G	4G	2^{64}
Clock speed (MHZ)	0.75	3	5/8	10-16	20-50	33-66	60-100
No. of transistors in 1000s	4	6	29	130	275	1000	3100

Table 5.3 : Comparison of Microprocessors.

5.6 MICROPROCESSOR - 8088

The Microprocessor is the main and the most important component of any computer. In this section you will be learning the following :

1. Features of 8088
2. Pinouts
3. Various signals it receives and sends.
4. Internal architecture.
5. Various registers in 8088 and their uses.
6. Advantages and disadvantages of maximum and minimum modes.
7. Differences between Memory mapped I/O and I/O Mapped I/O.
8. Concept of addressing the memory and I/O ports.

5.6.1 Features of 8088 :

* It has a 20-bit address bus.
* Has 8-bit data bus externally and 16 bit data bus internally.
* Has 16-bit ALU.
* Has 14 registers of 16 bits each.
* It can address upto 1 MB.
* It can address upto 64 KB of I/O ports.
* 8088 operates at 4.77 MHz.
* It can support slower memory and I/O ports by entering into a wait state.
* It can support a co-processor.
* It supports DMA type of data transfer.
* It supports both Maskable and Non-maskable interrupts.

5.6.2 8080 Pin Out

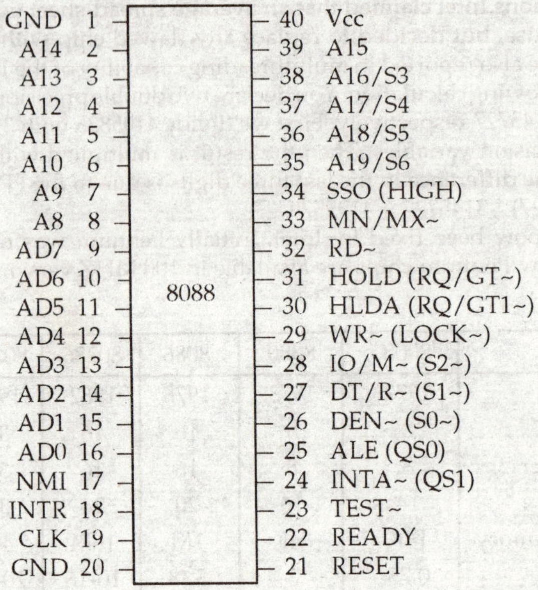

(The signals in the bracket denote maximum mode).

Fig 5.3 : Pin Outs of the 8088 Chip.

ADO - AD7	Multiplexed Address/data bus
A15 - A8	Address/Bus
A19/S6	Address/Status
A16/S3	
MN/MX	Mode Control
RD	Read Control
TEST	Wait on test
Ready	Wait State control
RESET	System reset
NMI	Non-maskable interrupt
INTR	Interrupt Request
CLK	System clock
Vcc	+5V
GND	Ground

MINIMUM MODE SIGNALS

Hold	Hold request
HLDA	Hold acknowledge
WR	Write Control
IO/R	IO/Memory Control
DT/R	Data transmit/receive
DEN	Data enable

ALE	Address latch enable
INTA	Interrupt acknowledge
SSO	SO Status

MAXIMUM MODE SOGNALS

RQ/RGT1	request/Growth bus
LOCK	Bus parity lock
Control	
S2 - S6	Bus cycle status
QSO-QS1	Instruction Queue Status

5.6.3 Internal Architecture :

* It has two units
* 1. Bus interface unit (BIU).
  2. Execution unit (EU).
* Bus interface unit interacts with the external bus and does fetching of opcodes and operands.
* Execution unit decodes the instructions and if it is a valid opcode, executes the instructions.
* The 8088 has a 4 byte Instruction queue and so it has|a feature of instruction prefetch.
* ALU is in the EU.
* The result is always in the main memory.

There are 2 types of general-purpose registers. They are

1. Four 16-bit registers of H and L group.
2. Four 16-bit pointers and index regs of P and I groups.

5.6.4 General Purpose Registers :

* AX,BX,CS,DX can be used as 8 bits or 16 bits each.
* These registers are known as Accumulator, Base register, Count register and Data register respectively.
* The pointer and Index registers are used for arithmetic and logical operations.
* There is a flag register which has 9 flags which are of two types i.e. status and control flags. Status flags are used to record the current status of any arithmetic operation
* The control flags are used to control the mp operation.

The different flags in 8088 are described as follows :

Carry flag (CF) : This flag is set if there is a carry from MSB position during addition or a borrow into MSB position during substration. Parity flag (F) : This flag shows as the odd parity bit for the eight LSB's of the result.

Auxiliary carry flag (AF) : This flag is used for BCD arithmetic. It is set if there is a carry from lower nibble to the higher nibble.

Zero flag (ZF): This flag is set if the result is zero, It is reset if it is non-zero,

Sign flag (SF) : This flag indicates whether the result is positive or negative.

Over flow (OF) : This flag is set when there is an overflow condition in the result of an addition or subtraction.

Trap flag (IF) : If this flag is set, the processor is put in single-step mode. After each instruction a trap (Internal Interrupt) is counted.

Interrupt flag (IF) : When this flag is set, the 8088 can recognize the INTR (Maskable Interrupt) and perform an interrupt.

Direction flag : (DF) : This is used by string manipulation instruction.

5.6.5 MIN MODE AND MAX MODE

8088 can operate in both the Min and Max mode.

(Min mode: In this mode all control signals are generated directly by the microprocessor itself. RAM, ROM, and peripheral chips can be directly interfaced to the microprocessor signals. There is no provision for multiprocessor configuration.)

Maximum Mode : In this mode the 8088 does not generate control signals directly. Instead it issues bus status signals. The bus controller, a special support chip, decodes the bus status and generates signals.

5.6.6 I/O Mapped I/O and Memory Mapped I/O

The 8088 supports direct I/O port addressing through input or output instructions. Each I/O port is assigned a 16 bit address. When an input instruction is executed by the 8088, it sends the I/O port address on the bus. This address is distinguished from memory address by IO/M signal(MIN MODE).

Hence memory does not respond to this address. A transfer between 8088 and I/O port is achieved by using Input or Output instructions only. This scheme of having separate I/O addressing is known as direct sI/O or I/O mapped I/O.

Memory Mapped I/O

In this scheme I/O ports are considered as memory locations. Each I/O port is assigned a 20 bit address, similar to a memory locations. In tis system Input/Output instructions are not used. There will be external decoding circuitry which decodes the address sent by the mcroprocessor and accordingly enables memory or I/O ports.

The 8088 follows a segmentation concept. The memory is logically divided into different segments (portions). The maximum size of a segment is 64KB. The whole 1 MB memory space can be logically organised into several segments. Though several segments are present, the 8088 can directly access only four segments namely code segment, stack segment, data segment and extra segment.

5.7 ADVANCED TECHNOLOGY PC AT/286/386

So far, the computer system based on Intel's 8088 microprocessor has been studied.

IBM developed an advanced version of the PC for obtaining higher performance levels. These systems were designed based on newer, larger and faster Intel microprocessors - 80286 and 80386. We shall see how they differ from the older PC's.

FEATURES	PC/XT	AT-286	AT-386
1. Processor	8088 V-20	80286	80386
a. Data Bus	8 bits	16 bits	32 bits
b. Address Bus	20 bits	24 bits	32 bits
c. Speed	4.77/8/10	6/12/16/20MHz	16/20/25/33MHZ
2. Co-Processor	8087	80287,8087	80287,80387
3. Memory Size (Max)	1 MB	16 MB	4 GigaBytes
4. ROM	8 KB	32 KB	32 KB
5. RTC	present	present	present
6. Serial Port	2 (max)	4	4
7. Printer Port	1	3	3
8. Expansion Slots	8 x 8bit slots	6 x 16 bits 2 x 8 bits	1 x 32 bits 5 x 16 bits 2 x 8 bits
9. Operating System	MSDOS	XENIX, OS2, IRMX,UNIX,MSDOS	XENIX, UNIX OS2, MSDOS

Table 5.4 : Comparative Study of PCs.

5.8 FEATURES OF 80286 MOTHERBOARD

1. **Microprocessor, Intel 80286 CPU working at 10/12/16/20 MHZ.**
2. **Socket for optional 80287/8087.**
3. 32 KB EPROM with support for DOS/UNIX/XENIX etc.

4. 4 banks of memory space available to expand memory from 1 MB to 4 MB.
5. 6 x 16 bit slots + 2 x 8 bit slots.
6. 82C201 Control signal generator.
7. 82C202 ROM/RAM decoder and latch.
8. 82C203 driver and buffer for CPU high address bus (A16-A22) Buffer and driver for CPU, system and local I/O control bus.
9. 82C204 Driver and buffer address (Ao-A15).
10. 82C205 Data bus buffer.
11. 82C206 (IPC) provides 16 levels of interrupts and 8 DMA channels.
12. On board battery backup or external battery backup for CMOS configuration and RTC.
13. Power supply requirements of +5V DC, -5V, -12V DC, +12V DC.

5.8.1 INTERNAL BLOCK DIAGRAM OF 80286 :

Figure shows the internal block diagram of 80286.

The 80286 is divided into 4 units :

1. Bus interface unit.
2. Instruction unit.
3. Address unit.
4. Execution unit.

BUS INTERFACE UNIT (BIU) :

This unit in the device performs all memory and I/O read and write. When the BIU is not using the buses for other operations it prefetches instruction bytes and puts them in a 6 byte prefetch queue.

When a jump or call instruction executes, the bus unit will dump the queue and start filling it from the destination address.

The BIU also controls transfer of data to and from the processor extension devices such as the **80287** math coprocessor.

INSTRUCTION UNIT :

This unit fully decodes upto 3 prefetched instruction and holds them in a queue; the execution unit can access them.

EXECUTION UNIT (EU) :

The unit sequentially executes instructions it receives from the instruction unit. It consists of index, pointer and general purpose registers identical to those of the 8086.In addition to a flag register it also has a 16 bit machine status word register.

The EU directs the BIU to access memory or I/O operands as needed.

ADDRESS UNIT :

The AU computes the physical addresses that will be sent out to memory or I/O by the BU. The 80286 can operate in one of the 2 memory addressing modes, real address mode or protected, virtual address mode.

5,8.2 80287

The numeric co-processor 80287 is a high performance processor extension that extends the 80286 architecture with floating point, extended integer and BCD data types.

The 80287 is implemented in N-channel depletion island, Silicon gate technology and packaged in a 40-pin ceramic package. It has the following features:

1. High performance internal architecture.
2. Implements proposed IEEE floating point standard 754.
3. Expands 80286 data types to include 32 bit, 64 bit, 80 bit floating point, 32 bit, 64 bit integers and 18 digit BCD operands.
4. Object code compatibility with 8087.
5. Operates in both real and protected mode 80286 system.
6. 8x 80 bit,indiviually adressable numeric register stack.
7. Directly extends 80286 instruction set to trigonometric, logarithmic, exponential and arithmetic instruction for all data types.

8. Operates with 80386 CPU without software modification.
9. Available in 40 pin Ceramic DIP package.

The 82C206 or the IPC as it is more commonly known is a 84 pin Quad chip. This device contains the equivalent of

1. 2 x 8237A DMA Controller.
2. 74LS612 Memory Mapper.
3. 2 x 8259A Interrupt controller.
4. 8254 Counter/Timer.
5. MC146818 RTC with RAM.

The IPC supports all the standard peripherals required for a standard system board implementation except the keyboard interface controller.

DMA

Two DMA controllers (8237) are connected in such a way as to provide the user.

a. (3) channels of DMA (DMA1) for eight bit transfers.

b. (4) channels of DMA (DMA2) for 16 bit transfers.

Included as part of the DMA subsystem is the page register (DMAPAGE) device used to drive the upper address lines when required.

DMA channel	Usage for PC AT-286 / AT-386
0	Memory refresh
1	SDLC
2	Floppy disk 3 SPARE
4	Cascade for DMAO-3
5	Spare
6	Spare
7	Spare

NOTE : The first 16 bit DMA channel of DMA2 is used for cascading with DMA1.

INTERRUPTS

82C206 has 16 interrupt channels. These channels are partitioned into 2 cascaded controllers (INTC,INTC2) with 8 inputs each. Of the 16 channels, 3 are connected internally allowing 13 user definable channels of interrupts.

The 3 internally connected channels are

CHANNEL 0 - Counter/timer counter .CHANNEL 2 - Cascade to interrupt controller (INTC2).

CHANNEL 8 - Real time Clock interrupt.The other interrupts are as follows

INTC 1	INTC 2	USAGE FOR PC AT286/AT386
0		Timer O/P o
1		Keyboard
2		Interrupt from INTC 2
	8	RTC
	9	Software redirected to IRO2
	10	Reserved
	11	Reserved
	12	Reserved
	13	Co-processor
	14	Fixed Disk Controller
	15	Reserved

3	Serial port 2
4	Serial port 1
5	Parallel port 2
6	Diskette controller
7	Parallel port 1

NOTE : Channel 0, 2, 8 are internally connected channels.

5.8.3 8254 COUNTER/TIMER

This subsystem contains 3 independent counters. All 3 counters are driven from a clock input pin which is independent from the other clock inputs to the device.

1. Counter 0 - is connected to interrupt 0 of INTC1.
2. Counter 1 - is used to generate pulses or square waves for use by external devices.
3. Counter 2 - it has a full function counter / timer which has a gate input for controlling the internal counter.

The RTC (Real Time Clock) is included in the 80286 for maintaining the time and date. This is taken care of by the MC146818 real time clock with RAM. This contains

1. RAM - 114 bytes
2. CLOCK / Calender.

The clock/calendar information and RAM are kept active by connecting the device to an external battery when system power is turned off.

1. AT 286 system board contains a 16 bit data bus and a 24 address bus making the memory address capacity to 16 MB.
2. Though under MS-DOS. the base memory is only 640 KB, it can address upto 16 MB through memory mapping.
3. Most add-on cards are the same as these that are used in the XT,s (8 bits). Exceptions are HDC Card, certain VGA display cards and certain LAN cards etc.

AT 286 COMPATIBLE CHIPSET CS8220 CONSISTS OF THE 82C201,02, 82C203, 82C204, 82C20 & 82C206. Features :

1. Fully IBM PC AT Compatible.
2. Flexible architecture in any 286 based system design.
3. Early ALE generation.
4. Eariy RAS generation.
5. **Low power CMOS process technology for 82C201 and 82C202 and lowpower Schottky process technology for 82C203,82C204, and 82C205.**
6. 10/8 MHz with one wait state on 6MHz with zero wait state capability.
7. Complete system board memory decode.
8. Configurable RAM select. 9. 16 bit to 8 bit conversion logic.
10. Variable wait state selection.
11. Single 5V supply.

The CS8220 PC/AT compatible is a 5 chip LSI implementation of most of the MSI/SSI logic to control the IBM personal computer AT. The flexible architecture of the chipset allows it to be used in any 286 based system design.

82C201 and 82C202 perform the function of 82284 clock generator and ready interface. 82288 bus controller for any 286 based sytem design.8284A clock generator and driver and replaces 30 other MSI/SSI devices in the IBM PC AT design.

Two signal ALE and RAS can be altered with the activation of the early mode select line (EMODE) ~. when EMOD~ is low,both signals become valid before the normal ALE and RAS signals. This allows the use of 120 n sec DRAMS in a 6 MHz zero wait state system or 150 n sec DRAMS in a 8 MHz one wait state system.

The 10 MHz one wait state system using 82C201-10 will require 120 nsec DRAMS. Variable wait state selection is also provided to accomodate slower memories and peripherals where necessary.

The 82c203, 82c204 & 82c205 include most of the buffers and drivers required in an IBM PC/AT compatible design.

82c20182c201 consists of the following functional blocks :

1. Clock generation.
2. Reset/Ready synchronization.
3. Command and control signal generation.
4. Conversion logic.
5. Wait state control.
6. DMA and refresh logic.
7. Numeric processor control.
8. NMI and Error logic.

CLOCK GENERATION

The clock generation circuitry contains 2 oscillators used to generate the system clock signals. Both oscillators are designed to use an external parallel resonant fundamental mode crystal to generate the basic operating frequency.

RESET

Two reset output signals are provided on the 82c201 for reseting the system.

COMMAND AND CONTROL SIGNAL GENERATION

This section of the 82c201 generates various I/0 and memory control signals for an 80286 based system.

CONVERSION LOGIC

The function of the wait state control logic is to match the speed of the various devices in the user's 8 bit peripheral devices.

Conversion will take place when either of the two conditions occurs :

A 16 bit transfer on 8 bit memory device.

A 16 bit transfer to an 8 bit I/0 device.

WAIT STATE CONTROL

The function of the wait state control logic is to match the speed of the varios devices in the user's system to the speed of the CPU.

DMA AND REFRESH LOGIC

Refresh in the IBM PC AT is handled by placing the CPU in a hold condition, executing the refresh and releasing the processor from the hold.

NUMERICAL PROCESSOR CONTROL

Incorporated in the 82c201 is the circuitry to interface 80287 numerical processor to the 80286.This circuitry handles the decoding required for selecting and resetting the numerical processor. Handling busy/error signals from 80287 to the CPU and generating interrupt signals for error handling.

NMI AND ERROR LOGIC

This section performs the latching and enabling of I/O and parity error condition which, if NMI is enabled will generate a non-maskable interrupt to the CPU.

82C202

It consists of the following functional blocks :

a. ROM/RAM Decode and latch.

b. Parity error detection logic.

c. I/O Decode logic.

a. ROM/RAM DECODE AND LATCH :

The 82c202 contains the circuitry to decode the CPU'S address bus and provide the necessary latched signals for controlling both ROMs on the user's system board.

b. PARITY ERROR DETECTION LOGIC :

During a memory read cycle, this section of the 82c202 will detect a parity error.

c. I/O DECODE LOGIC :

The I/O decode logic portion of the 82c202 provides the signals necessary for controlling the clock/ calendar, status/control port, NMI enable latch and keyboard controller.

82c203 :

82c203 chip provides the drivers and buffers the CPU, the system and local I/O control buses. The memory read and write and the I/O read and write signal are bidirectional.

82c204 :

The chip provides the driver and buffering for the address signal AO-A15.

82c205 :

The chip provides the data bus buffers and drivers for DO-D15. The 3 data buses controlled are the CPU bus (DO-D15), system data bus (SDO-SD15) and memory data bus (MDO-MD15), system data bus (SDO-SD15), memory data bus (MDO-MD15).

5.9 FEATURES OF 80386 MOTHER BOARD :

1. Microprocessor Intel 80386 CPU working at 16/20/25/33 MHZ.
2. Socket for optional 80287/80387 co-processor.
3. 32 KB EPROM with support for DOS/UNIX/XENIX.
4. Memory space available to expand from 2 MB to 16 MB.
5. Expansion slots are
   - 1 x 32 bit high speed expansion slots (124 pin edge connector)
   - 5 x 16 bit slots.
   - 2 x 8 bit slots.
6. The IPC provides 16 levels of interrupts and 8 DMA channels.
7. On board battery backup or external battery backup for CMOS configuration and RTC.
8. 82c301 bus controller.
9. 82C302 page interleave memory controller.
10. 82C303 high address buffer.
11. 82C304 address buffer.
12. 82C305 data buffer.
13. 82C305 control buffer.

The 80386 consists of :

1. Bus interface unit.
2. Code prefetch unit.
3. Instruction decode unit.
4. Execution unit.
5. Segment unit.
6. Paging unit.

The 80386 is more highly pipelined than the 80286. Instruction fetching, instruction decoding, instruction execution and memory management are all carried out in parallel.

The 80386 has a 32 bit data bus and produces a full 32 bit non-multiplexed bus. The 32 bit address bus allows it to address 2^{32} or about 4 giga bytes of physical memory. The 80386 can be operated either in the paged or nonpaged mode.

When operating in paged mode, the 80386 switches the paging unit on, after the segment unit. The paging unit allows memory pages of 4 Kb to be swapped in and out from the disk. The principle here is that only the pages that are actually needed from a larger segment have to be swapped in. This operation is called DEMAND-PAGED VIRTUAL MEMORY.

AT 386 CHIPSET

The 386 chipset CS8230 comprises of

82c301
82c302
82c303
82c304
82c305
82c306

AT 386 SYSTEM BLOCK DIAGRAM :

It has the following features :

1. 100% IBM PC-AT compatible.
2. Operates in page mode with interleave memory subsystem.
3. 16 MHz zero wait operation using 100 ns DRAM'S.
4. 1 MB to 16 MB of DRAM memory support.
5. A complete PC-AT requires only 40 IC's plus memory.

The cs8230 AT-386 chip set is a seven-chip VLSI implementation of most of the system logic to control iAP386 based system.

The flexible architecture of the chipset allows it to be used in any iAP386 based system design, such as CAD/CAE workstations etc.

cs8230 chipset + 82c206 IPC + 40 components + memory ——→ AT compatible system.

cs8230 consists of :

1. 1 * 82c301 Bus controller.
2. 1 * 82c302 Page/ interleave memory controller.
3. 1 * 82c303 High Address buffer.
4. 1 * 82c304 Low address buffer.
5. 1 * 82c305 Data bus interface.
6. 1 * 82c306 Control signal buffer.

The intel 80387 is a high-performance numeric processer extension that extends the 80386 architecture with floating point, extended integer and BCD data-types.

Using a numeric-oriented architecture, the 80387 adds over 70 mnemonics to the 80386 /80387 instruction set, making the 80386/80387 a complete solution for high-performance numeric processing. The 80387 is implemented with 1.5 micro, high performance speed CHMOS III technology packaged in a 68 pin ceramic pin grid array (PGA) package.

It has the following features :

1. High performance 80 bit internal architecture.
2. Implements ANSI/ IEEE standard 754 - 1985 for binary floating-point architecture.
3. 5 to 7 times 8087/80287 performance.
4. Upward object-code compatible from 8087/80287.
5. Directly extends 80386 instruction set to include trigonometric, logarithmic, exponential and arithmetic instructions for all data types.
6. Full-range operations for SINE, COSINE, TANGENT, ARCTANGENT and LOGARITHM.
7. Operates independently of real, protected and virtual modes of 80306.
8. 8 x 80 bit numeric registers usable as individually addressable general registers or as a register stack.
9. Available in 68 pin PGA package.

5.9.1 82c301 : BUS CONTROLLER

The 82c301 has the following features :

1. Optional independent AT bus clock.
2. Processor clock selection.
3. AT bus timing configuration.
4. CPU interface and bus control.
5. Port B register.

The 82c301 provides a clock generation circuitry to solve two basic problems :

1. To provide system designers the choice of a particular AT bus clock most adequate for the application.

2. To allow the processor to run at the full speed and optionally at a lower speed to match timing-dependent application software.

Since many AT adapters are designed with built-in timing assumption, independent programmable controls are provided for AT bus command timing and wait state generation for I/O access and for 8, 16 and 32 bit memory access.

The 820301 interfaces directly with the 80386 and implements the state machine required for controlling all bus accesses. It also features a status register, known as port B register, used in IBM PC/AT.

5.9.2 82C302 - INTERLEAVE MEMORY CONTROLLER

The 82C302 has the flowing features :

1. Page mode access with interleaved memory banks achieves higher performance than conventional DRAM arrays.
2. Zero wait state access at 16 MHZ using 100 n secs DRAMs.
3. Memory configurations of 1 bank of 36 bits, 1 MB using 256 x 1 or 16 MB using 1 M x 1 DRAMS.
4. Memory configurations of 1, 2, and 4 banks.
5. Shadow RAM features for efficient BIOS execution.
6. Staggered refresh to reduce power supply noise.

The 82C302 organizes memory as banks of 36 bits consisting of 32 bits of data and 4 bits of parity. The minimum configuration can be a single bank operating in non-interleaved mode or can be two pairs of banks operating in 2-way page interleaved mode at higher performance. The memory controller is such that the memory can be upgraded from one to two banks by making it a two-way interleaved organization. Due to the interleaved page operation, the third and fourth banks must be added as a pair. The DRAM types must be identical in each bank of a pair due to the interleaved configuration.

However pair of banks can use different DRAM types with one or two banks of smaller DRAM types and later upgraded with additional pairs of banks of larger DRAM'S.

82C302 performs the following main functions :

1. DRAM memory access arbitration.
2. DRAM memory access cycle control.
3. Memory mapping.

The 82C302 controls the DRAM memory access for CPU, DMA and refresh requests.

Features of 82c303 :

1. Provides direct Interface to AT bus.
2. Adapts advanced Schottky TTL technology.
3. Buffers for bits 31:12 of the local and system address bus.

FUNCTIONS :

1. Generates address decoding signal as required by other chips.
2. Provides interface between the local and system address bus.

The 82c303 interconnects the local and system address buses with bidirectional drivers connecting each bus and the internal buses.

Features :

1. Buffers for bits 11:00 of the local and system address buses.
2. Peripheral device decode.
3. Direct interface to AT bus.
4. Refresh address generation.
5. Advanced Schottky TTL technology.

82C305 has the following features :

1. Nibble slice of memory and AT data bus interface.
2. Data size conversion.
3. Advanced Schottky technology.

Funtional Description :

The 82c305 interface between the local memory and system (AT IO channel) data buses and provides data alignment and size conversion for AT I/O channel operations. It is designed as a nibble slice to reduce pin count and simplify system design. Two parts are used to interface all data buses. The 82c305 provides the data bus connections so that the data conversions are done correctly for CPU accesses to the AT bus.

It has following features :

1. 14.318 MHz oscillator and divide-by-12 counter.
2. Byte enable latch.
3. Parity checking.
4. Direct interface to AT bus.
5. Advanced Schottky TTL technology.

Functional description :

The colour reference oscillator is provided, eliminating the 8224 normally used in AT-compatible systems. A divide-by-12 counter is also included to generate the OSC/12 (1.19 MHz) signal used on the system board.

5.10 INTRODUCTION TO SUPPORT CHIP

The microprocessor alone cannot control all the functions required by the computer system. Many of the functions are exclusively dedicated to some ICs to perform dedicated controls. These chips could be used to control the flow of information within the computer logics like DMA control, interrupt control, input/output controls for controlling the functions of control devices like video display, disk drives, communication interface, printers and keyboard. Different ICs used in the microcomputer system board are :

1. 8284 - Clock generator.
2. 8288 - Bus controller.
3. 8253 - Programmable Internal Timer.
4. 8255 - Programmable Peripheral Interface.
5. 8259 - Programmable Interrupt Controller.
6. 8237 - Programmable DMA controller.
7. 8250- Universal Asynchronous Receiver Transmitter.
8. 8087 - Numeric coprocessor.

5.10.1 8284-Clock Generator

8284 clock generator and driver for 8086, 8088 processor : 8284 is a high performance clock-generator which supplies multiple clock signal outputs that are required to drive the CPU and other devices. The base frequency clock input to the clock generator is sourced from a crystal oscillator of a frequency usually three times the CPU clock frequency. This base frequency is divided by 3 for use as a CPU driver, and other frequencies required by different devices can be obtained by dividing the base frequency by the relevant factorial values.

The CPU operates at a clock of 4.77 MHz which is derived from a crystal oscillator of 14.318 MHz.

SPECIFICATIONS :

1. Generates the system clock for the 8086, 8088 processors.
2. Available in 18-pin lead plastic DIP.3. Uses a crystal or an external frequency source.
4. Provides local ready and multibus ready synchronization.
5. Generates system reset output from Schmitt Trigger input.
6. Capable of clock synchronization with other 8284's.
7. Low power consumption.
8. Single 5V power supply.
9. TTL compatible inputs/outputs. Multibus ready :

When multiple 8284's are connected together, the CSYNC allows 8284 to be synchronized to provide clocks that are in phase. Two ready inputs are provided to accomodate multimaster system bus. Each input has a qualifier AEN1 & AEN2 respectively.

Pin configuration of 8284 :

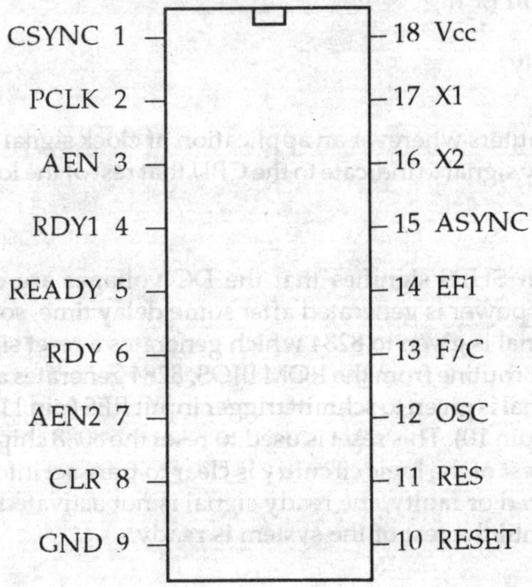

Fig 5.4 8284 is an 18-pin lead plastic DIP.

The pin configuration are follows :

AEN1 AEN2 - Address Enable AEN is an active low signal. AEN serves to qualify its respective bus-ready signal. AEN1 validates RDY1 and AEN2 validates RDY2. Two address enable signal inputs are useful in system configurations, which permits the processor to access two multimaster buses.

RDY1 RDY2 - Bus ready. Ready is an active high which is an indication from a device located on the system data bus that data has been received or is available. RDY1 is qualified by AEN1 while RDY2 is qualified by AEN1 while RDY2 is qualified by AEN2.

ASYNC - Ready synchronization select. ASYNC is an input which defines synchronization mode of ready logic. When ASYNC is low, stages of ready synchronization are provided. When ASYNC is high a single stage of ready synchronization is provided.

READY - Ready is an active high signal which is the synchronized RDY signal input. Ready is cleared after the granted hold time to the processor has been met.

X1, X2 - Crystal inputs. X1, X2 are the pins to which crystal is attached. The crystal frequency is three times the desired processor frequency.

F/C - Frequency/crystal select. F/C is a strapping option. When strapped low F/C permits the processor clock to be generated by the crystal. When F/C is strapped high, CLK is generated from the EF1 input.

EP1 - External frequency. When F/C is strapped high the CLK is generated from the input frequency appearing on this pin. The input signal is a square wave 3 times the frequency of the desired CLK output.

CLE - Processor clock CLE is the clock output used by the processor and all devices which directly connect to the processor local bus. CLF has an output frequency which is 1/3rd of the crystal or EF1 input frequency.

PCLK - Peripheral clock. PCLK is a TTL level peripheral clock signal whose output frequency is half that of CLK.

OSC - Oscillator output. OSC is the TTL level output of the internal oscillator circuitry, its frequency is that of a crystal.

RES - Reset in RES is an active low signal which is used to generate reset. The 8284 provides a Schmitt-trigger input so that an RC connection can be used to establish the power up reset of proper duration.

RESET - Reset is an active high signal which is used to reset the 8086/8088 family processor.

CSYNC - Clock synchronization. CSYNC is an active high signal which allows multiple 8284's to be synchronized to provide clocks that are in phase. When CSYNC is high the internal counters are reset.

When CSYNC goes low, the internal counters are allowed to resume counting. CSYNC needs to be externally synchronized with EF1.

GND - Ground

Vcc - Power +5V supply.

Applications :

It is used in microcomputers wherever an application of clock signal to the circuitry is required. For example, it generates a ready signal to indicate to the CPU that rest of the logic circuitry is clear to transmit information.

Reset Logic :

The power signal from SHPS signifies that the DC voltages are o.k. and can be used. During switching on the SMPS, the power is generated after some delay time, so that the power supply output voltages are stable. This signal is given to 8284 which generates a reset signal. This signal initializes the 8088 which initiates the post routine from the ROM BIOS, 8284 generates a ready signal, clear to transmit information. The power signal is given to schmitt trigger input RES (pin 11) and a synchronizing flip-flop to generate the reset signal (pin 10). This reset is used to reset the 8088 chip. 8284 generates a ready signal to indicate to the CPU that rest of the logic circuitry is clear to transact information. If the memory or the I/O devices are not initialized or faulty, the ready signal is not activated thus causing the CPU to stop initializing or processing until the rest of the system is ready.

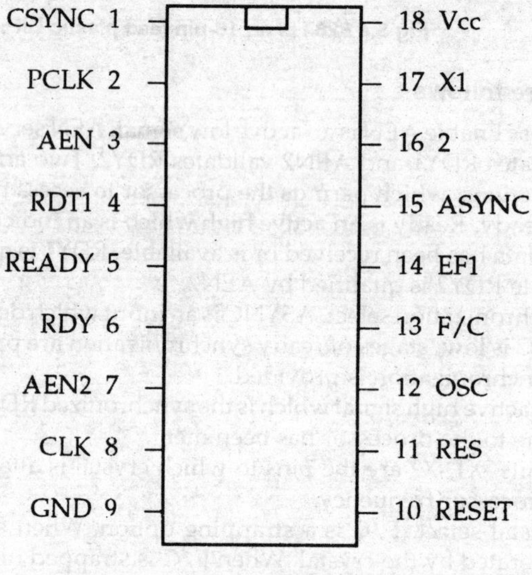

Fig 5.5 : Clock generator chip.

The clock generator has a crystal connected across two pins X1 and X2. The crystal operates at 14.31818 MHz. When turned or voltage is impressed on the crystal it oscillates. This is the master frequency. The clock generator internally divides the masterclock by 3. This produces the system operating frequency of 4.77 MHz.

The 8259 is used as an interrupt controller. Whenever an interrupt is generated from any device and sent to CPU, it is first sent to 8259, which interprets the signal and determines the level of priority of the interrupts with respect to other interrupts generated and then sends to the CPU, based on the priority determined. This enables the CPU, to communicate or control the program or device driver.

Specifications :

1. 8086, 8088 compatible
2. Eight level priority controller.
3. Expandable to 84 level by cascading.

4. Programmable interrupt modes.5. Individual mask capability.
6. Single +5V supply (no clocks)
7. 28-pin dual-in-line package.

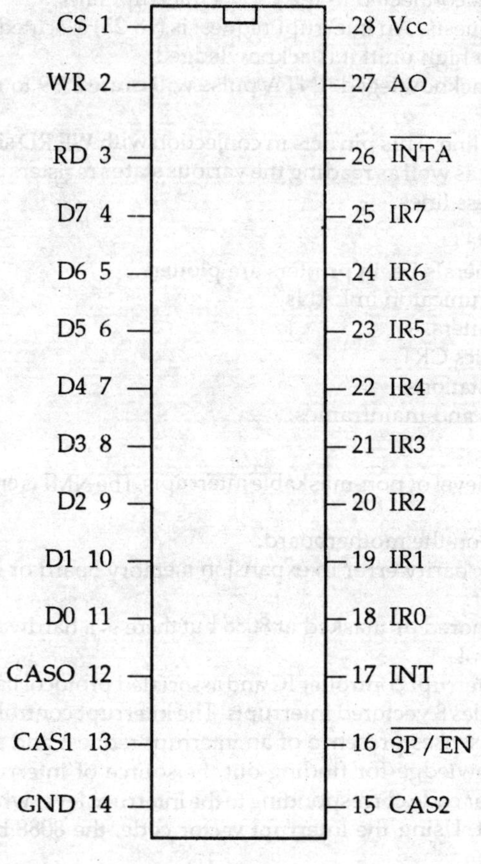

Fig 5.6 : Pin Configuration of 8259.

The Intel 8259 Programmable Interrupt Controller handles upto eight vector priority interrupts for the CPU. It can be cascaded to vectored priority interrupts without additional circuit. It is packaged in a 28 pin DIP. It requires a single +5V supply. It minimizes the software and real time overhead by handling multilevel priotity interrupts.

Pin descritions :

Vcc (28) - Supply +5V supply.

GEN (14) - Ground.

CS (1) - Chip select. A low on this pin enables read and write i.e. RD and WR communication between the CPU, and the 8259.

WR (2) - Write. A low on this pin when CS is low enables the 8259 to accept command words from the CPU.

RD (3) - Read. A low on this pin when CS is low enables the 8259 to release status onto the data bus for the CPU.

D0-D7 - Bidirectional databus. Control, status and (4-11) interrupts vector informations are transferred via this bus.

CAS0-CAS2 - Cascade lines. The CAS lines form a private 8259 bus to control a miltiple 8259 structure. These pins are used as outputs for a master 8259 and as inputs for a slave 8259.

SP/EN (16) - Slave program/Enable Buffer. This is a dual function pin. When in the buffer mode, it can be used as an output to control buffer transceiver (EN). When not in buffer mode, it is used as an input to designate a master or a slave (SP).

INT (17) - Interrupt. This pin goes high whenever a valid interrupt request is asserted. It is used to interrupt the CPU. Thus it is connected to the CPU's interrupt lines.

IR0-IR7 - Interrupt requests. An interrupt request is (18-25) executed by raising an interrupt input (low or high) and holding it high unitl it is acknowledged.

INTA (26) - Interrupt acknowleged. INTA pulse will cause 8259 to release vectoring information on to the data bus.

AO (27) - AO Address line. This pin acts in conjection with WE RD signals to write commands into various command registers, as well as reading the various status registers of the chip. This line can be tied directly to one of the address lines.

Applications of 8259 chip :

1. It is used in peripherals i.e. in printers are plotters.
2. It is used in communicaton in LANs.
3. It is used in computers.
4. It is used in graphics CRT.
5. It is used in workstations.
6. It is used in mini's and mainframes.

Interrupts :

The CPU supports one level of non-maskable interrupts. The NMI is created for any of the three error conditions.

1. RAM parity error on the motherboard.
2. I/O channel check parity error in expansion memory board or controller boards.
3. Co-processor error.

The NMI connot be ignored or masked at 8088 but there is a hardware overriding facility to block NMI, under software control.

With the addition of interrupt controller IC and associated protocol between the interrupt controller and 8088, the system provides 8 vectored interrupts. The interrupt controller assigns priority among the eight interrupt requests. It senses presence of an interrupt request and sends it to interrupt controller during the interrupt acknowledge for finding out the source of interrupt. It responds, the interrupt controller supplies the vector code corresponding to the interrupt level which has highest priority among the interrupt levels present. Using the interrupt vector code, the 8088 branches to the corresponding interrupt service.

The four DMA channels are used for :

Channel 0 - Dynamic RAM refresh.
Channel 1 - Reserved.
Channel 2 - Floppy Disk Controller.
Channel 3 - Hard Disk Controller.

Specifications :

1. Enable/Disable control of Individual DMA requests.
2. Four independent DMA channels.
3. Independent automation of ll channels.
4. Memory to memory transfers.
5. Memory block initialization.
6. Address increment or decrement.
7. High performance -transfers upto 1.6 MB/sec with 5 MHz 8237-5.
8. Directly expandable to any number of channels.
9. End of process input for terminating transfers.
10. Software DMA requests.
11. Independent polarity control for DREQ and DACK signals.
12. Available in express -Standard temperature range.
13. Available in 40 lead and plastic packages.

Specifications :

1. Provides support for 8086, 8088, 80186.
2. Low power operation.
   -Ir s = 100uA
   -Icc = 100mA
3. Provides advanced commands for multi-master buses.
4. 3-state command output drivers.
5. High drive capabiliity.
6. Configurable for use with an I/O bus.
7. Single 5V power supply
8. 8 MHz operation.

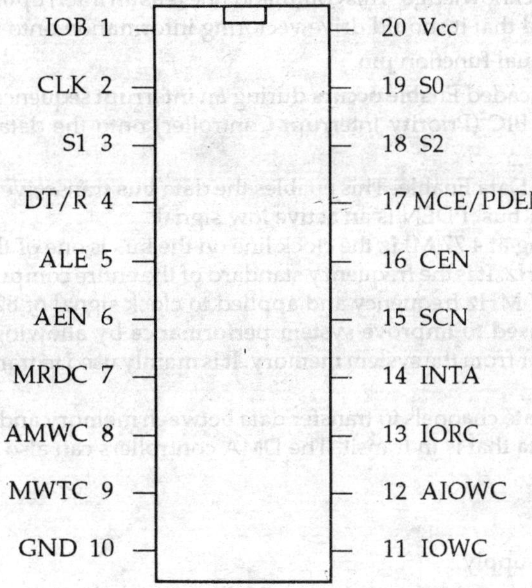

Fig 5.7 : Pin configuation of 8288.

Pin details of a 8286 :

Vcc - Power +5V supply.

GND - Ground.

CLK - Clock. This is signal from the 8284 clock generator and serves to establish when command and control signals are generated.

ALE - Address Latch Enable. This signal serves to strobe an addrss into the address latches. This signal is active high and occurs on the falling transitions. DEN - The signal serves to enable data transceivers into either local or system data bus.

D T/R - Data transmit/receive. This signal establishes the direction of data flow through the transceivers. A high on this line indicates transmit i.e. write to memory or I/O device and a low indicates receive signal.

AEN - Address Enable. AEN enables command is output of the bus controller.

CEN - Command Enable. When this signal is low, all command outputs DEN and PDEN control outputs are forced to their inactive signal. When this signal is high, these outputs DEN and PDEN are enabled.

IOB - Inputs/output bus mode. When IOB is high, it functions in I/O bus mode. When IOB is low, it functions in the system bus mode.

AIOWC - Advanced I/O Write Command. The AIOWC issues I/O devices an early indicator. of a write instrucion. AIOWC is active low signal.

IOWC - I/O Write command. This command line instructs an I/O device to read the data from the data bus. This is an active low signal.

IOEC - I/O Read Command. This command line instructs device to write its data onto the data bus. This signal is active low.

AMWO - Advanced Memory Write Command. The AMWC issues a memory write command earlier in the machine cycle to give memory device an early indicator of write instruction.

HMTC - Memory Write Command. This command line instructs the memory to record the data present on the data bus.

MRDC - Memory Read Command. This command line instructs the memory to drive its data onto the data bus.

INTA - Interrupt Acknowledge. This command line tells an interrupting device that its interrupt has been acknowledged and that it should drive vectoring information onto the data bus.

MCA/ - This is a dual function pin.

MCA - Master Cascaded Enable occurs during an interrupt sequence and serves to read a cascade address from a master PIC (Priority Interrupt Controller) onto the data bus. PDEN is an active low signal.

PDEN - Peripheral Data Enable. This enables the data bus transceiver for the I/O bus so that DEN performs for the system bus. PDEN is an active low signal.

When PC is working at 4.77 MHz the clock line on the bus is one of those signals derived form the oscillator of 14.31818 MHz. It is the frequency standard of the entire computer. This frequency is divided by three to obtain a 4.77 MHz frequency and applied to clock signal of 8288.

Intel 8237 chip is used to improve system performance by allowing external devices to directly transfer information to or from the system memory. It is mainly used to transfer data between disk drives and memory unit.

8237 has four separate channels to transfer data between memory and external devices and internal memory to store the data that is in transit. The DMA controllers can also be cascaded to provide more channels.

Pin description :

Vcc - Power : +5V supply

Vss - GND

CLK - Clock input. Clock input controls the internal operations of the 8237 and its rate of data transfers.

CS - Chips select. Chip select is an active low input used to select the 8237 as an I/O device during the idle cycle. This allows CPU to communicate to the data bus.

RESET - Ready. Ready is an input used to extend the memory read and write pulses from the 8237 to accomodate slow memories or I/O peripheral devices.

HLAD - Hold acknowledge. The active high hold acknowledge from the CPU indicates that it has relinquished the control of the system buses.

DREQ0-DRWQ3 - DMA request. The DMA request lines are used by peripheral circuits to obtain DMA service. DREQ0 has the highest priority and DREQ3 has the lowest priority.

DB0-DB7 - DATA bus. The data bus lines are bidirectional three state signal connected to the system data bus. The outputs are enabled in the program condition during the I/O read to output the contents of address registers, status registers and temporary registers to the CPU. The output are disabled and inputs are read during an I/O write cycle.

ADSTB - Address strobe. In memory to memory operations, data from the memory comes into the 8237 on the data bus during the memory transfer. In the write of memory transfer, the data bus outputs data into the new memory location.

8237 pin Configrations :
DMA Controller

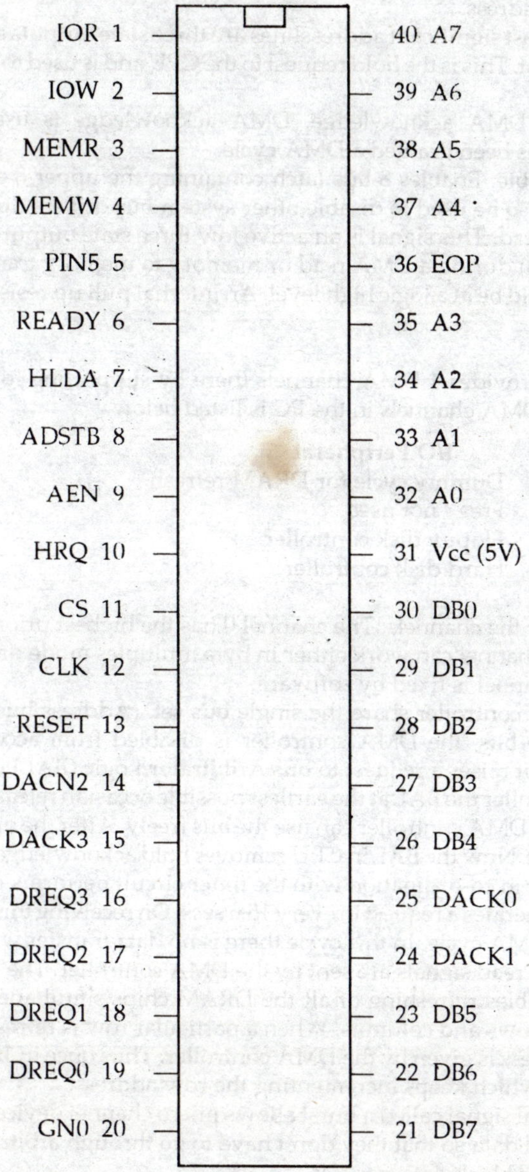

Fig 5.8 : 8237 is a Ceramic or plastic package.

IOR - I/O Read. I/O read is a bidirectional active low state line. It is an input control signal used by the CPU to read the control registers in an idle cycle. In an active cycle, it is an output control signal used to access data from a peripheral during a DMA transfer.

IOW - I/O Write is a bi-directional active low state line. In the idle cycle an input control signa is used by the CPU to load information. In the active cycle, an O/F control signal is used to load data to the peripheral during a DMA read transfer.

EOP - End of Process. It is an active low bi-directional signal. Information concerning the completion of DMA services is available at EOP lines.

A0-A3 - Address. These four least significant address lines are bidirectional three state signals. In the idle cycle, register is to be loaded or read. In the active cycle, they are outputs and provide the lower four bits of the output address.

A4-A7 - The four most significant addresslines are three state outputs and provide 4 bits of address.

HRQ - Hold Request. This is the hold request to the CPU and is used to request control of the system bus.

DACK0-DACK3 - DMA acknowledge. DMA acknowledge is used to notify the individual peripherals when one has been granted a DMA cycle.

AEN - Address Enable. Enables 8-bits latch containing the upper 8 address bits onto the system address bus. AFN can also be used to disable other system bus drivers during DMA transfers.

MEMR - Memory read. This signal is an active low three state output used to access data from the selected memory location during a DMA read or memory to memory transfer.

Pin 5 - This pin should be at a logic high level. An internal pull up resistor will establish a logic high when pin is left floating.

DMA Channels :

The PC hardware provides 4 DMA channels there by supporting four different I/O operations. Concurrently going on DMA channels in the PC is listed below.

Channel number	I/O Peripheral
0	Dummy cycle for DRAM refresh.
1	Free - not used.
2	Floppy disk controller.
3	Hard disk controller.

Provided system for the channels. The channel 0 has the highest priority followed by 1, 2 and 3 in decreasing order. Each channel can work either in byte multiples mode or in burst mode. The mode of operation for a given channel is fixed by software.

The CPU and DMA controller share the single bus set. (Address bus, data bus and control bus). When CPU is using the bus, the DMA controller is disabled from accessing the bus. When DMA controller needs the bus it raises a request to bus Aribitrator Logic (BAL) in CPU> On recieving such a request from DMA controller the BAL at the earliest possible occasion releases the bus to DMA controller and informs this so there DMA controller can use the bus freely. After the operation, the DMA controller removes the hold request. Now the BAL in CPU removes hold acknowledge and releases the bus to CPU.

The DMA controller in co-ordination with the timer circuit performs refreshing of the DRAM chip used in PC. The timer generates a request in every 15 u secs. On receiving this request, the DMA controller performs one dummy DMA cycle. In this cycle there is no data transfer with memory. Only 'Memory' address and 'MEMORY' read signals are sent by the DMA controller. The DRAM logic on seeing DMA channel 0 bus cycle, enables refreshing of all the DRAM chips simultaneously. The DRAM chips are organized internally as rows and columns. When a particular row is refreshed all the bits in that row is refreshed. The row address is given by the DMA controller. Thus once in 15 u secs, there is refresh cycle by the DMA controller which keeps incrementing the row address.

In burst mode, a final signal called a burst allows micro channel devices to retain control while they transfer blocks of related data so that they don't have to go through arbitration until the entire transfer is complete. It is used for block data transfer.

Applications :

1. It is used in peripherals i.e. printers.
2. It is used in mass storage devices like hard disk drive and floppy disk drives.
3. It is used in computers i.e. PC's
4. It is used in workstations.
5. In word processor and data entry terminals.

5.10.2 8253 - Programmable Internal Timer

The Intel 8253 is a programmable counter/timer chip designed for use as a microcomputer peripheral. It can generate upto 3 accurate time delays under software control. The input clock signal to this is given by 8284. It has 3 to 18 bit counters, each with a count rate of upto 2 MHz. These are used as software programmable counters by loading them with a count, start and stop instructions. It uses a single +5V supply and is packaged in a 24-pin plastic DIP. Specifications :

1. Intel 80XX family compatible.
2. Three independent 16-bit counters.
3. Programmable counter modes.
4. Count Binary or BCD.
5. Single +5V supply.
6. 24 pin dual inline package.

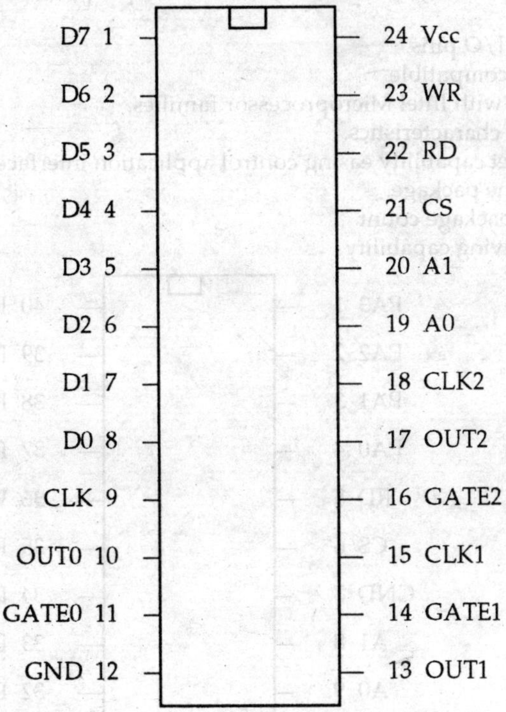

Fig 5.9 Pin configuration of 8253.

Pin connection.

DU - DMA data bus. The Tristate bidirectional buffer is usedto interface the 8253 to the system data bus. Data is transmitted or received depending upon the execution of input or output CPU instructions.

OUT - Counter outputs. The clock pulses from the counter are used as input to the channel C of the DMA controller which uses inputs to refresh the dynamic RAM. The output of counter C is used as input to the speaker through a driver to produce sound.

GATE N - Counter Gate inputs. The gate inputs on each counter is used to start or stop the particular counter with an external signal.

CS - Chip select. A low on this input enables the 8253.No reading or writing will occur unless the device is enabled.

A0-A1 - Counter select. Two address inputs to allow one of the three counters to be operated on and to address the control word register for mode.

Vcc - +5V

GND - Ground.

Applications :

1. It is used to generate sounds on the speaker internal to PC.
2. It is used in microcomputer system to generate accurateTime delays under software control.

3. It is used in real time clock circuitry.

4. The output or counter 1 is usually used in refreshing the dynamic RAM. The clock pulse from the counter are used as input to the channel 0 of the DMA controller which uses these inputs to refresh the DRAMS.

5.10.3 8255 - PROGRAMMABLE PERIPHERAL INTERFACE

8255 is a programmable peripheral interface device designedfor use in Intel microcomputer system. Its functons is that of general purpose I/O component to interface peripheral equipment to the microcomputer system . The functional configuration of the 8255 is programmed by the system software so that normally no external logic is necessary to interface peripheral devices.

Specifications :

1. 24 programmble I/O pins.
2. Completely TTL compatible.
3. Fully compatible with Intel Microprocessor families.
4. Improved timing characteristics.
5. Direct bit set/reset capability easing control application interface.
6 40 - pin dual in-line package.
7. Reduces system package count.
8. Improved DC driving capability.

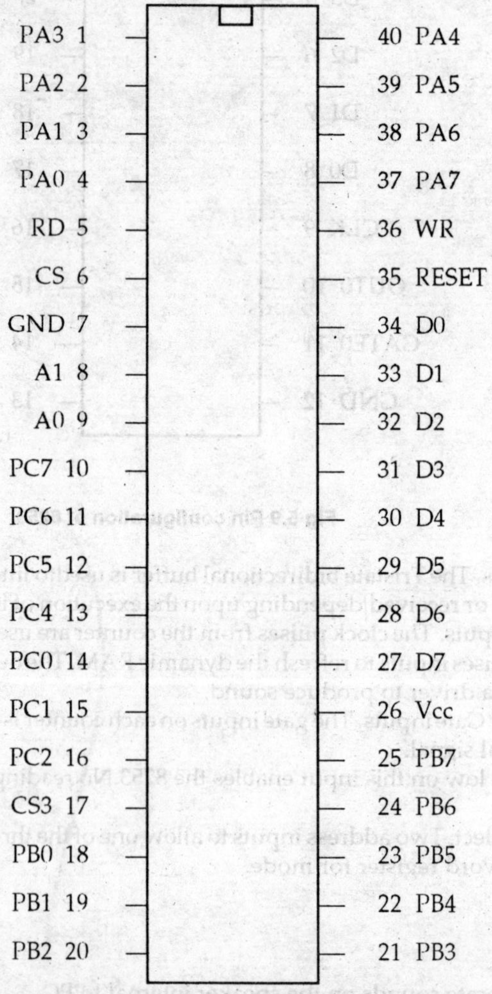

Fig 5.10 : Pin configuration of 8255.

Data bus fuffer : The 3-state birectional 8-bit buffer is used to interface the 8255 to the system data bus. Data is trasmitted or received by the buffer upon execution of input or output instructions by the CPU. Control words and status information are also transferred through the data bus buffer.

Read/Write : The functions of this block is to manage all internal and external transfers of both data ogic and control or status words.

CS - Chip select. A low on this input pin enables the communicatior between the 8255 and the CPU

RD - Read. A low on this pin enables the 8355 to send the data or status information to the CPU on the data bus. It allows the CPU to read from the 8255.

WF - A low on this input pin enable the CPU to write data or control words into 8255.

A0 and A1 - Port select 0 and port select 1 . These input signals in conjuction with the RD and write inputs, control the selection of one of 3 ports or the control word register. They are normally connected to the least significant bit of the address bus.

RESET - Reset. A high on this input clears the control register and all ports are set to the input mode.

In PC Peripheral devies are interfaced to the CPU through appropriate interface and controllers. Physically, the keyboard interface is present on the mother board where as the other interface and controllers are usually present as Add-on boards. Though the interfaces and controllers provide physical connection between the peripherals and the system it is the software which controls hardware interface and a software interface for each.

Table 5.5 below tells us the nature of hardware interface and software interface provided in PC for each peripheral device.

I/O Device	Hardware/Physical	Software Interface
Keyboard	Serial communication; seperate data line & clock line.	Parallel port along with to paraller converter (shift register).
Display Monitor	Serial interface; either composite video or TTL video interface	Shared memory as display buffer, programmable CRT controller.
Printer	Serial interface compatible to RS232C or parallel interface of centronics compatible.	Serial interface through UART, parallel interface directly under program control.
Floppy disk drive	Serial interface;MFM encoded data line which carries both data and clock.	Through intelligent floppy disk controllers commands and parameters are issued as chain of bytes.
Hard disk drive	Serial interface;MFM encoded data format. Data and clock on the same line/506417 compatible.	Through intelligent hard disk controller, commands and prameters are issued as a chain of bytes.

Table 5.5

The PC/XT architecture supports all three type of I/O techniques for data transfer :

1. Programmed or polled I/O.
2. Interrupt mode I/O
3. Direct memory assess mode.

The hardware design provides more than one option for some ofthe peripheral devices.
Summary of I/O Data transfer techniques used in PC :

I/O Device	I/O techniqies - Data transfer
Keyboard	Interrupt mode
Display	Data transfer through program mode, is transferred monitor by the CPU from its program memory to the video buffer which is a shared memory for both CPU and CRTC. Commands to CRT controller is used by the CPU in program mode directly to the CRT controller.
Printer - parallel interface	The PC hardware provides two options: 1. Interrupt mode of data transfer. 2. Program mode of data transfer.
The choice is made by software.	
Printer - serial interface	The PC hardware provides two options: 1. Interrupt mode of data transfer. 2. Program mode of data transfer.
The choice is mode by software.	
Floppy disk controller	Data transfer is in DMA mode. Command transfer to the controller is in program mode.
Hard disk	Data transfer is in DMA mode command transfer to controller the controller is in program mode.

5.10.4 8087 - NUMERIC COPROCESSOR

The Intel 8087 numeric data coprocessor provides the instructions and data types needed for high performance of a CPU alone. The 8087 is a numeric processor that provides arithmetic and logical instruction support for a variety of numeric data type. It also executes numeriç built-in-transcendental functions, eg. tangent and log functions.

The Specifications :

1. High performance numeric data coprocessor.
2. Adds arithmetic trigonometirc, exponential and logarithmic instructions.
3. CPU/8087 suports 7 data type; 16, 32, 64 bit intergers, 32, 64, 80 bit floating point and 18-digit BCD operands.
4. Compatible with IEEE floating point standard 754 .
5. Available in 5 MHz, 8 MHz and MHz.
6. Adds 8 X 80 bit individually addressable register stack to the 8086/8088 and 80186/80188.
7. 7 built-in exception handling functions.
8. Multibus system compatible interface.

Aplication areas

The 8087 provides functions meant specifically for high performance numeric processing requirements Trigonometric, logarithmic and exponential functions are built into the coprocessor hardware. These functions are essentialon scientific, engineering navigational and military applications. It is used in graphics CRT for extensive calculation of bit image graphic formation.

The 8087 is treated as an extension to the CPU providing register data types, control and instruction capabilities at the hardware level. At the programmer's level, the CPU and the 8087 are viewed as a single unified processor. As a coprocessor to an 8088 the 8087 is wired in parallel with the CPU as shown in figure.

The CPU's status (S0-S2) and queue status lines enable the 8087 to monitor and decode instructions in synchronization with the CPU. Once started the 8087 can process in parallel with, and independent of the host CPU. For resynchronization, the 8087's busy signal informs the CPU that the 8087 is executing an instruction and the CPU wait instrucion tests this signal to ensure that the 8087 is ready to execute subsequent instrucions. The 8087's interrupt request line is typically routed to the CPU through an 8259 programmable interrupt controller for 8088 systems. The 8087 uses one of request/grant lines of 8088 architecture i.e., RQ/GT0 to obtain control of the local bus for data transfer. The other request/grant lines is available for system use. A bus master can also be connected to the 8087 EQ~/GT1line. In this configuration the 8087 will pass the request/grant handshake signals between the CPU and the attached master when the 8087 is not in the control of the bus and will relinquish the bus to the master directly when 8087is in control. In this way two additional masters can be configured in an 8088 system. One will share the bus with the 8087 and the second will be guaranteed to be higher in priority than the 8087. The 8087 bus structure, operation and timing are identical to all other processors in the 8088 mode configuration. The address is time multiplexed data on the first 16/8 lines of the address/data bus. A16 through A19 are time multiplexed with four status lines S3-S6. The first 3 status lines S0 - S2 are used with an 8288 bus controller to determine the type of bus cycle being run.

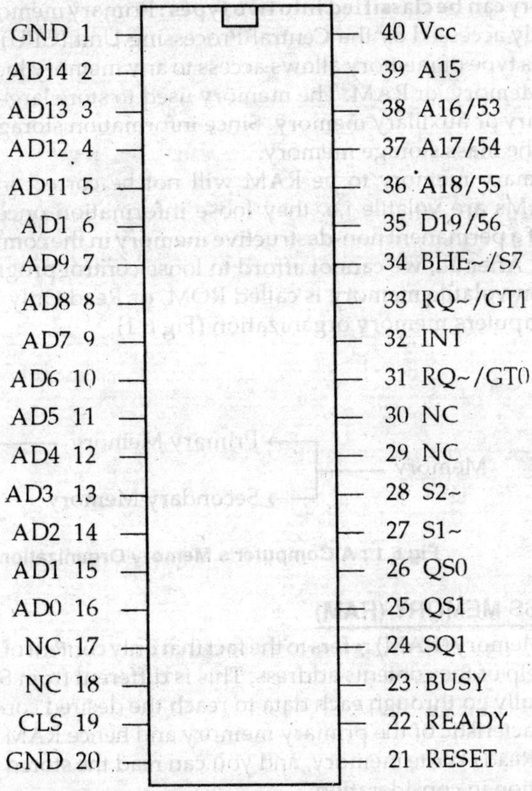

Fig 5.11 Pin configuration of 8087.

The 8087 includes the standard 8088 instruction set for general data manipulation and program control. It also includes 68 numeric instructions for extended precision integer, floating point trigonometric logarithmic and exponential functions. Any instruction executed by the 8087 is the combined result of the CPU and 8087 activity. The CPU and 8087 is the combined result of the CPU control over all program execution while the 8087 uses the coprocessor interface to recognize and perform numeric operation.

Chapter Six
MEMORY

6.0 INTRODUCTION

The memory of a computer is the place where programs and processed data is stored by the computer. This one line definItion itself highlights the importance of memory in a computer. As is evident from the block diagram of a computer in its barest form, the processing unit and memory always interact with each other. The basic memory unit is defined as the memory cell. A memory cell is a device capable of storing a binary digit. Generally a group of memory cells are organized into an addressable word. Generally eight bits make up a byte, and two bytes makes up a word.

Computer memory can be classified into two types : Primary memory and Secondary memory. The memory that is directly accessed by the Central Processing Unit (CPU) is called the main memory, or primary memory. This type of memory allows access to any memory location and hence it is also called the Random Access Memory, or RAM. The memory used to store larger bulk of programs and data is known as the secondary or auxillary memory. Since information storage is allowed in large quantities it is often dubbed as the mass storage memory.

Defining the primary memory to be RAM will not be correct in the present state of memory technology. Most RAMs are volatile i.e. they loose information once the power is shutdown. This necessiates the need of a permanent non-destructive memory in the computer which can be used to keep the control programs. After all, we cannot afford to loose control programs due to power failure. This type of permanent non-volatile memory is called ROM, or Read Only Memory. Now we give a small figure illustrating computers memory organization (Fig 6.1).

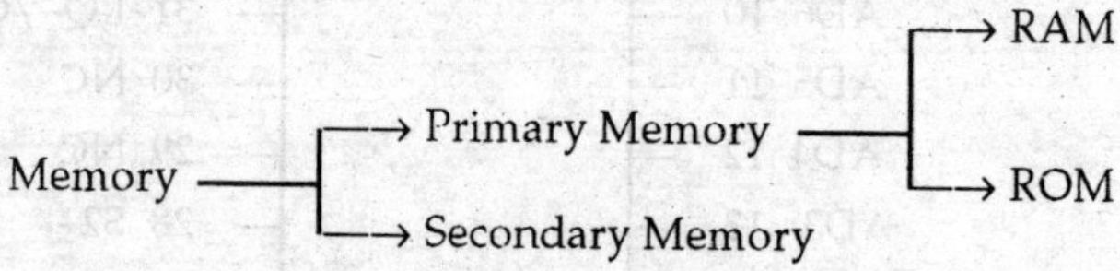

Fig 6.1 : A Computer's Memory Organization

6.1 RANDOM ACCESS MEMORY (RAM)

Random Access Memory (RAM) refers to the fact that only content of such a memory can be instantly referenced with the help of the contents address. This is different from SAM, or Serial Access Memory, where one has to serially go through each data to reach the desired contents. Immediate data access is thus a important characteristic of the primary memory and hence RAM is one of its constituents. RAM is often referred to as Read/Write memory, and you can read the stored contents or write new contents into the memory location in consideration.

Conceptually both RAM and ROM are random access memories. That is why both are used to make the computers primary memory. But RAM is used to refer to random access purely on the grounds of tradition reasons. The various types of RAM memories are considered next.

6.1.1 Core RAMs

The core RAM was the primary memory for most first generation computers. In those days, engineers relied on manipulation of magnetic dipoles to read and write on the RAM. But slowly this technology faded away, giving way to newer technologies. The analog of magnetism, electricity was clever enough to take the lead. It is because of this historical reason that computer users still refer to the primary memory as the core or core memory. It will surely occur to the exprienced Unix System User, that he has seen the ominous message : Segmentation fault-core dumped a number of times.These core RAMs are expensive and harder to work with, resulting in their slow demise from the memory scene.

6.1.2 Semiconductor RAMs

Semiconductor RAMs are now used to fabricate the modern generation of Computers. Semiconductor RAMs can be further classified into two types : Static RAM or SRAM, and Dynamic RAM or DRAM.

SRAM uses bipolar or MOS flipflops whereas DRAM uses MOSFETs and capacitors to store data.

Static RAM (SRAM) :

The memory cell of the SRAM is constructed from flip-flop, which may be either bipolar or MOS. Figure 6.2 shows a bipolar flip-flop used as a memory cell. In the above figure, each collector drive is shown to drive the base of the other transistor. Consider that the transistor Q_1 is saturated. This implies that the collector voltage of Q_1 is approximately 0 volts, and hence there is no drive voltage for the transistor Q_2. This results in the transistor Q_2 being cutoff, resulting in a +5V collector. This high collector voltage is sufficient enough to produce the required base current to retain transistor Q_2 in saturated state. This +5V collector voltage is obtained accross Q_2 and is called the high state, representing a binary one.

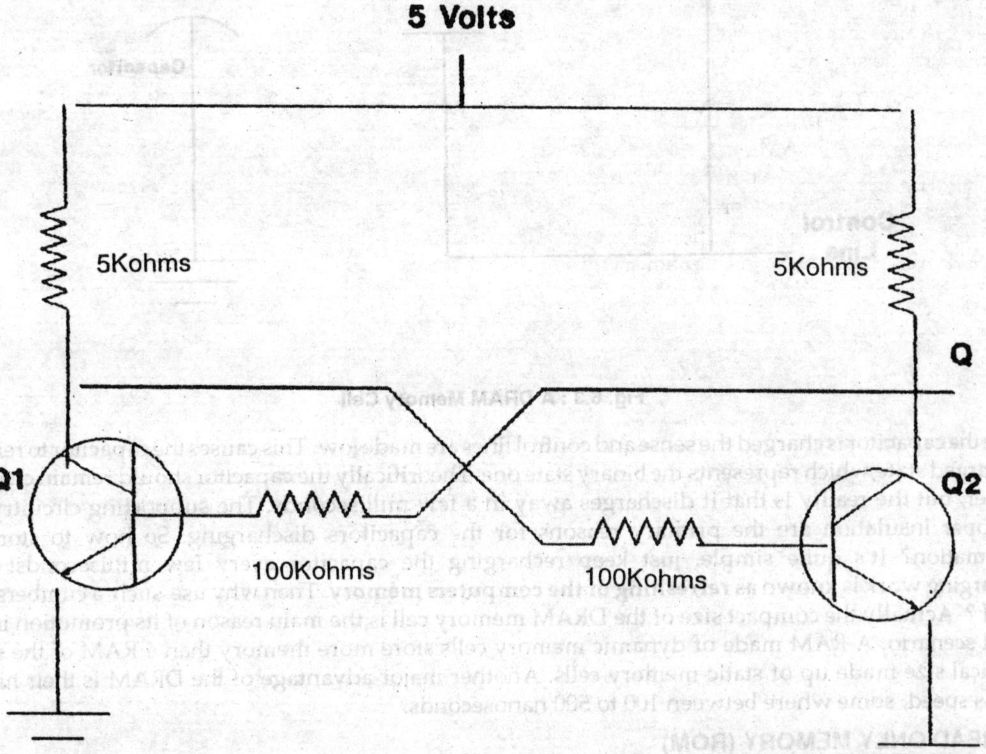

Fig. 6.2 : A SRAM Memory Cell.

Similarly if transistor Q_2 is saturated, Q_1 will be cutoff resulting in a zero volt output across Q. This represents the low state or binary zero.

When one transistor is saturated, the other is cutoff. This condition remains as long as an external force tries to change the condition of one of the transistors. Thus it is said that a flip-flop works like a latch, and the first case can be described as a latched condition with the transistor Q_1 saturated and transistor Q_2 cutoff.

A static ROM will contain thousands of flip-flops like this, each one storing a bit. As long as power is available (uninterrupted), the flip-flop remains latched and stores a bit. This is one of the primary reasons for describing this memory as static.

Dynamic RAM (DRAM) :

Dynamic RAM is a special semiconductor circuitry made of MOSFETs and Capacitors. A DRAM memory cell is shown below in Fig 6.3.

When the sense and control lines become high, the MOSFET conducts, charging up the capacitor.

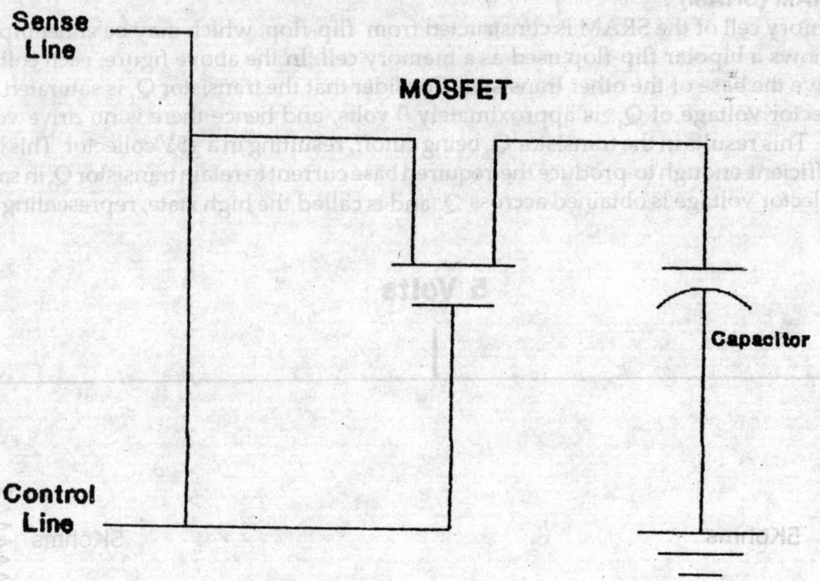

Fig. 6.3 : A DRAM Memory Cell

Once the capacitor is charged the sense and control lines are made low. This causes the capacitor to remain in charged state, which represents the binary state one. Theoritically the capacitor should remain charged forever, but the reality is that it discharges away in a few milliseconds. The supporting circuitry and improper insulation are the primary reasons for the capacitors discharging. So how to store the information? It's quite simple, just keep recharging the capacitor every few milliseconds! This recharging work is known as **refreshing of the computers memory.** Then why use such a cumbersome RAM ? Actually the compact size of the DRAM memory cell is the main reason of its promotion in the RAM scenario. A RAM made of dynamic memory cells store more memory than a RAM of the same physical size made up of static memory cells. Another major advantage of the DRAM is their higher access speed, some where between 100 to 500 nanoseconds.

6.2 READ ONLY MEMORY (ROM)

All memories should not be endowed with the capability to change its contents. Examples of such memories are ROM, which allow only the memory to be read. Most control programs are loaded in the computers ROM. The manufacturer does not want them to be lost due to power failures, or accidental tampering. Thus they resort to using the ROM. They are essentially non-volatile in nature. Examples of the basic elements used for constructing the ROM are diodes, MOSFETS, and even bipolar transistor. The various types of ROMs available are Mask ROM, EPROM, EEPROM, and Flash RAM. Details of these ROMs are considered next.

6.2.1 Mask ROM

When such a ROM is to be fabricated on a chip, the programming is done during their fabrication itself. Their contents cannot be altered easily. But why the name mask? The mask is the master pattern used to draw the circuit elements on the substrate during the fabrication of the IC. Hence the name.

The masked ROM has many advantages. We list a few of them :-

(i) High storage density.

(ii) Low production cost, when produce in large quantities.

(iii) Non volatile in nature ,

But they have quite a few stumbling disadvantages. First its production is a time taking process. This is so because the mask with all circuit elements marked is to be made before any further step can be taken. Secondly its production is feasible only when produced in large numbers. The biggest disadvantage is its non-changability. One just can't modify its contents, if for any reason the produced ROM turns out to be faulty. All that one can do is to throw it away! Not surprising, many more types of ROM have come to our rescue.

6.2.2 PROM

Programmable Read Only Memory is an alternative to the mask ROM. This type of ROM allows the user to program the ROM using a device known as the ROM programmer. PROM is actually an array of fusible links, originally made of nichrome or polysilicon. When all the unprogrammed rows of the metallic array are linked together. This represents the logic 0. When the programmer wants a logic one at a particular location of the memory, he generates a high intensity electric current to burn away the link. This represents the logic one. This process of burning of the metallic links is called **burning of the PROM.**

During its early years of existence, PROM users noticed a peculiar problem. The fused links sometimes healed establishing a link, by condensation of the vapourized metal. Thus a memory location programmed to represent binary one, becomes a binary zero, all by itself. This is dubbed as the **'grow-back'** phenomenon by the researchers. Researcher, were able to get rid of this unwanted phenomena by using special alloys to make the metallic array.

After this discussion, the reader may be carried away to beleive that PROM is something tuned to be perfect in a world full of turmoil. So, here is a word of caution! Once PROM is programmed, it is not possible to get the fused links established, unless the 'grow-back' comes as a saviour. So once programmed wrongly, the PROM has to be thrown away. Thus using PROM during the early developmental phase of any control programme, would essentially lead to waste of many PROMs, resulting in escalation of production cost. This drawback made the electronic people think about other possibilities. To get over these difficulties the EPROM (Erasable Programmable ROM) was made available.

6.2.3 EPROM

Erasable PROM, as the name suggests is a programmable ROM which allows the user to erase what he programs. This facility allows repeated programming of the chip, until the desired programming is done. To erase all the previous contents, U V rays are focussed through the window on the EPROM chip. For programming the EPROM a special programming kit, known as the EPROM programmer is used.

6.2.4 EEPROM

EEPROM is the acronym for Electrically Erasable Programmable Read Only Memory. It is very much similar to the EPROM, except that it is erased electrically. The major disadvantages of these chips is that they can be erased a fixed number of times only.

6.2.5 FLASH RAM

This is a chip belonging more or less to the EEPROM group. EEPROM uses a constant current flow for a few microseconds to erase the contents of the chip. This returns all the memory cells of the chip to zero state. Instead of using a constant current flow, the flash RAM uses current in a flash, and hence the name. It also is erasable a fixed number of times.

6.3 MEMORY ORGANIZATION

So far, the discussion concentrated on various types of memories and their uses. The concept of memory cell was also introduced in the previous discussion. This section is devoted towards understanding memory organisation. Typically, the bits used for storing information in a semiconductor memory, are organized into groups. A group of 8 bits, usually form a byte or word. Words of different lengths are possible, from one byte to any number of bytes. Information is grouped, in such a way that the word is the least addressable unit of the computer memory. A block diagram of a 8 bit word memory organization (fig 6.4) is shown below.

Addresses in a memory block are contiguous from 0, to the last memory location number. To read or write a word, a particular memory location is to be addressed by the computer. The contents of the address location is data.

As shown in Fig. 6.4, the main memory is more or less like an array of pigeon holes, each containing some information. To get a particular information, the relevant address location (the collection of a group of pigeon holes) has to be obtained. Each pigeon hole is associated with a fixed number of other pigeon holes. The length of such pigeon holes varies according to the size of the memory location used. This length of pigeon-holes or bits, is called the word length.

Each memory location is addressed using same number of bits. If n bits are used to create the address, you can have a total of 2^n addresses. Thus the total number of addressable memory location using n bits is 2^n .

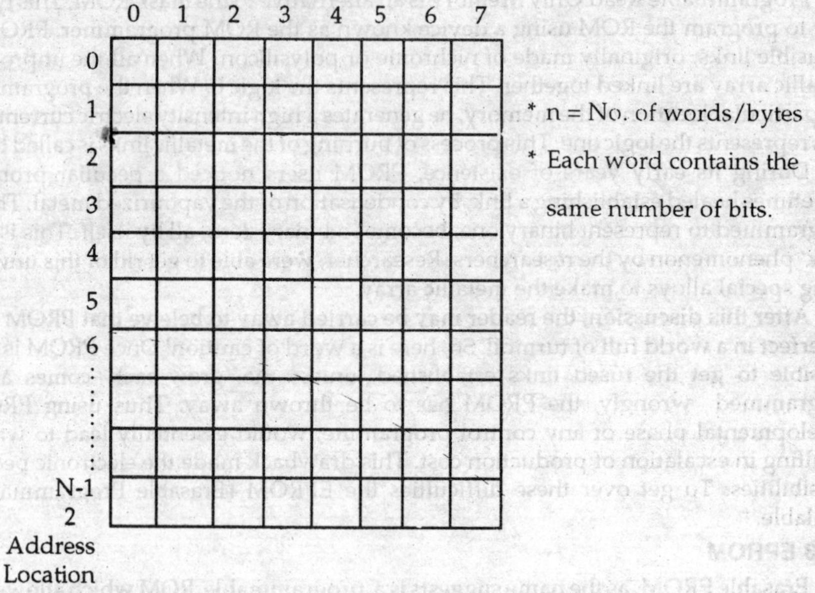

Fig 6.4 : Block Diagram of A Hypothetical Memory.

Originally 16 bit addresses were used. This could generate a total of 2^{16}, or 16,256 addresses. In the first IBM PC, a word was made up of 8 bits. Thus using 16 bits, the microprocessor could address 16,256 words, or bytes in this particular case. This went on to be referred to as 16kb of memory, and this configuration was referred to as 8/16 bit memory in short.

The 32 bit intel microprocessors - The 386 and 486 keeps a full word at each address, where a word refers to two bytes. But the smallest addressable unit of these latest microprocessors is four double words, i.e 16 bytes. This smallest addressable unit is described as a memory line.

6.4 PROCESSOR SPEED

The performance of a microprocessor is generally evaluated in terms of its processor speed. But what is the processor speed ? The processor speed is the frequency at which a microprocessor can execute instructions. This speed is measured with the help of an electronic clock, which is always ticking inside your computer (it doesn't matter whether the system is powered on or not). Measurement of frequency is done in MegaHertzs,that is the clock beats in the order of millions per second.

The original PC used the 8088 chip that had a 4.77 MHz clock. At a clock speed of 1MHz, one clock cycle takes 1,000 nanoseconds. Thus the original PC cycle duration was around 200 nanoseconds. The original 80286 chip base had a 6 MHz clock, reducing the cycle duration to 167 nanoseconds. As the processors improved, the cycle duration went on reducing it is now common to see PCs with 25 MHz clocks, making the clock duration as small as 40 nanoseconds. Thus a 25 MHz PC is about 6 times faster than the 4.77 MHz original PC.

Now lets consider the number of bits that can be handled at one go. Originally the 8088 allowed only 8 bits per instruction. But the processors have grown over the year, and the 80286 handles 16 bits per instruction, where as the 802386 and 80486 handles 32 bits per instruction. Thus a 486 machine handles instructions four times faster than the 8086.

The combined effect of these two features increases the processor speed many fold. Thus a 25 MHz

486 machine is approximately 24 times faster than the 4.77 MHz 8088 machine.

6.5 WAIT STATE

Before wait condition is explained, it is necessary to have a sound understanding of memory speed. The memory speed is the time taken by the memory chip to access a particular memory location, once the address has been obtained. It is measured in nanoseconds, and it will be worth mentioning that the fastest DRAMs have a rated speed of 60 to 70 nanoseconds.

After the above consideration, it is easy to notice the trade off between the processor speed and memory speed. In the early days of the PC, processors limped at around 4 MHz. Thus an average memory chip of rated speed 200 nanosecond had no problem with reading or writing. But the processor speed increased manyfolds when compared with the memory speed. Today most average PCs have processor speed of around 25 MHz, (a cycle of 40 nanoseconds), leave aside Pentium driven systems which cruse at around 100 MHz and thus a 70 nanosecond memory chip cannot keep up with the processor. As a result, the processor is made to wait in idle state, while the memory chip reads from or writes to the memory location. This idle state of the processor during a read/write operation is defined as the **Wait State**. Wait states serverly reduce computer speed, chopping away all the advantages that could be reaped from the higher processor speed.

6.6 SOLVING THE WAIT PROBLEM

The first possible solution is to use faster DRAMs. But the fastest DRAM cannot match a 25 MHz processor. Another problem is associated with the DRAMs. The DRAMs do not perform at their rated speeds due to their intermediate charging. Thus the DRAM never reads or writes at the rated speed when you make a few consequtive read/write. Memory speed can be made to increase, if SRAMs are used. SRAMs have speeds of about 40 nanoseconds, thus giving almost zero wait state. But the cost of SRAMs being more, hikes the cost of such memories.

Researchers have found a few clever solutions to the wait problem. They changed the memory architecture to increase memory speed. The most popular architectures are interleaved,static-column and page mode RAM.

6.6.1 Interleaved RAM

In this technique the memory is divided into two or more banks, and the sequential bits are arranged in alternating banks. To illustrate the point, consider that the DRAMs memory is divided into two banks, say bank1 and bank2. The first bit is read from bank1. To read the next bit it has to switch to bank2, and so on. This method thus allows one part of the memory to be used, while the other one can be refreshed. Thus there is no time delay in read/write due to refreshing. The biggest advantage of this inter leaving memory structure is the fact that there is no need for a specialized DRAM. The same chip can be used, provided a proper controller is built into the PC. It is observed that memory interleaving by a factor of two, increase memory speed by almost 50 percent.

6.6.2 Static Column RAM

This type of RAM uses a different chip technology. The memory is divided into rows and columns. Adjacent bits are placed in a column. Thus sequential reading of a bit from a particular column doesnot result in wait states. But jumping over to the next column. does result in wait states. The structure of such DRAMs some how resemble SRAMs, and give almos[illegible] percent increase in efficiency.

6.6.3 Page Mode RAM

In this memory architecture, the DRAM is divided into pages or modules, each containing about 2K bits. Consequtive bits can be read from a particular page without any wait states. But reading from a new page does result in wait states.

6.7 MEMORY CACHING

This is the most popular method of increasing the memory speed, and widely implemented in the latest 386 and 486 machines.In this technique, a high speed memory, generally made of SRAM, is placed between the primary memory and the microprocessor. **This high speed SRAM is known as the memory cache, and is responsible for storing those instructions, which may be required by the processor during its processing.** Special controller circuits are used to control what fills the cache. This control circuit can be implemented in both hardware and software. If the information requested by the processor is obtained from the cache, it is called a **cache hit,** else we call it a **cache miss.** Needless to mention that higher cache hit increase memory performance.

Most 386 and 486 based machines use a fast SRAM cache of capacity in the range 32-64K. This enhances the memory speed extraordinarily. A DRAM having a rated speed of about 100 nanosecond seems to run at about 40 nanosecond ! The usefulness of this caching technique prompted manufacturers to incorporate caches into their processor chips itself. The 486 processor comes with a 8K SRAM built in it. PC manufacturers add external caches to increase the performance further. But always try to settle with a modest sized SRAM, as the cost of the system drastically increases with larger capacity SRAMs.

6.8 BUS

What is a bus ? A bus is a set of wires used to transmit a group of bits in parallel under control of an associated controller. The components of a computer system, i.e, the memory, input-output devices and processor etc., must be connected to form a computer system. The manner in which these components are connected and communicate among themselves, profoundly detemine the systems performance.

In the first generation computers, the CPU was directly connected to each of the system components, i.e. memory unit, input-output devices etc. This architecture was termed as the **two bus system**, as the CPU was connected to the I/O device and memory unit using seperate bus connections. Fig. 6.5 illustrates a two bus system connections. Every bus structure consists of an address bus which carries the address of the system components or memory location as the case may be, a control bus which carries the control signals and a data bus which actually carries the data. All these buses are illustrated in fig. 6.5. This method of interconnection requires n bus systems to interconnect n devices with the CPU.

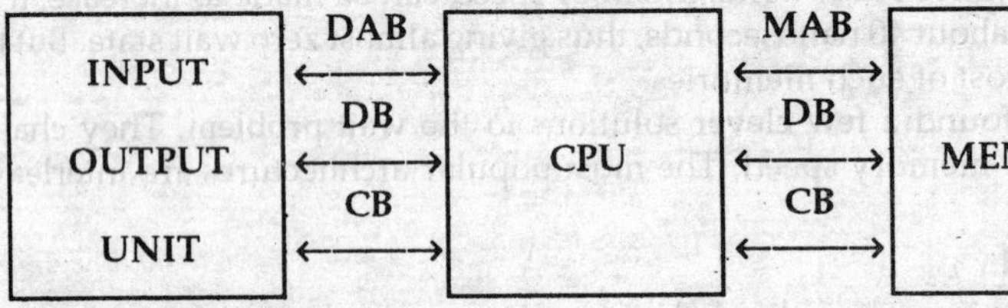

DAB - Device Address Bus
DB - Data Bus
MAB - Memory Address Bus
CB - Control Bus

Fig. 6.5 : A Two Bus System.

This considerably increases system cost and increases the use of interface logic. To make the interconnection of system components less expensive and to standardize the interface logic used, a popular technique involving interconnection of all components on a single BUS system is used. This system connection is called the **unibus structure**. The unibus architecture is illustrated in fig. 6.6.

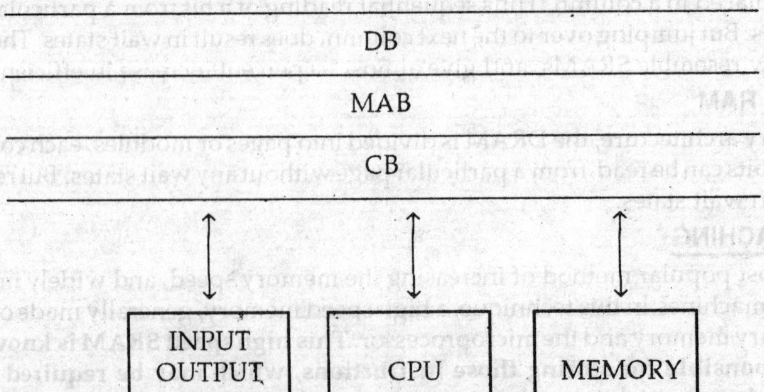

Fig. 6.6 : A Unibus Architecture.

The bus used by the original IBM PC (based on INTEL 8088) had a total of 62 separate lines of wires to it. They are identified by the codes A0 through A31 and B0 through B31 ; numbering scheme corresponds to the physical layout of the lines on the option boards; the 'A' side is on the right, the 'B' on left, with the number runing from back to front.

There is quite a variety of signals passed in all these lines. Five of them are used to pass the four different power voltages, with one voltage duplicated. Another three are used as ground lines to be used along with the power lines.

Eight of the lines are used to pass the eight bits of data in a byte,so that they can transfer data byte-by-byte at a time.Twenty lines are used for addressing to indicate which part of the computer has to has to communicate. With 20 address lines we can access 2^{20} addresses, thus making the memory capacity one megabyte. There are two addressing methods :

1. Memory addressing.
2. I/O port addressing.

Which ever mode is being used, the address is signalled on the address lines, while data passes on the eight data lines. The remaining lines of a PC are used for a variety of control purposes. One line indicates whether the bus is busy or free for use. Another set of lines handles interrupt requests, which are basically hardware signals indicating that one part of the computer or another needs attention.

A number of differrent types buses exist and consequenty several different standards are available for the buses. All buses can be divided into three major sections, the address,data and control sections. These were explained in the very beginning itself.

Most buses use tri-state drivers to write data on the data lines. In the most straight forward systems, the address lines are completely controlled by the bus master, while the remaining devices connected to the bus are called slaves. Each slave then has an address number and the bus-master uses the address lines to control who is to use the bus. In this case, a controlling device is called the bus-master only when it has control and at that time, the responding devices are called slaves. For buses in which control is shared among several devices i.e. more than one device can take control of the bus, the address lines are also driven by tri-state drivers. The bus uses synchronous or an asynchronous technique.

For synchronous transfers, the bus works as follows. Let us assume that the CPU wishes to read and write from peripheral devices. Each device is given a separate number, and a device is selected by the CPU placing the required number on the address lines.

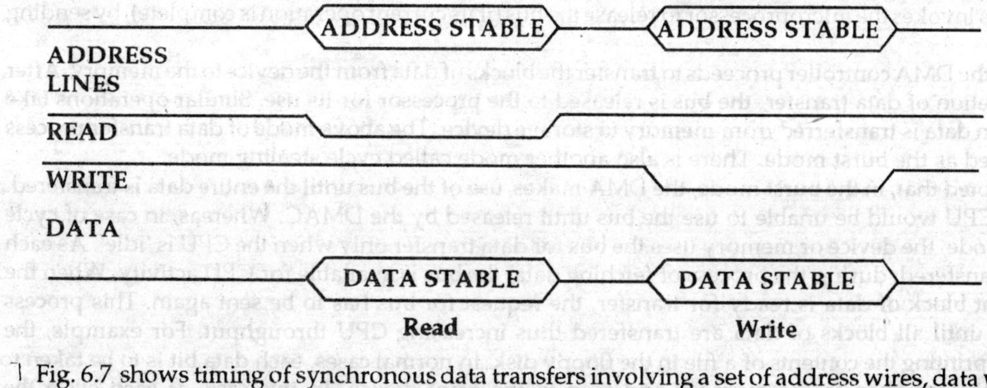

Fig. 6.7 shows timing of synchronous data transfers involving a set of address wires, data wires and read write control line. All transfers are made by the CPU.

For reading, the CPU places the number of the devices to be read from, on the address lines. Then the CPU lowers the read and the selected device must place data on the data lines which means enabling its tristate drivers connected to the bus data wires. When the new line goes back to a '3', the device must disable its tristate drivers.

When the CPU desires to write data, the device number is placed on the address line and then data are placed on the data lines.The CPU activates write line and the device must read the data.

Synchronous transfers are generally thought to be the fastest way to transfer data and are used for memory data transfers and sometimes for transferring data to other types of devices. The problem is that all devices must respond at the same speed. To avoid the problem of speed mismatch, the asynchronous transfer technique is often used.

When an asynchronous bus transfer technique is used, another control line called data valid is required. This line is controlled by the devices and not the CPU. If there is more than one device on the bus, a tristate driver will be required for each device using this line.

The asynchronous procedure involves handshaking. The effect is that the CPU tells which device is selected for either reading or writing and then waits for the selected device to respond with a handshake before continuing.

6.8.1 AT BUS

The AT bus uses the standard PC bus and adds another 36 lines to it. The physical and electrical layout of the AT bus is designed to be compatible with the PC bus, so that the AT class of machines can use as many PC option boards as possible. The 36 new lines are numbered C1 through C18 and D1 through D18, similar to PC bus address lines to extend the range of addressing and five more interrupt request lines.

6.9 DIRECT MEMORY ACCESS

In a microcomputer the data transfer occurs between any of the following two devices :

1. Memory and microprocessor.
2. Microprocessor and I/O devices.
3. Memory and I/O devices.

These transfers of data can be done by two methods :

1. Program I/O mode (through microprocessor)
2. Direct memory access.

In programmed I/O data transfer, a program residing in the memory, request the device for data transfer to or from the microprocessor. During every data transfer, the microprocessor is involved making itself redundant for other operations. Also, this method of transfer is very slow, since data is transferred byte by byte.

In DMA mode of transfer, as the name implies, the data transfer is taking place directly between memory and I/O devices or vice versa. Thus it will reduce the overhead of the microprocessor. Also the operation is considerably speeded up, as the transfer of data is in blocks. For this purpose a separate device known as the DMA controller in used. When data is to be transfered from a block storage device (FDD/HDD) to memory, the DMA controller has to request the microprocessor to release the bus from its usage, by sending a signal called DRQ. The channel of DRQ (0-3) depends on the device that is currently active. This invokes the microprocessor to release the bus (if its current operation is complete), by sending a signal.

Then the DMA controller proceeds to transfer the blocks of data from the device to the memory. After the completion of data transfer the bus is released to the processor for its use. Similar operations take place when data is transferred from memory to storage device. The above mode of data transfer process is described as the burst mode. There is also another mode called cycle stealing mode.

It is noted that, in the burst mode, the DMA makes use of the bus until the entire data is transfered. Thus the CPU would be unable to use the bus until released by the DMAC. Whereas, in case of cycle stealing mode, the device or memory uses the bus for data transfer only when the CPU is 'idle'. As each block is transfered, during the process of fetching data, the bus is available for CPU activity. When the subsequent block of data is ready for transfer, the request for bus has to be sent again. This process continues until all blocks of data are transfered thus increasing CPU throughput. For example, the process of printing the contents of a file in the floppy disk. In normal cases, each data bit is to be taken to the accumulator, then to the memory and then to the print device. In this case, at each cycle the microprocessor is able to send one word of data and is slow. If the same is done without the intermediate transfer to the accumulator, it will be much faster. If this is to be done, ther the microprocessor must be able to relinquish control of data address buses so that logic is taken over by some other chip. This particular chip should be capable of transfering the data en-masse, given the address and length of data. Such transfer is known as direct memory access.

Whenever there is bulk data transfer, the DMA controller requests the microprocesser by raising an interrupt, after getting the interrupt acknowledge, the DMA transfers the data, and then releases the bus. Here for a certain amount of time, the DMA takes control of the bus and the microprocesser will be idle for that period.

7.0 INTRODUCTION

The Keyboard is the most user friendly input device for most computer systems we encounter in our applications. It consists of a set of type-writer like keys, which are used for inputing data, programs and issuing commands to the computer.

PLATE 4 "A KEYBOARD"

The original layout of keys on the IBM PC/XT series was called the **QWERTY** arrangement, corresponding to the six characters of the top row of the keyboard (refer fig 7.1). The QWERTY key layout is due to Christopher Soles. This layout pattern came under heavy criticism from the press and alternative layout patterns started evolving. The most popular alternative is known as the **Dvorak-Dealey** layout, named after its inventors (refer fig 7.2). The IBM has stuck to the original QWERTY layout, while some of its clones have gone for alternative layout patterns.

The original IBM PC/XT Keyboard had a total of 83 keys. The IBM AT Keyboard then brought out some modifications on the original PC/XT keyboard and increased the no. of keys to 101. The number of keys on the keyboard kept on varying from one manufacturer to the other.

7.1 KEYBOARD SPECIFICATIONS

These days most IBM PC's and their clones come with 101 keys.

The **standard spacing** between two keytops (the distance measured from the center of a key to that of an other adjacent key) is about 0.75 inches.

The standard keytravel (the distance a key has to travel to effect a "key") ranges from 2.5 to 4.5 mm.

Fig 7.1 : QWERTY LAYOUT

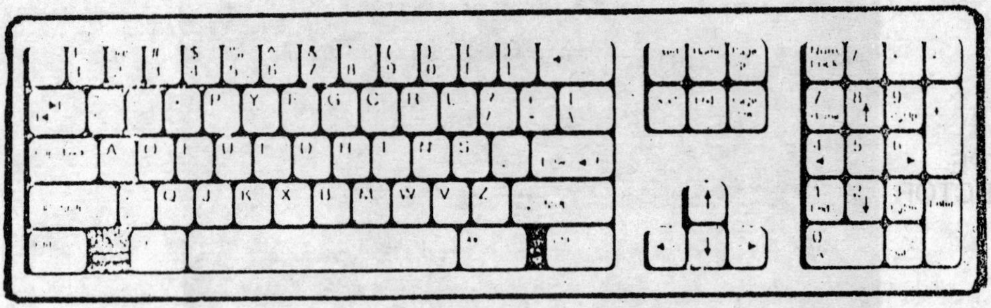

Fig 7.2 : DROVAK OEALY LAYOUT.

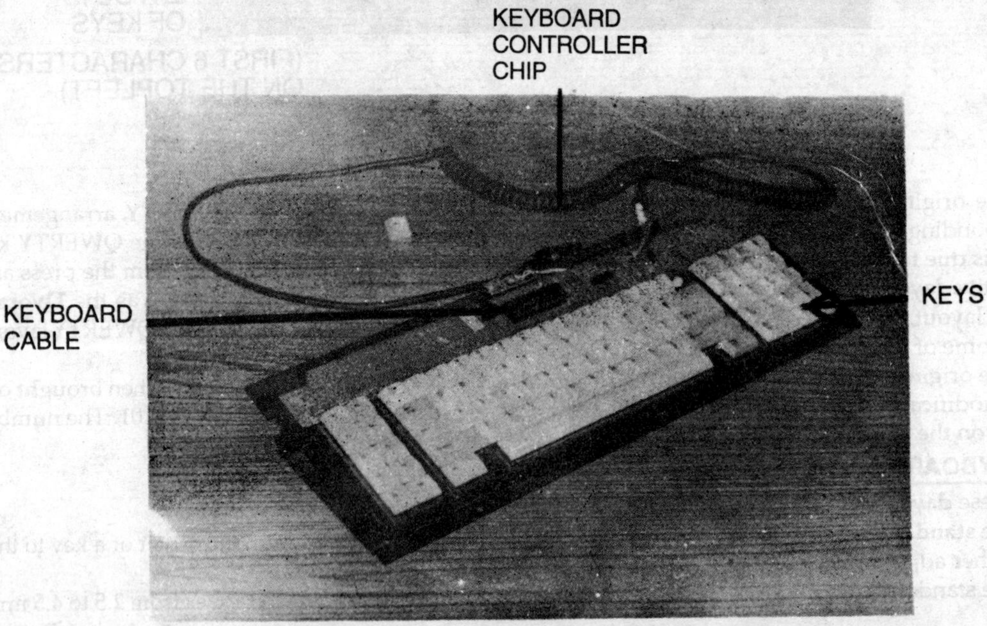

PLATE 5 "Inside the Keyboard"

Usually the **keyboard cable** is approximately 6 feet long, and is coiled like a telephone cable. Most commonly a standard 5 PIN DIN is used as the connector to the main computer system. The pin connections of the 5 PIN DIN are as follows:-

1. Keyboard clock
2. Keyboard Data
3. Keyboard Reset (unused)
4. Ground
5. 5.0 V D.C.

The notch on the PIN DIN allows the pin connections to be made in only one particular way. This prevents wrongs pin connections being made to the computer system.

7.2 KEYBOARD INTERNALS

The block diagram of a 4 by 4 keyboard is shown in fig. 7.3. The keyswitches are arranged in a matrix form. Each keyswitch has a set of co-ordinates, corresponding to its row and column.

The keyboard electronics is concerned with sensing the key depression, encoding and then sending the code to the computer. The function of sensing the keydepression is done by a standard method known as **scanning.**

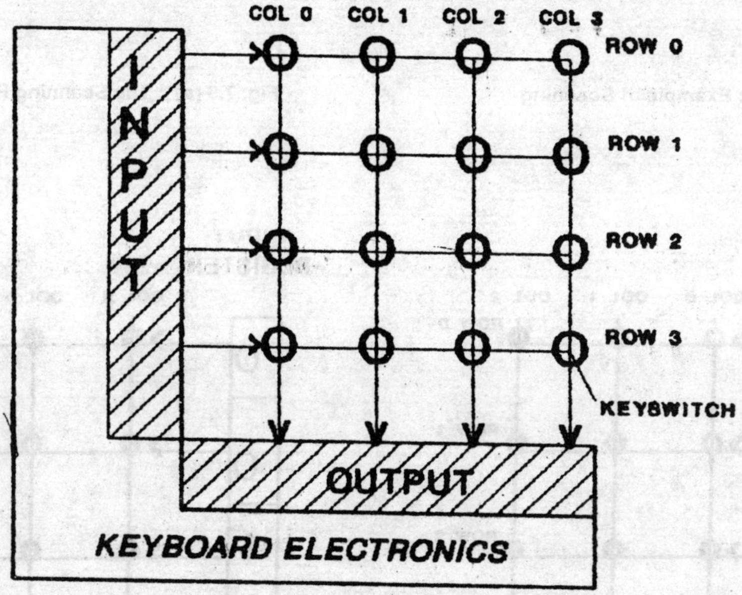

Fig. 7.3 : Block Diagram of a 4 by 4 Keyboard

Various types of keyswitches are available. The most popular ones are:-

1. Capacitive Keyswitches
2. Hard Contact

All IBM PCs and most of the clones use the capacitive keyswitches. This technology is explained in the next section.

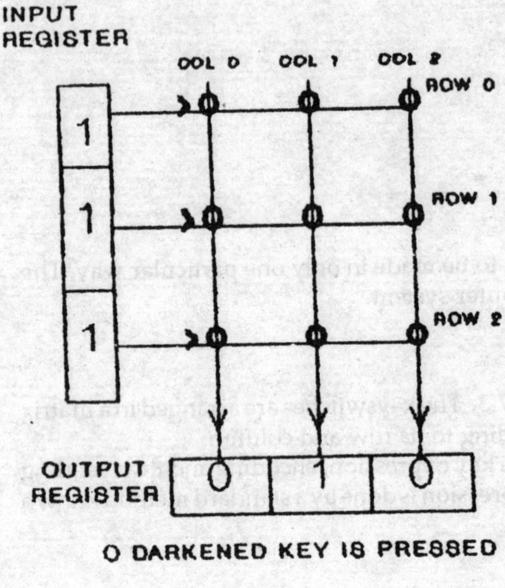

Fig. 7.4 : Example of Scanning

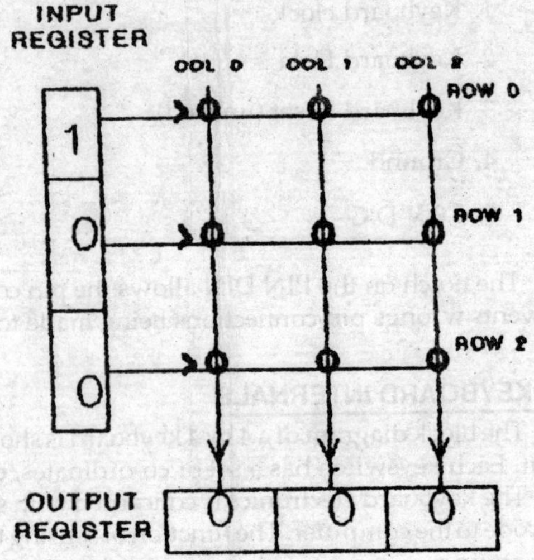

Fig. 7.5 (a) : The Scanning Process

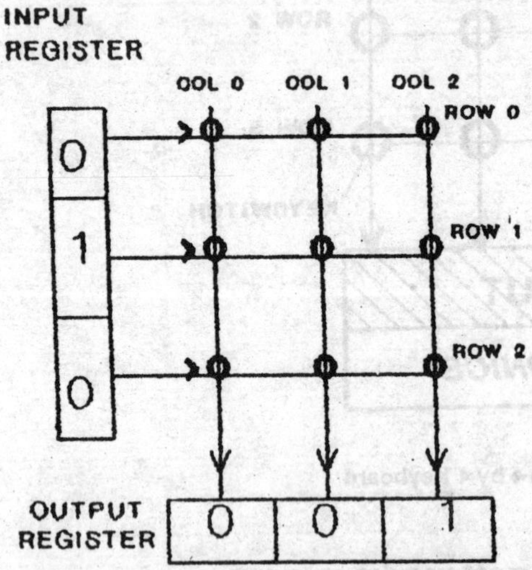

Fig. 7.5 (b) : The Scanning Process

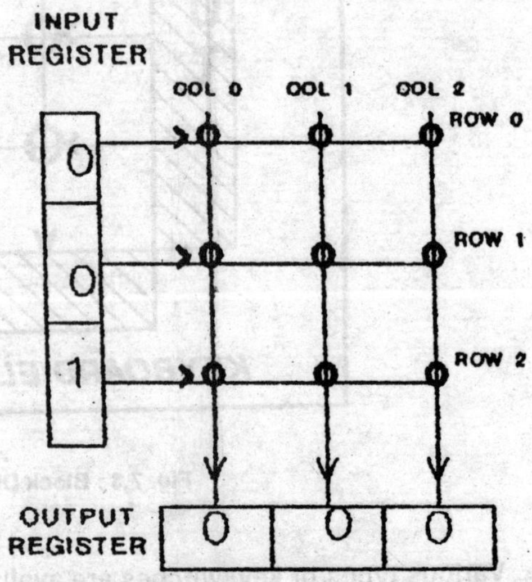

Fig. 7.5 (c) : The Scanning Process

7.2.1 Capacitive Keyboards

The very fact that all IBM PCs and most clones use this type of keyboard makes it the most widely used keyboard technology.

Capacitive keyboards are fabricated on etched circuit boards. Each keyswitch actually consists of two capacitor. The capacitor plates are usually tin/nickle plated circular plates, separated from each other such that they work as a capacitor. Pressing a key causes the concerned capacitor plates to come together. This change in distance between capacitor plates effect a change in capacity of the capacitor, which results in a small current to flow. The keyboard microprocessor (MUP) scans the matrix of keyswitches for current flows (scanning is explained in keyboard operation). When a current flow is detected, it generates a **scancode**. Actually each press of a key generates two scancodes. The first scancode is generated when the key goes down, and the next scancode is generated when the key goes up. This two-time scanning is incorporated as a precautionary measure. Random noises can also cause similar current flows which may be detected by the keyboard MUP, and can be a source of confusion. The process of scanning the matrix twice may initially seem to hold the key speed. But the fact is that this process is still faster than the most efficient typists typing (typically 200-300 characters/sec can be detected by MUP). The scancodes are converted to serial data and relayed to MUP in the computer system.

7.2.2 Hard Contract Keyboards

This capacitive keyboard technology is complex and costly. It has the advantage of long lasting service. A cheaper alternative to this technology is known as the **hard contact Keyboard technology.**

In place of using capacitors, and depending upon the change in capacitance for current flows, actual contact is established when a key stroke is made. This method allows simpler design, but is prone to faster degradation.

7.3 KEYBOARD OPERATION

As explained in the capacitive keyboard section, each keydown movement results in a serial code to be generated by the keyboard MUP (intel 8048), and a similar serial code is generated for the keyup movement. If the key remains pressed for move than half a second, the keyboard sends out Make Codes repeatedly ten times/second. Thus the 8048 is mainly concerned with watching the key movements and representing their status to the ROM-BIOS. The 8048 also has a buffer which can store 20 key actions. The 8048 is explained in detail later.

The traditional method of identifying which key has been pressed is known as the **scanning method** is and explained next.

A 3 by 3 keyboard (fig.7.5) is used to illustrate the basic principle of scanning. If all the bits of the input register are high, then the corresponding O/P on the output register will be observed to be high only for col 1. This identifies that a key of column 1 had been pressed. It would have been easy to find out the corresponding row number also, had a shift register with only one high bit been used. For the purpose of clarity actual polarity is not considered.

Let us consider a 3 by 3 matrix and consider the darkened key to be pressed.

High O/P is observed only in phase B, which corresponds to high I/P on row 1 and high O/P on column 2. Thus the key with co-ordinates (1,2) was pressed.

7.4 ROLL-OVER

A problem known as roll-over occurs when a user accidently or deliberately presses more than one key at the same instant of time. Roll-over is defined as the number of simultaneous key presses detectable by the keyboard. The basic matrix form has a roll-over of 2 keys. Most recent PC keyboards provide multiple roll-over to permit the user to key multiple keys at the same time.

7.5 KEYBOUNCE

In most applications involving electromechanical components, the actual stable contact is established only after several oscillations (bounces). Usually 10-20 milliseconds are required after a keypress for the oscillations to cease. The same problem is encountered during key release. Both hardware and software solutions are available for this problem.

Many hardware solutions are possible. But all the solutions, be it in hardware or software are concerned with screening the oscillations from being scanned by the keyboard electronics. A R-C filter can be used to filter the oscillation. A Delay Flip-flop can also be used to delay the scanning. These solution are costlier and thus the software solution is more preferred. The software solution consists of checking the keyswitch again after n milliseconds (n = 10 to 20ms, the time taken by oscillations), where the value of n varies for various keyboard implementations. If a key press is detected after n milliseconds, the key press is considered to be genuine, else the initial detection is attributed to noise. The time delay employed is called the **debounce time**. Figure 7.6 illustrates the key-Bouncing phenomena.

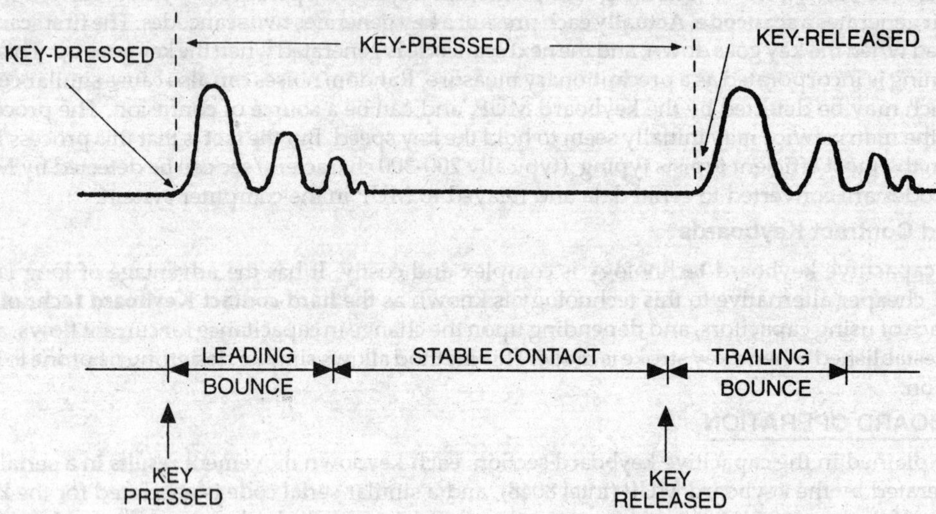

Fig. 7.6 : The Keybouncing Phenomena

7.6 KEYBOARD CONTROLLER

The microprocessors used in most PC keyboards is the intel 8048. The intel 8048 is a single chip microprocessor with a RAM and ROM.

7.6.1 INTEL 8048

It is a 8 bit parallel microcomputer fabricated on a single chip. It has 27 I/O lines, a 8 bit timer/counter and an on board clock/oscillator. It has a **1 Kilobyte ROM** and a **512 byte RAM.**

7.6.2 INTEL 8048 Pin Configuration

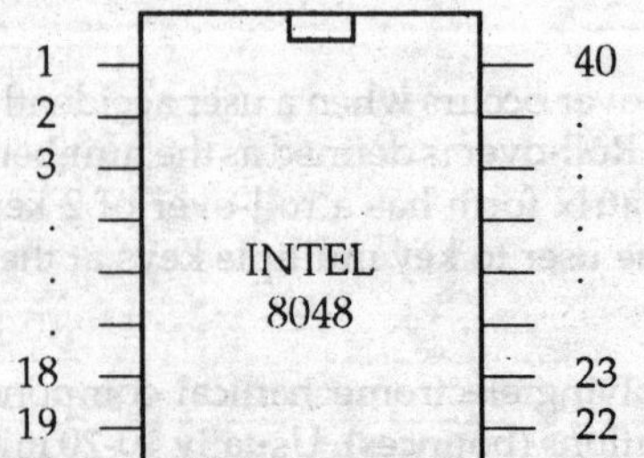

Fig 7.7 : Pin Out Diagram.

The Pin-connections are:-

Pin No :

1. Input testable pin
2. One side of crystal I/P for internal/external oscillator
3. Other side of crystal I/P
4. (Active low) to initialize the processor
5. Step I/P
6. Interrupt I/P it initiates an interrupt if interrupt is enabled.
7. External access input which forces all program memory fetches to reference external memory.
8. O/P strobe activated during a BUS Read.
9. Program strobe enable
10. Output strobe during a bus write
11. Address latche enable

12-19. Bidirectional port which can be read/writes

20. GND.

21-24. 8 bit bidirectional port

25. O/P strobe

27-34. 8 bit bidirectional port

35-38. High order programme counter bit

39. I/P testable pin

40. Power supply (+5 V)

The main functions of the keyboard microprocessors (such as Intel 8048) are as follows:-

1. Scanning keyboard matrix.
2. Detection of key press.
3. Debouncing.
4. Transmitting the keyboard data to the mother board serially.
5. Performing power on self-test when required by the PC system.
6. Typematic action (i.e. repeating the transmission of a particular scancode, when a key is pressed continuously).

7.7 KEYBOARD LOCK

Keyboard lock facility is provided on most IBM PC's and their clones. When the keyboard is locked, the keyboard data line is disabled. Thus the data from the keyboard never reaches the computer. This lock facility is generally provided on the front panel of the system. This feature is known as ALPM (Automatic Ledger Posting Mechanism). This facility prevents unauthorized use of the computer system.

7.8 MAKE AND BREAK CODES

Most keyboard follow IBM Keyboard specifications and use the Intel 8048 microprocessor. As described in the keyboard operation section, the microprocessor sends a scancode (serial bit codes) when the key is pressed. This is called the Make code. When the key breaks contact, another code is sent which is called the **TABLE 7.1 Breakcode.** The make and break codes of a particular key differ only by the M.S.B. (D7). D7 is 0 in the make code and 1 in the break code.

Key	Make Code	Break Code
Left Alt	38	B8
Right Shift	36	B6
Right Alt	E0 38	E0 B8
Right Ctrl	E0 1D	E0 9D
Caps Lock	3A	BA
Backspace	0E	8E
Tab	0F	8F
Space bar	39	B9
Enter	1C	9C

Numeric/Cursor Keypad

Key	Make Code	Break Code
Scroll Lock	46	C6
Num Lock	45	C5
*	37	B7
-	4A	CA
+	4E	CE
Enter	E0 1C	E0 9C
1 or End	4F	CF
2	50	D0
3 or Pg Dn	51	D1
4	4B	CB
5	4C	CC
6	4D	CD
7 or Home	47	C7
8	48	C8
9 or PgUp	49	C9
0 or Ins	52	D2
Num Lock	E0 35	E0 B5

NOTE : *When the keyboard is in a shifted state, the make code of the Num Lock key change to AA, and the break code changes to E0 B5 2A.*

Function Keys
(F11 and F12 on Advance and Compact keyboards only)

Key	Make Code	Break Code
Esc	01	81
F1	3B	BB
F2	3C	BC
F3	3D	BD
F4	3E	BE
F5	3F	BF
F6	40	C0
F7	41	C1
F8	42	C2
F9	43	C3
F10	44	C4
F11	57	D7
F12	58	D8

NOTE : *When the keyboard is in a Shifted state or the Ctrl key is held down when the Print Screen key is pressed, it sends out a make code of E0 37 and a breack code of E0 B7. When the Alt key is hold down, the make code of Print Screen becomes 54, and the break code becomes D4. The Pause key also acts differently in the shifted or Ctrl state, sending out the make code E0 46 E0 C6.*

Embedded Cursor Keypad (Compact keyboard only)		
Key	**Make Code**	**Break Code**
; or : or *	37	B7
- or _	4A	CA
= or +	4E	CE
J or 1	4F	CF
K or 2	50	D0
L or 3	51	D1
U or 4	4B	CB
I or 5	4C	CC
O or 6	4D	CD
7 or &	47	C7
8 or *	48	C8
9 or (	49	C9
0 or)	52	D2

NOTE : *When Shift is active, the Scroll Lock key sends a scan code of 45 C5, which switches on the embedded numeric keypad on the Compact Keyboard. The sacn keys of the following keys change to the indicated value during this state.*

Table 7.1

7.9 TYPEMATIC ACTION

If a key remains pressed for more than half a second, the keyboard sends out the scancode of the key repeatedly ten times/second. This feature enables the user to type in a particular key multiple number of times withouthiting the key again and again. In IBM terminology this is kown as the **Typematic action.** IBM specifications say that the typematic action works for all except the shift keys.

7.10 IBM AT KEY BOARD

When compaired with the PC keyboard, the AT keyboard has a new switch called SYS REQ.Using this key a special software interrupt signal generated by the keyboard BIOS is made available. Software control of the three status lights eg.Caps Lock,Scroll Lock and Num Lock can be achieved.The keyboard data format is also different,but details of the signal pattern is not considered here.

7.10.1 XT/AT SWITCH

Most IBM PC keyboards come with a XT/AT switch on the rear side of the keyboard. An IBM AT requires the switch to be in the AT position, else after booting, the computer will flash a keyboard error. Similarly an IBM XT requires the switch to be in the XT position. This switch has been incorporated so that the same keyboard serves both the XT and the AT. The necessity of this switch is due to the fact that the keyboard data format for a XT and AT are different.

7.11 KEYBOARD FAULTS AND REMEDIES

The most common problem associated with the keyboard is that of dead or stuck-up key switches. Dead key switches refer to those keys which do not result in a key stroke after a key is pressed. Reasons for such a fault can be improper keyboard usage, mechanical fault and most frequently gradual degradation of the key due to repeated use. The same reasons result in a stuck-up key switch. When a key switch remains pressed after pressing it once and a series of key switch characters appear on the screen, the switch is said to be stuck-up.

When this problem is encountered, the most cost effective solution is keyswitch replacement. This process is explained next. First the keyboard is disconnected from the computer system by removing the 5 pin cable. Next the keyboard is inverted and the screws opened. The board enclosed inside the keyboards outer case is removed. Next the required key's positions are searched in the PCB of the keyboard and removed from it by using a soldering iron. It is generally observed that many key's in the keyboard are left unused. Examples of such keys are those present on the right-most side of the keyboard. One such key is removed by searching the particular key position in terms of rows and columns. This removed key is assumed to be functionally ok. This key is put in the faulty keys position and the faulty one is placed in this keys position, and soldered. Putting back the screws,the keyboard is connected to the computer and tested whether this replacement works. If it works, it is well and good else this procedure is repeated with some other key.

The keyboard microprocessor becoming faulty is another frequently seen problem in the keyboards. If the microprocessor is mounted as chips are mounted on the the bread board,one can get rid of this problem by simply replacing the chip. Else, if the chip is soldered, the only solution is to replace the keyboard as a whole. With this discussion on keyboard faults and remedies, this section is concluded.

8.0 INTRODUCTION

The Computer System as a whole comprises of many sub-assemblies interconnected to the processing unit, to enable the user to implement the system according to his need. From the diagram showing the various components and slots in the PC Block Diagram; given in chapter One (PLATE 1), it is easy to understand what expansion slots are for. Anyway, the expansion slots are used to add adapter cards for any device whose control circuit is not present on the system board. If one goes by the literal sense of the word "expansion" it may be misleading, though not in the present state of PC making.

In the early days, devices like Floppy drives and Display systems used separate adapter cards, which were fitted in the expansion slot. Now if "expansion" slot boards are considered to be optional, why not throw away the display board and disable the screen ! So in this context the adapter cards fitted into the expansion slot may not necessarily be optional. But with the advent of integrated motherboards, all peripheral devices control are available on one system board. Now in this present context, it will be right to describe the cards fitted on the expansion slot as optional.

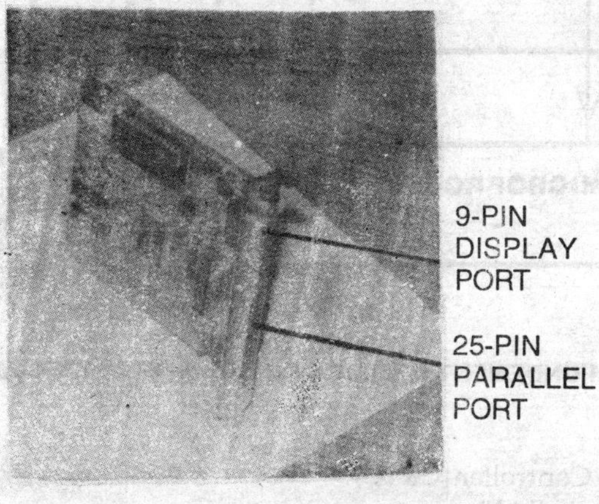

PLATE 6 "THE DISPLAY ADAPTER"

What does the display adapter do? The display adapter provides the right interface between the computer and the Video Display Unit (VDU). It is thus responsible for conversion of data to image. With this rudimentary understanding of the display adapter, lets proceed to understand some fundamentals.

8.1 FUNDAMENTALS

In an IBM PC or a compatible system, the display information is an add-on card, which plugs into the expansion slot of the system. The display adapter can be divided into the following four functional blocks (Fig 8.1).

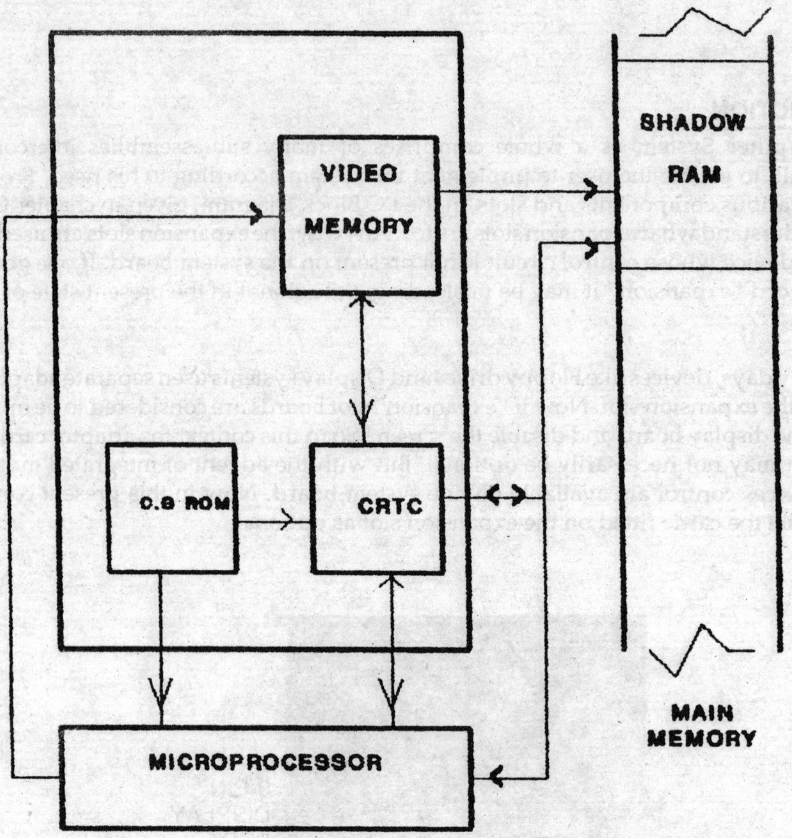

Fig. 8.1 : FUNDEMENTAL BLOCK DIAGRAM OF A VIDEO ADAPTER

These are :

i. Cathode Ray Tube Controller (CRTC)
ii. Video Memory (Static RAM)
iii. Character Generator ROM (CGROM)
iv. CPU Interface Circuits

The computer's Video Display Unit (VDU) is used to display information. But for this display to occur, the information has to come from some place. The place from which the information comes is called the Video memory or display memory. It is physically a SRAM located on the display adapter card. The speciality of this SRAM is that it directly communicates with both the CPU and CRTC. Hence it is **often called the dual ported static RAM.** Why is this memory provided physically on the adapter card ? This question might have already started jolting you. So lets see the answer. By having the SRAM physically on the adapter card, it is possible to get maximum flexibility and speed. But there is another reason also. This is considered later.

The functional block directly controlling the VDU is called the CRTC (Cathode Ray Tube Controller). The programs responsible for screen display are loaded in the microprocessor. When display is to be generated, the CRTC sends the image read from the Video memory to the VDU. The CRTC does all things necessary to put the digital data onto the screen in image form. The computers display screen is refreshed with the display memories content 50 times every second.

How is character mapping done ? The CRTC reads the data from the video memory and sends the appropriate addresses to the microprocessor. The microprocessor uses these addresses to read screen contents from the shadow RAM (Fig. 8.1). For each character read, the corresponding dot pattern is obtained from the CGROM (Character Generator ROM). The CRTC processes the contents read from CGROM and sends it to the video display unit. Video Display Unit does whatever is necessary to cause the screen display. This is the basic working of the video adapter in text (alpha-numeric) mode.

Two modes of operation are provided by the video adapter cards. These are text and graphics mode. The mode of information transfer for text mode has already been discussed, and the graphics mode of information transfer is considered in a later section. As the mode of operation determines the amount of video memory required, the RAM is provided on the adapter card. This facilitates proper selection of the RAM.

Let us now proceed to display fundamentals. Whatever be the type of adapter used, the screen is always divided horizontally and vertically into a number of tiny dots called pixels. Pixels mean Picture Elements. Pixels are fundamentally the smallest displayable unit. What actually detemines the mode of operation is the manner in which these pixels are treated. In text modes the screen is divided into a number

0		32		64	@	96		128	Ç	160	á	192	└	224	α
1	☺	33	!	65	A	97	a	129	ü	161	í	193	┴	225	ß
2	☻	34	"	66	B	98	b	130	é	162	ó	194	┬	226	Γ
3	♥	35	#	67	C	99	c	131	â	163	ú	195	├	227	π
4	♦	36	$	68	D	100	d	132	ä	164	ñ	196	─	228	Σ
5	♣	37	%	69	E	101	e	133	à	165	Ñ	197	┼	229	σ
6	♠	38	&	70	F	102	f	134	å	166	ª	198	╞	230	µ
7	•	39	'	71	G	103	g	135	ç	167	º	199	╟	231	τ
8	◘	40	(	72	H	104	h	136	ê	168	¿	200	╚	232	Φ
9	○	41	)	73	I	105	i	137	ë	169	⌐	201	╔	233	Θ
10	◙	42	*	74	J	106	j	138	è	170	¬	202	╩	234	Ω
11	♂	43	+	75	K	107	k	139	ï	171	½	203	╦	235	δ
12	♀	44	,	76	L	108	l	140	î	172	¼	204	╠	236	∞
13	♪	45	-	77	M	109	m	141	ì	173	¡	205	═	237	φ
14	♫	46	.	78	N	110	n	142	Ä	174	«	206	╬	238	ε
15	☼	47	/	79	O	111	o	143	Å	175	»	207	╧	239	∩
16	►	48	0	80	P	112	p	144	É	176	░	208	╨	240	≡
17	◄	49	1	81	Q	113	q	145	æ	177	▒	209	╤	241	±
18	↕	50	2	82	R	114	r	146	Æ	178	▓	210	╥	242	≥
19	‼	51	3	83	S	115	s	147	ô	179	│	211	╙	243	≤
20	¶	52	4	84	T	116	t	148	ö	180	┤	212	╘	244	⌠
21	§	53	5	85	U	117	u	149	ò	181	╡	213	╒	245	⌡
22	▬	54	6	86	V	118	v	150	û	182	╢	214	╓	246	÷
23	↨	55	7	87	W	119	w	151	ù	183	╖	215	╫	247	≈
24	↑	56	8	88	X	120	x	152	ÿ	184	╕	216	╪	248	°
25	↓	57	9	89	Y	121	y	153	Ö	185	╣	217	┘	249	∙
26	→	58	:	90	Z	122	z	154	Ü	186	║	218	┌	250	·
27	←	59	;	91	[	123	{	155	¢	187	╗	219	█	251	√
28	∟	60	<	92	\	124	¦	156	£	188	╝	220	▄	252	ⁿ
29	↔	61	=	93	]	125	}	157	¥	189	╜	221	▌	253	²
30	▲	62	>	94	^	126	~	158	₧	190	╛	222	▐	254	■
31	▼	63	?	95	_	127	⌂	159	ƒ	191	┐	223	▀	255	

Table 8.1 : THE PC CHARACTER SET

of pigeon-hole like boxes. Each pigeon-hole represents the character box. Thus in text mode, the smallest physical unit of the screen is the box, which in turn is composed of a matrix of pixels. In the graphics mode every pixel can be independently addressed. This means that the smallest physical unit of the screen in a graphics mode is a pixel.

To understand this differentiation between text and graphics mode, it is very much necessary to understand what is meant by resolution. Resolution is a measure of sharpness of the display and is represented by the number of pixels used to form the horizontal lines and vertical lines of the screen.

Consider a screen of 720 X 350 resolution. Thus a total of 720 X 350 pixels make up the displayable area of the screen. In text mode, the screen is vertically divided into 25 character blocks, and horizontally divided in either 80 character blocks or 40 character blocks. Consider the 80 X 25 mode. If the screen resolution is 720 X 350, then the character box matrix is formed from 9 X 14 pixels. It is not necessary that all pixels will be used to form the character. Thus in text mode the 9 X 14 pixel box is fundamentally our smallest unit. On the other hand the graphics mode offers 720 X 350 fundamental units (i.e all pixels), which is much larger in number than the 80 X 25 units for the text mode. It is although of the same physical size.

Before ending this section it is worth mentioning one more point. Text mode offers the maximum flexibility of displaying 256 characters only (i.e the PC character set). This character set is included as Table 8.1 for reference, and contains a few graphics symbols which can be used to create crude graphics.

The various types of display adapters are considered next.

8.2 MONOCHROME DISPLAY ADAPTER (MDA)

As the name itself suggests, this interface is designed to work with single-colour display units. MDA was introduced with the first IBM PC and is an Alpha/Numeric display controller in which no graphic display capabilities are incorporated. It is used exclusively for text processing applications. This gives a display of 40 X 25 or 80 X 25 characters on a screen of 720 X 350 pixel resolution.

Each character is formed in a box or matrix of 9 X 14 pixels. Of these, 7 X 9 pixels are used to form the character, and the remaining pixels are used to separate the characters by allowing inter-character and inter-line spacing, for easy readability.

MDA uses the very versatile video controller/processor - 6845 of Motorola. MDA has 4Kb of dual ported RAM to store character information to be displayed. The RAM is dual ported due to the fact that both the microprocessor and the video controller can access it independently.

The video controller accesses the RAM buffer to store information that is processed by it for displaying. Subsequent updation to the screen page stored in RAM buffer is done by the microprocessor.

The starting address of the video buffer RAM for MDA and CGA are

MDA - | B000 | - 4 Kb RAM <out of 32Kb allocated> Static RAM
CGA - | B800 | - 16 Kb RAM < " > Dynamic RAM

EGA starts at either B000 when in MDA mode or starts at B800 when in CGA mode. But, when working in EGA modes it starts at some location in the A block.

80 X 25 mode has 2000 characters displayed on the screen. Hence 2000 unique byte locations are in use. Considering that 2 bytes are required for a character display i.e., data byte & attribute byte, 4000 bytes would be required. On adding 96 unused bytes, resulting in a total of 4096 bytes, it makes the complete 4Kb RAM size.

8.2.1 Formation Of Characters

As mentioned earlier, in a screen displaying 80 X 25 characters, each character is formed in a matrix of 9 X 14 pixels. Of these pixels in the matrix, 7 X 9 pixels are used to actually display the character, whereas the remaining pixel spaces are used to form inter-line spacing and inter-character gap.

The extra dots on top and bottom of the matrix are used for characters with descenders, viz. g,j,y,etc.

The character to be displayed is the information sent by the microprocessor up via the I/O slot to the video RAM in the display card. The microprocessor also sends the information to the CRTC, which in effect, does the micro programming of the CRTC and inputs to the registers there in. This in effect enables the CRTC to perform relevant functions and to generate video RAM addresses in sequence to fetch required data.

The fetched data (ASCII) points to the Character Generator ROM, which in turn outputs the relevant character bit pattern. This parallel bit pattern is then serialised and sent along with attribute byte to the video logic card of the display unit, via the output connector. This output connector also connects Horizontal-synchronous and Vertical-synchronous signals generated separately at the CRTC.

Apart from this, the CRTC also generates the cursor displayed on the screen. This is a feature offered by the CTRC itself, upon micro-programming. The cursor is called hard cursor because its rate of flashing cannot be altered.

The monochrome display can have the following attributes. It uses two bytes to represent one character. The even byte has the ASCII value(character value) while the odd byte has the attribute value.

EVEN-BYTE : ASCII character value

7	6	5	4	3	2	1	0

ODD BYTE: Display attribute

	7	6	5	4	3	2	1	0
Non-blinking characters	0	x	x	x	x	x	x	x
Blinking characters	1	x	x	x	x	x	x	x
Non-display	x	0	0	0	x	0	0	0
Underline	x	0	0	0	x	0	0	1
White-on-black	x	0	0	0	x	1	1	1
Reverse video	x	1	1	1	x	0	0	0
Normal intenalty	x	x	x	x	0	x	x	x
High intenalty (bright)	x	x	x	x	1	x	x	x

Key : x = don't care
0 = binary 0
1 = binary 1

Fig 8.2 : Monochrome Text Display Attributes.

8.2.2 CRT CONTROLLER (CRTC - 6845)

As per IBM PC Compatible standards, most display adapters in the range of MCA, HGA, CGA, etc., use Motorola's 6845 CRT controller.

8.3 COLOUR GRAPHICS ADAPTER (CGA)

Now, we know how a character is formed/displayed in the monitor screen using monochrome display adapter, i.e., Alpha-Numeric display. Let us now find out how a graphic image is formed on a screen, with various colours using a CGA interface.

This is an IBM PC Compatible display card. This display interface is capable of providing various display modes.

Alpha Numeric	Monochrome
Text/Graphic	Colour

In text mode, 80 X 25 or 40 X 25 characters are displayed on the screen. Both these modes can be displayed in colour or monochrome depending on the type of the display unit. In Graphic mode, the two main display modes are medium and high resolution. The medium resolution offers 320X200 pixel resolution with 4 colours, whereas the high resolution offers only monochrome (2 color) display with 640X200 pixel resolution.

Video output is provided by a 9 pin female 'D' type connector for TTL level, or composite video output - RS170 standard, is provided at co-axial RCA connector.

8.3.1 CGA Operation In Text Mode

In text mode, the character displayed on the screen is defined in a matrix of 8 X 8 dots (pixels). Of these, only 7 dots are used horizontally, allowing one dot for inter-character spacing. The interline space is normally one dot, but in case of descender characters (eg g,y,j) the 8th dot is also used. Apart from the standard ASCII characters, there are special characters with shapes of graphic symbols. These are called block graphics or semi-graphic characters, that can be displayed in text mode. Similar to the MDA operation, the text mode of CGA achieves the function of displaying characters on the screen.

The CGA card consists of 16Kb of RAM for video memory. This allows to store 4 pages of screen memory, each page of 4Kb. In 80 X 25 character display mode, 2Kb is used for character information and 2Kb is used for attribute information which amounts to the use of 4Kb out of 16Kb chunks used for screen paging.

EVEN BYTE : ASCII character value

7	6	5	4	3	2	1	0

ODD BYTE : Display attribute

7	6	5	4	3	2	1	0

FOREGROUND COLOR :

	7	6	5	4	3	2	1	0
Black	x	x	x	x	0	0	0	0
Blue	x	x	x	x	0	0	1	0
Green	x	x	x	x	0	0	1	0
Cyan	x	x	x	x	0	0	1	1
Red	x	x	x	x	0	1	0	0
Magenta	x	x	x	x	0	1	0	1
Brown	x	x	x	x	0	1	0	1
Light gray	x	x	x	x	0	1	1	1
Dark gray	x	x	x	x	1	0	0	0
Bright blue	x	x	x	x	1	0	0	1
Bright green	x	x	x	x	1	0	1	0
Bright cyan	x	x	x	x	1	0	1	1
Bright red	x	x	x	x	1	1	0	0
Bright magenta	x	x	x	x	1	1	0	1
Yellow	x	x	x	x	1	1	1	0
White	x	x	x	x	1	1	1	1

EVEN BYTE : ASCII character value

7	6	5	4	3	2	1	0

ODD BYTE : Display attribute

BACKGROUND COLOR	7	6	5	4	3	2	1	0
Black	x	0	0	0	x	x	x	x
Blue	x	0	0	1	x	x	x	x
Green	x	0	1	0	x	x	x	x
Cyan	x	0	1	1	x	x	x	x
Red	x	1	0	0	x	x	x	x
Magenta	x	1	0	1	x	x	x	x
Brown	x	1	1	0	x	x	x	x
White(light gray)	x	1	1	1	x	x	x	x
Non-blinking characters	0	x	x	x	x	x	x	x
Blinking characters	1	x	x	x	x	x	x	x

Key : x = don't care

0 = binary 0

1 = binary 1

Fig. 8.3 : Color Text Display Attributes.

Fig 8.3 shows various attributes that are possible in text mode in a CGA card. The first four significant bits of the attribute byte determine the foreground colour while the least siginificant four bits determine the background colour.

In CGA text mode, as told earlier, a character requires 2 bytes, the first one being the data and the other is attribute. The colour graphics adapter in text mode is capable of displaying 16 foreground colours with 8 background colours and allows blinking.

8.3.2 CGA Operation In Graphics Mode

As seen earlier, the colour graphics adapter card can operate in various modes, viz., A/N-80 X 25, A/N-40 X 25, Medium resolution in solution Graphics/Colour Graphics, High resolution Graphics / Monochrome Graphics.

In the previous pages, the workings of the CGA card in text (A/N) mode was explored. Following is the explanation on the operation of CGA card in Graphics mode.

Medium resolution graphics offers 320 X 200 pixel resolution with 4 colours. Thus, graphics mode is also known as All Points Addressable Mode. In this graphics mode, each pixel can be individually set to show some colour. **The main difference between text mode and graphics mode is that the smallest entity in text mode is a full character matrix, whereas in graphics the smallest image is a pixel, which is just a splash (dot) of light, without any form or shape of its own.**

In text mode, the image displayed has a colour which is contrasted with the surrounding area by a different colour, which is called background colour.

In graphics mode, the image displayed is formed by individual pixels (dots), each set to a specific colour. The colour of pixels that are not used to form the image are set to a different, contrasting colour or the default of no-colour. Hence, there is no such thing as background colour in graphics mode. In graphics mode, text or A/N character is also displayed as a graphic pattern.

Another characteristic of the displayed image, i.e., the blinking feature of the character, is available only in text mode and not in graphics mode. This feature of blinking characters is not available in graphics mode due to limitations of hardware design and firmware. However, this feature too can be achieved through software programs.

Also, there is no such a concept as cursor in graphics mode. The 6845 cursor generation is only applicable to text mode, as the cursor occupies one character matrix space. The cursor seen in the graphics mode is generated as a graphics pattern by software program.

8.3.3 CGA BIT Mapped Graphics

To display graphics information on the screen, the method used to form the graphical image on the information is called bit mapping. This entails in assigning some part of the memory to each pixel. (As in case of character display, 2 bytes are assigned to each character).

Since data controlling each pixel is stored in one or more bits of memory, it is called bit-mapped-graphics. And, since each pixel can be individually controlled or addressed through memory, this method is also known as **All-Point -Addressable** graphics display system.

The best graphic display possible using the CGA card is High-Resolution 2 colour, 640 X 200 pixels, which require 16Kb of video RAM.

Each pixel state of glowing would be set by one bit. To draw a graphic image, relevant bits on every relevant byte has to be addressed and set appropriately. Since no standard image pattern is assumed, every display image has to be generated in the memory, by calculating the position of the correct pixels to be illuminated.

This process of calculations to form the image with reference to the displayable data output by the CPU is the function of the software programs written by the programmers or programs built in to the ROM-BIOS. Due to elaborate calculations required, the CRTC (microprocessor) has to do elaborate bit - manipulations, resulting in slow operations compared to text display.

For example, High order bit of the first byte i.e., bit 7 is set for the first pixel on the screen. Subsequent pixels - 2,3,4,5,6,7,8, are set by bits 6,5,4,3,2,1,0 of the first byte. As the first byte sets the status of the first 8 pixels on line one of the screen, successive pixels are similarly set by subsequent bytes.

8.3.4 Colour Graphics

So far, the explanation was related to graphics image formation only.

There are two modes of operation of CGA in graphic mode supported by IBM. These are

(1) Medium resolution graphics.

(2) High resolution graphics.

Low resolution graphics is not supported by IBM.

Medium resolution Graphics :

This mode offers 320 X 200 pixel resolution, with 4 colour display, To achieve this display in colour, it is required that each pixel is formed by two bits representing two dots. These two bits can have a combination of 2 or 4 colours, from two palettes of colours, using either one palette. Thus one byte of data can represent 4 unique pixels.

To determine the colour to be displayed by each pixel, the colour information is sent along with the image information. This is achieved by the software program, by programming the CRTC to generate required colour attribute. This colour attribute information is sent to colour encoding circuitry and sent along with the dot bits.

The signals generated by the colour encoder, control the intensity of the corresponding colour given in the CRT. Thus assigning a specific colour, including the default or black, to every pixel that is displayed.

High Resolution Graphics :

This mode offers 640 X 200 pixel resolution, in single colour. Each pixel is represented by one bit. Since CGA card memory is limited to 16Kb, only one bit can be allocated to one pixel. Thus limiting the possibility to displaying only one colour (either in on or off state). The formation of graphic image is as per earlier explanation.

8.4 HERCULES GRAPHICS ADAPTER (HGA)

This is an advanced version of monochrome adapter, offering higher resolutions of 720 X 348 pixels and graphic display. The text formation is in a character matrix of 9 X 14 pixels. Due to high dot density, the higher horizontal frequency of 18.1 KHz is used (whereas in CGA, it is 15.525 KHz). This display has a frame rate of 50Hz. Long persistance phosphorus screens reduce the amount of flicker due to this low frame rate. The enhancement is only in higher resolution and graphic capability. The attributes used are same as in MDA.

Though the text mode is MDA compatible, the graphics mode is not compatible to IBM graphic display standard.

The CRT controller or display control processor used is same as in MDA, i.e., Motorola 6845. The video output is given by 9 pin 'D' type, female connector.

8.5 ENHANCED GRAPHICS ADAPTER (EGA)

This card offers a resolution of 640 X 350 pixels. The characters are formed in 8 X 14 pixel matrix. But the actual size of character is 7 X 9 as in the case of MDA. This EGA works at a frequency of 22.1 KHz and the frame rate is 60 Hz. This card offers 64 different colour hues. It displays 16 colours from a palette of 64 colours.

In standard minimal configuration, EGA card has 64Kb of RAM, split into 4 banks. To the host system, the adapter looks like a CGA board as long as the advanced EGA modes and their bank-switching is not brought into play.

But this 64Kb of RAM is not sufficient for the wide palette and high resolution modes of EGA. Hence IBM provided expansion upto 256Kb through memory expansion card, so that the maximum configuration gives 4 banks of 64Kb each. Thus in EGA mode, the base address is shifted to A0000 instead of B0000.

The EGA card has a 9 pin female connector for connecting to the monitor.EGA is also available with parallel port.

EGA can also work in various modes offered by CGA, making it downward compatible. The various modes can be selected by setting the DIP switch bank provided. EGA uses VLSI IC for display control. It is an ASIC (Application Specific Integrated Circuit).

8.6 VIDEO GRAPHICS ARRAY (VGA)

This offers a maximum resolution of 1024 X 768 pixels. It gives a display of 256 colours from a palette of 256 colours.

This also works in the various display modes offered by MDA, CGA, EGA and HGA, thus making it downward compatible to various display units and application software. The character matrix size is 9 X 16 pixels. This requires VGA compatible monitor to make use of all its capabilities.

Various modes of operation giving different display outputs are listed below.

Mode	Colours	Text	Chr.matrix	Pixel Res
Text	16k	40 X 25	8 X 8	320 X 200
Text	16k	80 X 25	8 X 8	640 X 200
Text	16k	40 X 25	8 X 14	320 X 350
Text	16k	50 X 25	8 X 14	640 X 350
Text	16k	40 X 25	9 X 16	360 X 400
Text	16k	80 X 25	9 X 16	720 X 400
Graphic	4k			320 X 200
Graphic	2k			640 X 200
Text	Mono	80 X 25	9 X 14	720 X 315
Text	Mono	80 X 25	9 X 16	720 X 400
Graphic	16			320 X 200
Graphic	16			640 X 200
Graphic	4			840 X 350

Mode	Colours	Text	Chr.matrix	Pixel Res
Graphic	16			640 X 350
Graphic	2			640 X 480
Graphic	16			640 X 480
Graphic	256			320 X 200

Table 8.2 : Modes of Operation and Characteristics.

VGA horizontal frequency is of 31.5 KHz. With a frame rate of 70Hz in most of the modes and 60Hz frame rate in VGA mode (to squeeze in more characters).

VGA offering 256 colours at high resolutions requires larger memory size of 256KB. This can be enhanced upto 512 KB. Due to this complexity of the video signals to be output, it is not possible to use only a 9 pin female connector, as in previous cases. If TTL - Digital signals have to be retained, it would require to have many more signal pins, about 18, to generate the display image. Also the colour bit pattern combinations would be of the order of 2 to the power of 18. To avoid such complexities, VGA sends out analog form of signals to the monitor. This also reduces the complexity of monitor circuitry. The data to be displayed is converted from digital to analog voltage levels. This enables the use of only three signals for 3 colours (RGB), with varying voltages to vary the intensity of each other.

8.7 SUPER VGA (SVGA)

Super VGA is an enhancement of VGA, that significantly distinguishes itself from the EGA modes. It offers 640 X 480 resolution in 256 colours and 800 X 600 resolution in 16 or 256 colours. Seeing that Super VGA based PCs have the potential of competiting with specialized workstations, manufacturers of adapters and monitors formed an association called Video Electronics Standard Association (VESA). The VESA specified a resolution of 800 X 600 pixels with 16 colour for Super VGA graphics mode while maintaining downward compatibility with most of the previously discussed text/graphics modes. It also laid down guidelines for 1024 X 768 resolution.

PLATE 7 "DISPLAY MONITOR"

8.8 COMBINATION OF DISPLAY ADAPTERS

Most system have one display adapter. It is also possible to install two display adapters in the same system. Possible combinations are one Colour Graphics Adapter and one Monochrome Adapter. Usually EGA or VGA cards can co-exist with monochrome adapter or CGA working in mono mode. The colour adapter port address is between 3DO - 3DF and that of monochrome display adapter is 3BCD - 3BF. This allows the co-existence of display adapter without clashing of addresses.

8.9 VIDEO DISPLAY UNIT : INTRODUCTION

In the last topic various types of display adapters have been considered. These adapters work as an interface between the processing unit and the display unit. We have also seen how the information display, which is in digital form, is manipulated into a format that is used by the monitor to display the information which has already been considered in sufficient detail.

PLATE 7 Coming to the circuitry that takes in the outputs of the display controller(CRTC), we shall now see, how these electrical signals are used to project a visual image.

Video Monitors are of various types, depending on the type of display controllers, they are connected to. The four most commonly used video monitors are listed below.

1. Monochrome Monitor
   - Green CGA
   - Blue MDA
   - Amber HGA
   - Softwhite Dual frequency
2. Colour Graphics Monitor
3. Enhanced Graphics Monitor
4. Video Graphics Array Monitor - Multi sync.

In each of these types of monitors various features are included by different manufacturers.

8.10 CONTROL OF A MOINITOR

The common control functions provided in most monitors are :

1. Power ON/OFF switch
2. Power ON indicator
3. Brightness control
4. Contrast control
5. Vertical Hold
6. Horizontal Hold
7. Focus
8. Vertical size
9. Horizontal shift
10. Vertical linearity
11. Power fuse

A photograph of a monitor is shown (PLATE 7). Some or all of these functions may be accessible by the user or the service personnel (either located externally or internally). The monitors are also provided with input connectors for signal and power. Power input usually is the utility AC supply voltage, but in some cases it could also be DC voltage (+12v). Care must be taken to ensure that correct input power is made available. The signal input connector could be either 9 pin, 'D' type, female or RCA jack, or in some cases - Special connectors, such as 15 pin, 'D' type sub-miniature connector (for Analog input).

8.11 DETAILS OF THE DISPLAY UNIT

Monitor or Display unit consists of mainly 3 sub-assemblies.

1. Cathode Ray Tube
2. Video Logic Circuitry & Controls
3. Power Supply & Control.

8.11.1 Cathode Ray Tube

Figure (8.5) gives an explanation for the operating principle of CRT. The cathode is a small metallic oxide disk placed at the end of a narrow tube that covers the heater. Although the cathode is heated to produce thermionic emission, it is electrically insulated from the heater. Next, along the tube axis is the control-grid <G1> cylinder. A small aperture in G1 allows the electrons to pass through. The negative bias voltage at the control grid with respect to the cathode enables the G1 to control the space charge of electron emitted from the cathode. As a result the current beam can be varied and the brightness modulated by the voltage that is applied between G1 and the cathode.

Next is the screen grid G2,which also considers the beams to be made up of electrons in the beam because of the applied positive voltage. The G2 cylinder contains the internal baffles to restrict the beam to a narrow path. Following G2, the focus grill cylinder G3 focuses the electrostatic 'lens' with G2 to force electrons into a path that merges to a single point at the phosphor screen.

All the cylinders are made up of Nickel alloys. They are supported by glass or ceramic insulated rods that are parallel to the gun axis. Connections to all the elements are made at the base pins, except G4, which is the part of anode. This cup has metallic spring fingers that makes the contact with the inner Aquadag coating for the anode voltage.

Because the electron beam passes through narrow apertures, they move straight to the screen as though the electrons were ejected from the electron gun as a point source.

Electrostatic focus :

Electrons emitted from the cathode tend to diverge because they repel one another. However the electrons can be forced to converge by an electric field. The action is similar to the focusing of a beam of light by optical lenses. The first is the electrostatic field between the cathode and the control grid which is produced by their difference in potential. This voltage causes the beam to converge to a spot (P). The second lens may be either electrostatic field or electromagnetic field, and it focuses the beam just before the point of deflection.

High Voltage Focus :

G3 is the focus grid with a voltage of several kilovolts,normally 1/5 of anode voltage.

Magnetic deflection :

All picture tubes, either colour or monochrome, use magnetic deflection with Vertical and Horizontal deflection coils, in an external yoke around the neck of the tube, rather than electrostatic deflection plates which takes saw tooth voltage. For magnetic coils, saw tooth current is required.

Deflection is much easier with magnetic scanning, especially when very high anode voltage picture tubes are used. In electrostatic scanning the deflection angle is inversely proportional to the amount of high voltage whereas in magnetic scanning deflection is inversely proportional to square root of the high voltage. Thus using the magnetic deflection scanning shortens tube length.

In magnetic scanning, two pairs of deflection coils are used which are mounted externally around the neck of the tube. The pair of coils above and below the beam axis produces horizontal deflection, the coils to the left of the beam produces vertical deflection. This perpendicular displacement results because the positive current in each coil has a magnetic field that reacts with the magnetic field of electron beam. The resulting forces deflects the electrons at right angles to both the beam axis and the deflection field.

The electron beam thus generated, focussed and deflected is made to strike a point on the inner surface of the tube/screen.

A screen coated with a layer of phosphor material is used. The phosphors are crystals to which an activator material such as Manganese or Silver can be added to distort the crystal lattice. Then high velocity electrons excite the Phosphor, causing them to emit light. Electrons within the atoms of the phosphor get excited and are found to move to higher energy level. As these electrons fall back to a lower level,light energy is radiated. The radiation of the light from the screen is called luminescence.

Colour Picture Tube :

In this, the light emitting screen is made up of a trios of phosphor. Each dot of a trio is capable of emitting light in one of the three primary colours (Red, Green or Blue). A shadow mask mounted near the screen of tube contains over 10,000 apertures, one for each of the phosphor dot trios. This mask provides colour separation by shadowing two of the three phosphor dots of each trio. Three closely spaced electron guns, built as a unit, provide separate beams for excitation of the three different colour-phosphor dot arrays. Thus it is possible to control the brightness of each of the three colour independently of the other two. The three guns are mounted with their axes tilted towards the central axis of the envelope, and spaced 120 degrees with respect to each other. The focusing electrode of the three guns are interconnected internally, and their potential is adjusted to cause the separate beams to focus at the phosphor of screen.

All the three beams must be made to converge at the screen while they are simultaneously being deflected. Convergence is accomplished by the action of static and dynamic magnetic field setup by the radial converging magnet assembly mounted on the neck of the tube. These fields are coupled into radial converging pole pieces within the tube. Another pair of the lateral converging magnet also mounted on the neck of the tube. These pole pieces permit lateral shift in position of the blue beam in opposition to the lateral shift of the green and red beams.

A purifying magnet is used with the colour picture tubes to provide a magnetic field, adjustable in magnitude and direction, to affect register over the entire area of the screen. a magnetic shield is used to minimize the effects of the earths magnetic field.

8.11.2 Operation Of The Video Logics In A Monitor

The input signals received by the typical monitor are :-

1. Ground
2. Video Signal
3. Horizontal Synchronous Frequency <18.1 KHz>
4. Vertical Synchronous Frequency (50Hz)
5. Intensity - Positive going.

There are two methods of interfacing a CRT monitor to a computer depending on whether the monitor is of TTL type or of Composite type. In the TTL type all signals sent to the monitor are on separate signal lines, while in the Composite type all the signals are bundled together. The video logic is responsible for proper interpretation of the signals and controlling the various elements of the CRT to plot the image. Deflection of the three beams is accomplished simultaneously by the deflecting yoke using four electromagnetic coils similar to the deflecting yoke used for black and white picture tubes.

8.11.3 Power Supply and Control

Two modes of power supply is generally used in PCs. These are switch mode power supply and linear power supply. Some of the monitors are using linear power supply and others, SMPS. In case of mono, either SMPS or linear power supply are available where as for colour and EGA, SMPS is used. The theory and operation of power supply is considered in detail in chapter eleven.

Chapter Nine
FLOPPY DISKDRIVE

9.0 INTRODUCTION

With the growth of the microcomputer market, the floppy disk has evolved as the most frequently used data exchange medium. Nowadays the softwares are available mostly in floppies and almost every PC user resorts to using floppies for storing valuable work. Reasons for such a phenomenal appreciation of the floppy disk are many. In one line it can be said that the floppy disk is the cheapest, easiest and most simplest method of data storage and exchange.

Today's floppies have also evolved after a long evolution process, some thing which Darwin would have liked to mould in a theory of evolution. In the early days of the PC, most computers came with disks measuring 8 inches in diameter. The IBM introduced the 5.25 inch floppies in the late seventies. This floppy became immensly popular and slowly wiped out the 8 inch floppy from the market. Till recently the 5.25 inch floppy was considered as the defacto standard for the floppy size, but the arrival of the 3.5 inch stronger and larger capacity floppy has already started eating into the 5.25 inch floppy market. Nowadays most PC's give you both the 5.25 inch and 3.5 inch floppy drives.

In the earlier floppy disks only one side of the disk was used to store information. Such disks were described as **Single sided disks.** Actually these floppies had the magnetic oxide coated on both sides of the disk, but the manufacturers guaranted the use of only one side. This implies that the necessary testing was done on only one side of the disk, and this lucky side was generally the bottom surface of the disk. But most currently manufactured disks allow the user to use both the sides of the floppy disk, thus doubling the storage capacity of the floppy disk.

9.1 SINGLE/DOUBLE DENSITY DISKS

On the basis of the technique used for recording information on the floppy disk by the floppy disk drive, floppy disks are classified as single density and double density floppy disks.

In the early days of the microcomputer industry most floppy drives used a technique known as Frequency Modulation, or FM reording. This recording technique resulted in the **single density floppies.** This recording method remained as the standard for many years till the Modified Frequency Modulation, or MFM technique came up.

The MFM recording technique could store twice the information that could be stored using the FM recording technique. Consequently such floppy disks were termed as the **double-density disk.** These days most floppy disk drives use the MFM recording technique, and consequently the market is flooded with double-density disks.

9.2 HIGH DENSITY DISKS

Recording on the floppy disk is largely dependent on the magnetic material used to fabricate the disk. Different manufacturers have different formulae for creating the magnetic coating on the Mylar film of the floppy disk. Due to these differences in the magnetic material the **high density** disks have evolved, which allow more informations to be packed on a smaller space.

9.3 THE 5.25 INCH FLOPPY

The 5.25 inch floppy gained ground in the late seventies with the IBM adopting this floppy size. The 5.25 inch floppy was smaller than the 8 inch floppies previously in use, they went on to be termed as **diskettes** in the microcomputer jargon. The name diskettes somehow suited the computer user and authors and the name eventually spread to floppies of all sizes. The impact of the term diskette was so much that it has become a synonym for disk.The 5.25 inch diskette is also known as **mini-floppy** (fig.9.1)

The 5.25 inch diskette consists of a 5.25 inch plastic cover inside which a magnetic oxide coated Mylar circular disk of 5.25 inches in diameter is placed. The layout of the 5.25 inch floppy disk is shown in the figure 9.1.

The large hole in the center of the plastic cover is used to fit the **drive hub** of the floppy disk drive. The drive hub is like a truncated cone with the diameter increasing while travelling down from the top of the drive hub. This truncated cone shape ensure proper clamping of the disk. The **hub clamp** presses against the disk to prevent the disk from slipping when the disk rotates. The area of the disk pressed by the hub clamp is most vulnerable to wear and tear. The centre of the disk can be damaged due to any malfunctioning of the floppy disk drive or even due to regular pressing of the hub clamp. To prevent this damage, most manufacturers provides the disks with protective **hub rings** in the **disk clamping zone.**

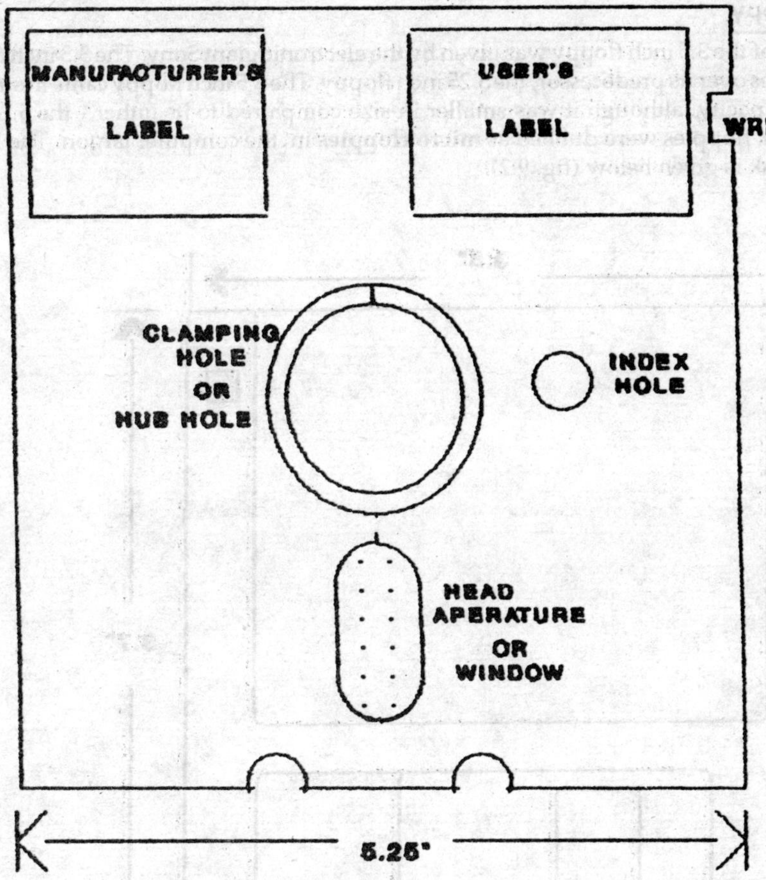

Fig. 9.1 : PHYSICAL LAYOUT OF 5.25" FLOPPY DISK

A small hole towards the right of the clamping hub is observed in the floppy shell. If the disk inside the shell is rotated slowly (mechanically), a small hole in the floppy disk can be made to allign with that of the shell's hole. This small hole is known as the **index hole.** This is the reference point for the track count. Each track begins (sector 1) when the floppy disk drive senses the index hole. A light sensor is placed in the floppy disk drive, and when the index hole coincides with that of the shells hole, light passes through the disk and reaches the light sensor. This indicates the begining of a track. Nowadays, most floppy disk drives have given up this method of referencing the begining of a track. Instead they opt for magnetically marking their sectors, but the index hole has been preserved from the original design of the diskette.

The large oval aperture in the shell located below the clamping hole, is provided to allow the read-write head to make physical contact with the disk. The read-write head is provided on a common assembly in the floppy disk drive.

A small notch located on the right edge of the shell is known as the **write protect notch.** The functioning of this notch is similar to that of the index hole. A light source is constantly focussed over the notch, and a light sensor is laid down with the responsibility of sensing whether or not light passes through the notch. If the notch is covered with an opaque tape, light does not reach the sensor, and the floppy drive is read only. This means that nothing can be written to the floppy. Once the notch is uncovered, light passes through and write permission is given. Now you have the permission to write to the disk. This notch can be said to resemble the tab of the video and audio tapes and serves the same purpose of preventing accidental erasure of previously recoded data.

9.4 THE 3.5 INCH FLOPPY

The original design of the 3.5 inch floppy was given by the electronic giant Sony. The 3.5 inch floppy had numerous advantages over its predecessor, the 5.25 inch floppy. The 3.5 inch floppy came in stronger shells, and had larger capacity, although it was smaller in size compaired to its father - the 5.25 inch floppy. These small sized floppies were dubbed as **micro floppies** in the computer jargon. The layout of the 3.5 inch floppy disk is given below (fig. 9.2).

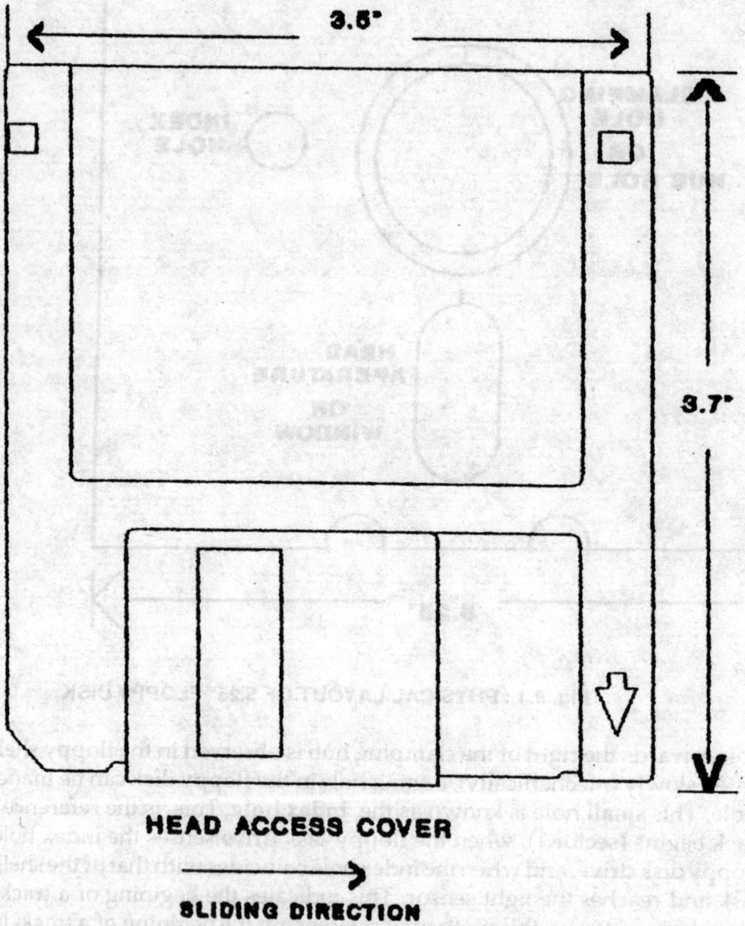

Fig. 9.2 : LAYOUT OF 3.5" FLOPPY DISKETTE

Apart from the small size, the most notable difference between the 5.25" floppies and 3.5" floppies is the stronger shell. This stronger shell prevents accidental damage of the disk inside the shell.

Instead of having a large head aperture, the 3.5" floppy design goes for a **head access** which is covered and equipped with a spring. The head access cover has a small aperture which moves to the floppy disk area below the head access cover when the head access cover is slided. The sliding head access is again an improvement over its predecessor. This design prevents dirt from entering the floppies when the floppies are kept in storage. The head access automatically slides when the disk is inserted inside the drive.

To prevent improper insertion of the disk in the disk drive,the 3.5 inch floppy has a bent corner on the top left hand side. This bent corner is referred to as the **insert key.**

Instead of using a write protect notch, these floppies use a **write protect slider** and hole. When the hole is visible the disk is read only. When the slider slides to cover the hole, the write permissions are available. Many software distributors donot provide the slider to make the disk write protected only.

The IBM standard says that all 3.5 inch floppies are double sided.So single sided 3.5 inch floppies are ruled out in the present discussion. To pack more data into this small floppy disk, the number of tracks were increased. A total of 80 tracks were provided on the 3.5 inch floppy at 135 TPI (Tracks Per Inch). Ordinarily the DSDD (Double Sided Double Density) 3.5 inch floppy has 9 sectors per tracks and a storage capacity of 720 KB. This can be calculated as follows :

Capacity = No.of Tracks x No.of Sectors/Track x No.of kb/Sector x No. of heads
= 80 x 9 x 1/2 x 2
= 720 KB

The high density floppies increased the number of sectors per tracks to 18, thus increasing the storage capacity to 1.44 MB. A notch on the bottom left corner of the disk is used to indicate that the disk is a high density disk. If the hole is not present, the floppy drive assumes the disk to be an ordinary DSDD.

9.5 DISK PROBLEMS

Floppy disks are mostly damaged due to physical and magnetic forces. Physical damage of the disk can occur due to a large number of reasons. Any physical damage is generally concerned with the destruction of the magnetic coating on the mylar film. Accumulation of dust is the major coating destroyer. Improper usage is the next enemy of the disk. Many new comers to the computing environment touch the floppy with their finger. This may cause oil and dirt to stick to the disk, which will continue to accumulate more dirt, ultimately destroying the disk. Sometimes the disk gets folded, accidently causing the disk to cease. All these disk problems are mostly associated with the 5.25 inch floppy. The harder protective shell of the 3.5 inch floppy prevents most of these problems. Magnetic forces are capable of altering the data stored in the disks. Thus it is generally advisable that floppy disks should not be kept near sources of magnetic flux.

9.6 HARD AND SOFT SECTORING

In hard sectoring method, the number of sectors on each tracks was designated by the manufacturers. Each sector was marked with an sector hole, indicating the begining of the sector. **Soft sectoring** method, the number of sectors on each tracks is software dependent. There is no need of sector holes in this method of sector organization.

9.7 THE FLOPPY DISK DRIVE

The first PC rolled out by IBM used DOS 1.0 and worked on the soft-sectoring principle. DOS 1.0 used 40 tracks on one side of the 5.25 inch floppy disk, and divided each track into eight sectors. This original organization used single sided disks and had a total capacity of 160 KiloBytes. Each sector is equivalent to 512 bytes or half a KiloByte. Thus the total capacity can be calculated as shown below :

Total Capacity = No. of Tracks x No. of Sector/Track x No. of Kilo bytes/Sector
= 40 x 8 x 1/2 = 160 Kilo bytes.

The DOS 2.0 brought an additional format. It allowed 40 tracks and 9 sectors per track. It also allowed the use of double-sided disks. To maintain compatibility with the DOS 1.0 format, it allowed backward compatibility i.e. it worked properly for floppies formatted using the DOS 1.0. The disk capacity of a double-side floppy disk is calculated below :

Total Capacity = No. of Tracks x No. of Sectors/Track x No. of Kilobytes/Sector x No. of heads
= 40 x 9 x 1/2 x 2 = 360 Kilobytes

These days most IBM PCs use the 360 Kilobyte capacity FDD. With the arrival of DOS 3.0, the disk capacity further increased. It allowed 80 tracks on the high density disks, and made 15 sectors per tracks. Thus the total capacity of an high density double sided floppy disk can be calculated to be 1.2 Megabytes. The 1.2 Mbyte FDD was introduced by the IBM only for its AT machines, but clones have adopted it elsewhere also.

The microcomputer manufacturers have paid the price of introducing write the high density disks. The cost paid is in the from of backward compatibility. To read all the 80 tracks, the read-write head was made narrower, and thus a floppy formatted using the 1.2 Mbyte FDD cannot be used in a 360 Kilobyte FDD, although the reverse is possible.

S.No.	FEATURE	DOUBLE SIDED DOUBLE DENSITY 360 kB FDD	DOUBLE SIDES HIGH DENSITY 1.2 MB FDD
1.	Formatted Capacity	360 KB	1.2 MB
2.	Unformatted Capacity	456 KB	1.6 MB
3.	No. of Heads	2	2
4.	No. of Tracks per side	40	80
5.	No. of Sectors per Track	9	15
6.	Bytes per Sector	512	512
7.	Disk Speed	300 rpm	360 rpm
8.	Tracks Per Inch (TPI)	48	96

Table 9.1 : Disk Drive Characteristics.

The DOS 5.0 and higher versions support extra high density FDD.

9.8 COMPONENTS OF THE FLOPPY DISK DRIVE

Floppy disk in itself is not a part of the system. As a sole indiviual it does not make much sense. The other system components required are FDD, FD controller and the Disk Operating System (DOS). In the preceeding sections the medium (Floppy disk) has been discussed. Now we proceed to understand FDD.

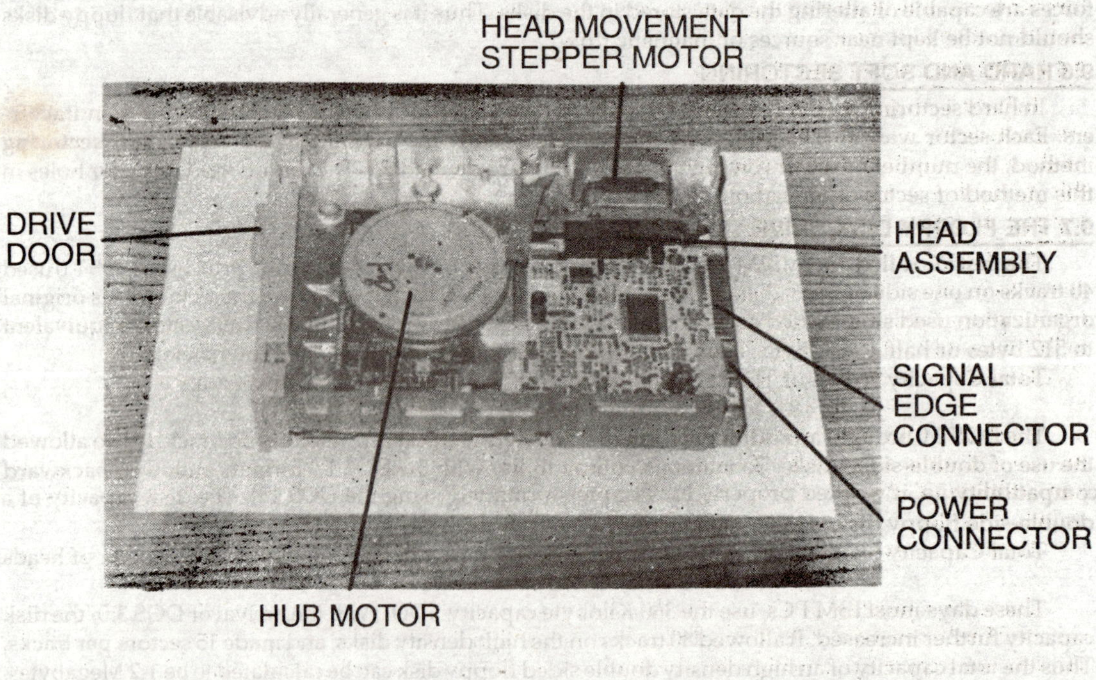

PLATE 8 "FLOPPY DISC DRIVE"

A Floppy drive mainly consists of the following parts :

(i) Mechanical Assembly
(ii) Sensors
(iii) Logic Card
(iv) Motors

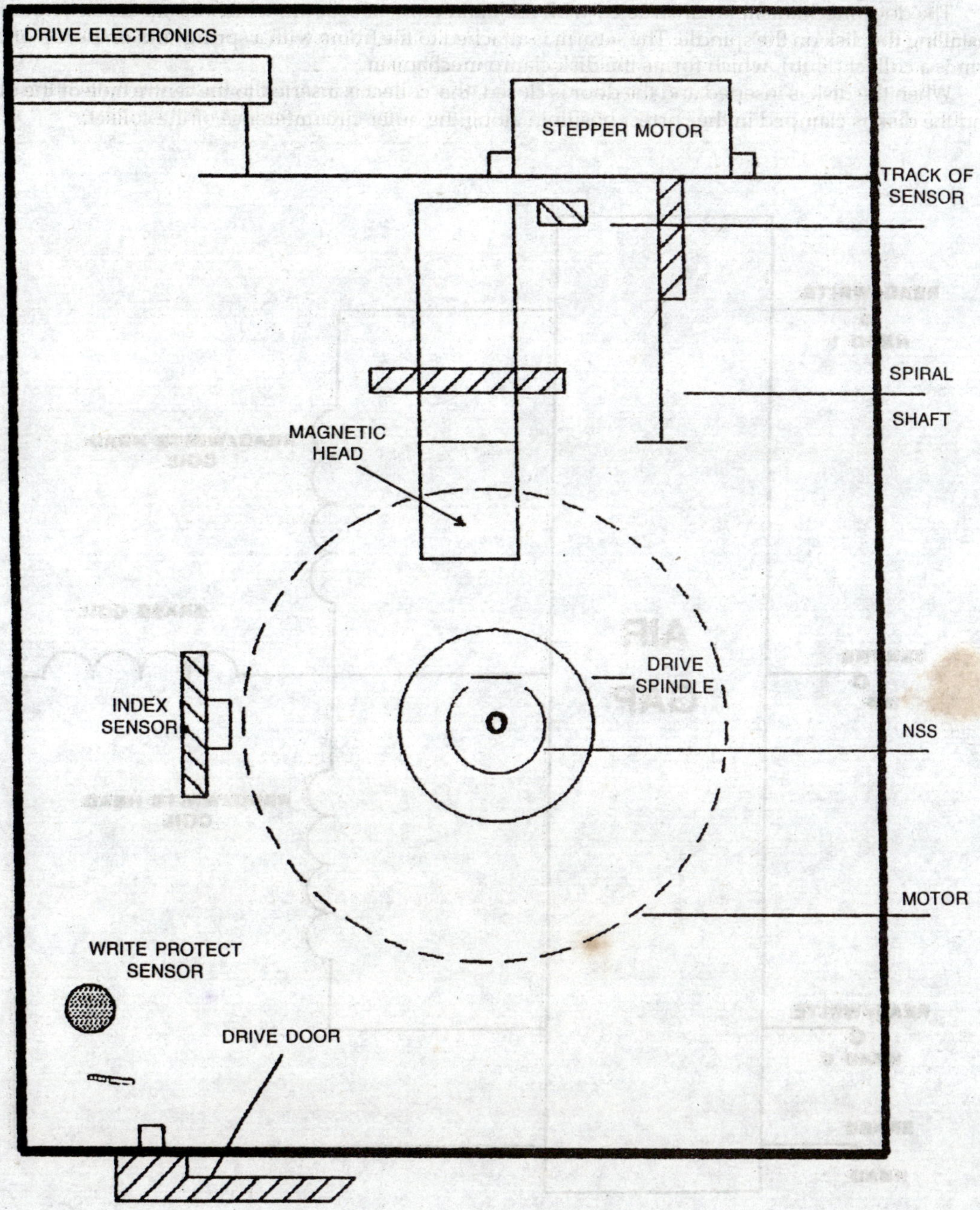

Fig. 9.3 : BLOCK DIAGRAM OF FDD

9.8.1. Mechanical Assembly

This assembly consists of the frame (chassis), door lever mechanicsm, magnetic R/W head and its carriage head, load mechanism, head seek mechanism etc.

Frame:

This is the main structure for mounting the various components and printed circuit boards. It is made up of Aluminium die cast to maintain stability of FDD in strength, precision etc.

Door mechanism and disk clamp mechanism :

The door mechanism is constructed with the main parts of set arm, which forms the structure for installing the disk on the spindle. The set arm is attached to the frame with a spring and on the top of the arm is a collect (Hub), which forms the disk clamp mechanism.

When the disk is inserted and the door is closed, the collect is inserted to the centre hole of the disk and the disk is clamped in the correct positioin along the outer circumference of the collect.

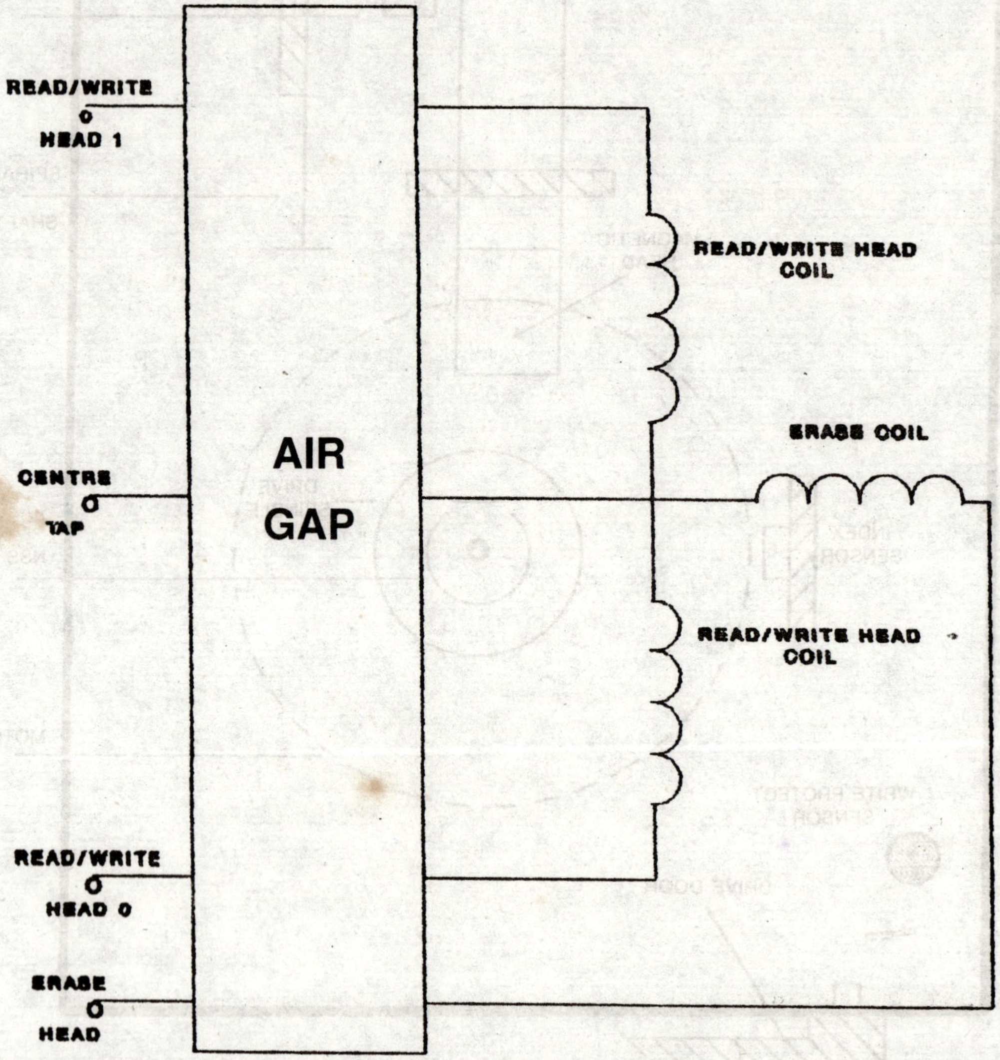

Fig. 9.4 : FDD HEAD CONFIGURATION

Disk Rotation Mechanism :

This unit comprises of Disk drive motor assembly which includes a spindle motor.

The spindle motor is a rotor type DC brushless motor.It rotates at a speed of 300 rpm in 360 KB FDD and 360 rpm in 1.2 MB FDD, and is maintained at a constant speed against the load variations and environmental changes. This is achieved by a feed back signal from the internal AC tachometer.

The Hub (collector) and spindle are combined precisely to maintain the centre position correctly, without damaging the centre hole of the disk.

FDD functional block diagram :

Figure 9.3 shows the functional block diagram of FDD.

Magnetic Head and Carriage Assembly :

Figure 9.4 shows the Magnified view of magnetic R/W Head. The magnetic head assembly is of 'button' type. It is mounted on the carriage assembly and the head is assembled so that the window area (head aperture) of the floppy disk is in contact with the head when loaded.

There are two magnetic heads. One is in contact with the bottom surface of the disk and the other with the top surface. These are called side 0 and 1 of the disk. The top head is in contact with side 1 and is called head 1, whereas the bottom head is in contact with side 0 and is called head 0. The head is constructed with Read/Write coils used for reading and writing data on the disk, and erase coils to erase the recorded track edges, trimming the magnetic flux.

Head seek mechanism :

The head seek mechanism consists of a stepper motor with a capstan (pulley), steel belt, and a guide shaft. The head carriage assembly is connected to the capstan of the stepper motor through a steel belt and is slided along the guide shafts.

The stepper motor will rotate at a pre-determined value, in terms of degree, when a pulse is given.

The stepper motor used in FDD is typically moving two steps (3.6 degrees) for a single pulse in 360 KB FDD and one step (1.8 degrees) for a single pulse in 1.2 MB FDD. The mechanism is constructed in such a way that the distance between the shaft and the center line of the disk is a constant (means the parallelism is kept). In designing it, great care is taken to overcome the thermal expansion of belt, carriage, etc.

Head loading :

Unlike single sided drives, where head was made to come in contact with the disk by actuating a solenoid, the present day drives achieve this mechanically by closing the front door lever.

9.8.2 Sensors

These are devices used to find the status of physical positions and conditions of the various mechanisms. In the FDD, mainly three sensors are present viz.,

(i) Write protect sensor
(ii) Index sensor
(iii) Track 00 or head home position sensor.

Write protect sensor :

This is a photo sensor constructed with a LED (Light Emitting Diode) and photo transistor to detect the state of the write enable notch on the disk. If a disk in which the notch is not covered is inserted, light emitted will pass through the notch, thus making the photo transistor active. The signal output is used to form the logic condition enabling the write operation on the disk. For this purpose the photocell is mounted on Disk Drive assembly in a position where the disk's notch is present.

Index sensor :

In a floppy, an index hole is present. This sensor is used for indicating the starting sector of the disk. As in the case of write protect sensor, index sensor is also a combination of LED and photo transistor. This is located at the index hole area of the disk.

The LED-Photo transistor assembly is mounted in such a way that, they are on either side of the disk, at the position of the index hole.

Track 00 sensor :

In a floppy disk, the outer most track is known as track 00. The track sensor assembly is also made up of LED-Photo cell combination. This assembly is mounted on the rear side of the FDD. The head carriage assembly is equipped with a protruding tab which cuts the light falling on the photo cell, indicating the reference position of the head. This is called the home position of the head or the track 00 position.

This sensor also ensures that the head carriage is unable to move outward beyond track 0.

9.8.3 Logic Card

The electronics of the FDD has 3 sections viz.,

(i) Read/Write circuit
(ii) Control circuit
(iii) Servo circuit

Read/Write circuit :

The read/write circuit consists of a mode selector, read circuit, write circuit and a low voltage sensor. These are all packed in a single LSI chip.

The mode selector is used in 1.2 MB FDD, for increasing the current while writing on the outer tracks (00 to 43). It also contains a filter circuit to eliminate the saddle wave form.

The read circuit consists of head matrix switch (selecting 0/1 head), pre-amplifier, low pass filter, differentiation amplifier, peak detector, time domain filter and output driver.

When a coil is placed in the magnetic field, this induces an electromagnetic field in the coil. This minute voltage induced in the read/write head, during read operation, is the input to the pre-amplifier via matrix switch for selecting side, 0/1 heads, (amplifier has about 100 to 200 gain). The pre-amplifier output is supplied to a differentiation amplifier via the low pass filter and switch filter to eliminate the undesirable noises. The differentiation amplifier phase shifts the peak position of the reproduced wave form to zero cross point, and at the same time it amplifies the signal. It is then passed through the peak detector, so as to get the square wave.

The write circuit consists of write control logic, write current source, erase driver, common driver, etc. and most of these are integrated in LSI chip.

The common driver output terminals, com0, com1 are connected to common terminals of the side 0 and side 1 heads respectively. The output of the common driver are controlled by the side one select (S1) input signal, and write gate (WG)/erase gate (EG) signals, supplied through the write control logic when the com 0 or com1 is high level (11.5V approx), the power to the read coil is cut off in read operation.

During write operation, to ensure current in the coil, the levels of com0 or com1 are to be kept low, depending on the side selected.

The write data input pulse is latched by write data latch to the write control logic. An appropriate write current from write current source is supplied to the read/write head & is controlled by turning ON & OFF the two write drives alternately.

Control Circuit :

The control circuit consists of a jumper circuit, LED & read/write/erase head control circuit, motor-ON gate, ready detector, stepper motor control circuit, interface driver, etc.

All the circuits except the driver are integrated in the control LSI chip.

Strap circuit means the jumpers available on the PCB. This selects various options, which are defined by the user viz, select drive as first, select drive as second, put do motor always 'ON', etc.

LED indicator is optionally activated either when the drive is selected or when the motor-ON condition prevails. Usually LED is used to indicate the active state of motor to indicate access to media. This is controlled by the motor-ON signal line,

Write Operation Timing :

Write/erase control circuit consists of write/erase gate and erase timer. It is enclosed in the LSI chip. This write/erase gate judges whether new data has to be written on the disk. If so, the circuit supplies WG (write gate) signal for read/write circuit and erase timer.

Ready detector :

It consists of 50% speed detector, pre-ready latch, ready latch, motor ON delay circuit. The motor control signal for controlling the spindle motor is input to the ready detector, which enables the operation all above circuits. As the motor speed increases, 50% speed detector first, and then pre-ready latch is set when the pulse interval becomes less than twice the nominal condition (i.e., 50% of disk speed).

Then the +- 2% speed detector starts its operation and sets the ready latch when the pulse interval at the IDXS terminal becomes with in +- 2% of the rated speed condition. The ready latch is set where more than 3 index pulses are detected after the motor starts. In typical cases, the motor speed reaches within

+- 6% of the rated speed when the next pulse is detected after the pre-ready state. The ready latch will be set at that time.

Operation modes of the two speed detectors are changed by the speed signal and the index pulse interval time will be detected appropriately from 360 rpm or 300 rpm.

The MOTORON (MON) delay circuit generates two delay signals after the MC signal becomes true. One of them is MON delay 1 signal to be suppiled to the write/erase gate and the other is MON delay 2 signal. The MON delay 2 signal and the ready latch output coincide through AND gate are output from the control LSI as ready signal. It indicates that the FDD is in read/write state.

Stepper Motor Control Circuit :

This circuit consists of direction latch, internal step generator, shift register phase drive selector, over drive timer, coil driver and over drive circuit.

(i) Direction latch :

At every input of the step (ISTP) pulse from the host controller, the direction latch samples and holds the head seek direction designated by the direction select (IDIR) signal. The latched output is supplied to the bidirectional shift register and changes the activating direction of the stepping motor coil.

(ii) Internal step generator :

This circuit generates an internal step pulse approximately after the STEP input pulse. This function is executed only when the signal level at track terminal is low (48TPI). When TRK is high (96TPI Mode) it is not executed, the stepping motor rotates for one step space in response to one step pulse. When it is low stepper motor rotates for two step space (3.6 degrees) in response to one step pulse.

Shift register and phase driver select :

This generates appropriate timing signals for the uni-polar 1-2 phase drive of a 4 phase stepper motor. Input for the shift register is given from step pulse and the output of the direction latch.

In order to improve the torque margin in the seek iteration, partial 2-phase drive period is provided at the initial stage when the drive phase is changed.

Track counter :

The track counter gives the track position and outputs track which (SP) signal for the read/write circuit. It also outputs T00 (Track 00) status signal to the host controller.

The output signal from the track 00 sensor is supplied to terminal of LSI and output as the T00 signal through the gate in the track counter.

Interface drive :

The output from the R/W LSI and the control LSI is supplied to the host controller via the interface driver. Normally AND gates are used as drivers. The output is valid only when the drive/select input is active.

Servo ciruit :

The servo circuit maintains the constant rotational speed of the spindle motor at a per-determined speed. The drive motor having 3-phase coils and bipolar drive system. Energization and magnetised direction of the coil are controlled by the signal from the hall element mounted on the servo PCB around the motor so that they are changed corresponding to the desired rotational direction.

So far, we have discussed individual part operation. Now we can see how the FDD is working when put together.

+5V +12V and GND signal are given for the FDD. +5V for logic circuits, +12V for motor and the GND for reference/return path.

The interfacing is done between the FDD and CPU through floppy disk drive controller. It is a 34 pin flat edge connector coming from the FDC connected to FDD. There are data signals and control signals.

When data is to be written on the floppy, contorl signal moves the head to appropriate position on the floppy.

Since the serial data in the MFM code format energizes the write coil and correspondingly the magnetic field of the floppy disk changes ensuring the right data is stored.

For reading the data, the emf induced in the coil is given to per-amplifier and then through edge connector to controller.

Terminator :

Terminator resistance network is used in cases where logic signals are daisy chained, i.e., signals reaching more than one destination. When any signal line is open or floating, it is bound to pick-up electrical noise, thus reducing the reliability of the circuitry. This is overcome by terminating each signal at its last point by a pull-up resistor.

Jumper of FDD :

In order to select drive 0, drive 1, etc., there are normally 6 bank jumpers available. Suppose it is required to select second drive as B, then the second drive jumpers corresponding to DSI should be shorted.

Differentiation between 360 KB & 1.2 MB FDD :

- Observe the drive closely and check for the rpm rating of the dc motor. It will be stamped either with 300 rpm or 360 rpm. If it is 300 rpm then it is confirmed as 360 KB FDD. If it is 360 rpm the drive capacity is 1.2 MB. (In some drives it wil be present).
- If this is not available then check for the model.

With this understanding of the FDD electronics we are now poised to understand hard disks properly.

Chapter Ten
HARD DISK

10.0 INTRODUCTION

Most personal computers available today definately have a hard disk. A PC without a hard disk is like a store without a godown, at least for most PC users. In principal the hard disk is an auxillary storage device, just like the floppy disk, which can store large data and program files. But what is actually an hard disk ? This will be covered in detail in the next section, but in a nutshell it can be described as a set of magnetic disks mounted on a spindle to form a disk pack. When this disk pack is mounted on a drive, the drive is called the **hard disk drive (HDD)**.

10.1 WINCHESTER HARD DISK

This type of hard disk is the most popular brand and was introduced in the early seventies by IBM. The first **winchester** hard disk was describe as the 30/30 hard disk to exemplify that it consisted of two disks of 30 Mb each, packed in a single unit. Since this hard disk technology was advocated and used by IBM, it has some how become a defacto standard for hard disks today.

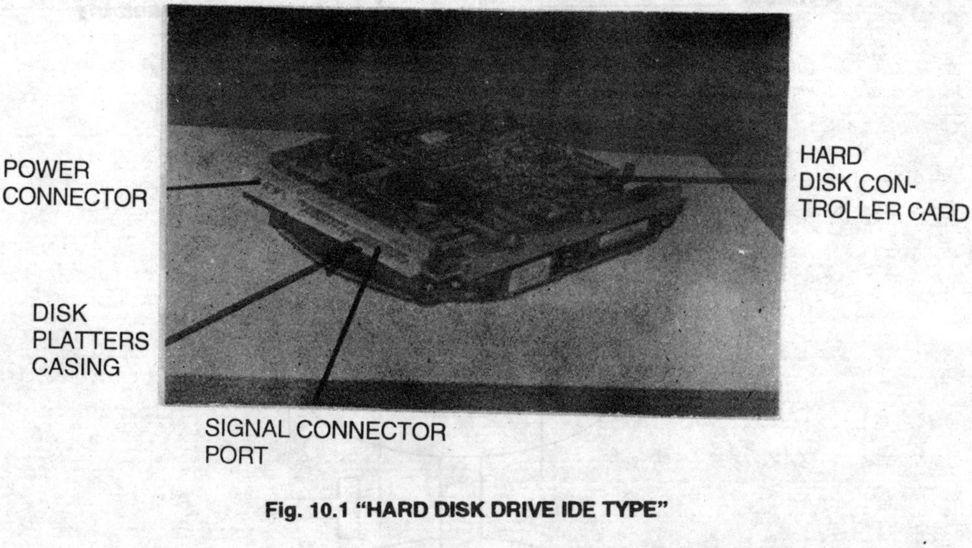

Fig. 10.1 "HARD DISK DRIVE IDE TYPE"

Before understanding the physical structure of the winchester hard disk, it would be necessary to understand the basic hard disk structure. In fig. 10.2 set of magnetic disk are shown to be mounted on a spindle to form a **disk pack**. To start, the discussion concentrates on the magnetic disk only. The magnetic disk can be considered to a platter coated with magnetic oxides.

The platter is the hard metallic disk made of aluminium. Reasons for using aluminium as the substrate material are many. The most important ones being :- (i) aluminium disks are easy to machine and are generally very smooth (ii) aluminium does not react with the oxide coat due to its non-magnetic nature.

Many new substrate materials have come up recently. Glass is being seriously considered as a potential substrate material by the hard disk manufacturing industries, while ceramic substrate are trying to creep into the consideration list.

The original hard disk was coated with iron oxides, namely ferrous and ferric oxides. This coating gives the hard disk a typical rust brown colour, similar to the one found in audio and video tapes. Now the oxides coated media is fading away, giving way to new media formulae. The primary reason for abandoning the oxide coated media is that they do not allow high density of recording when compared to the newer ones. Also these coated magnetic oxide particles lose their information storing capacity with time, reducing the disks storage capacity. Most recent hard disk use a thin film of magnetic material to work as the media.

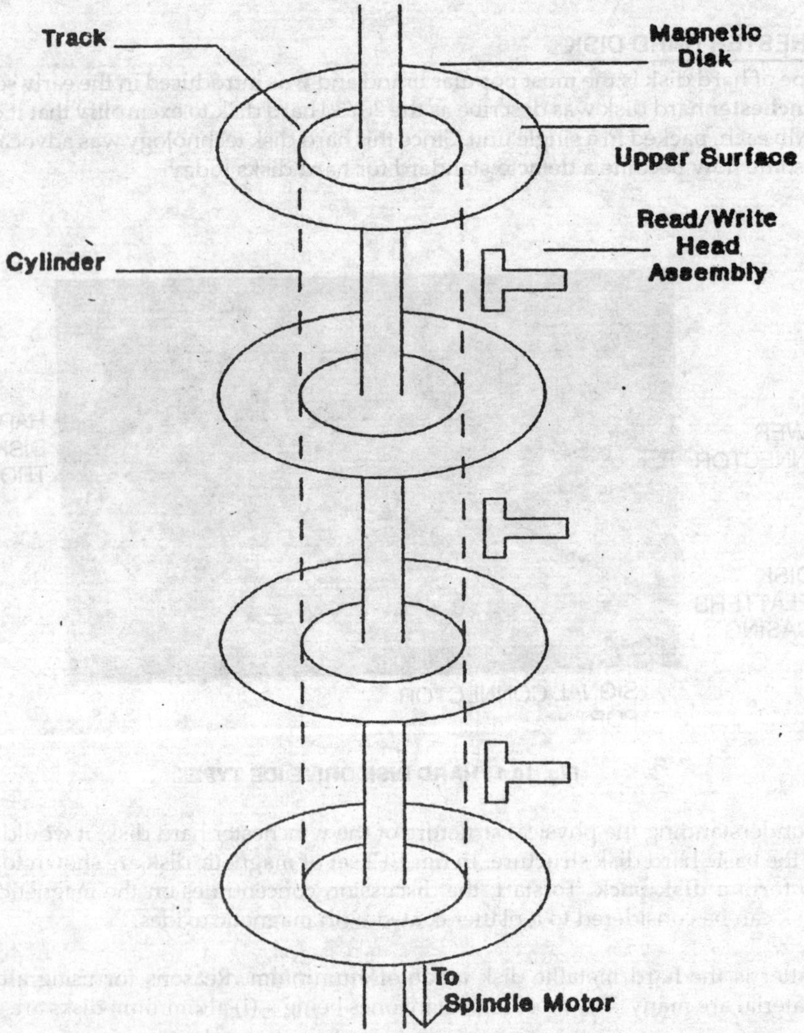

Fig. 10.2 : SECTION OF HARD DISK PACK

The primary reason for using the thin film media is higher area density. Area density refers to the amount of information that can be stored on a given area of the disk surface. We do not go into the details of the factors influencing area density in this discussion.

Depending upon the capacity of the hard disk drive, there could be one or more magnetic disks (platter and Oxides coating) mounted on a shaft known as spindle (refer fig.10.1).

At this junction it would be appropiate to mention why hard disks are also known as fixed disks. The platters which are mounted on the spindle are fixed and not removable, unlike the floppy disk, which is a removable media and hence the name **fixed disk**. The spindle is connected to a spindle motor, which is laid down with the responsibility of rotating the entire assembly of platters. Originally synchronous motors were used, which rotate the assembly at an approximate speed of 3600 r.p.m. Most recent hard disk have opted for new technology known as the servo controlled DC motor. The biggest advantage of this new technology is that it gets feed-back on the disk speed and adjusts the disk speed accordingly.

A note of caution. The number of platters has no direct relationship to the amount of data a hard disk can hold. This largely depends on the hard disk format. The various formatting procedure are considered later.

Figure 10.2 has been included to illustrate the basic hard disk organization. After understanding the magnetic disk, the next topic of interest is the read-write head. The read-write head is made from coils, which electrically induce magnetic flux on the recording medium. The read-write head section covered in the floppy drive chapter holds good. Every recording surface is provided one head. Conventionally, the top most and bottom most surfaces in the disk pack are not used for recording information. But with the cost of manufacturing touching new heights, most hard disks now use both of these surfaces. Each read-write head is connected to a long arm, which is responsible for moving the read-write head. It is generally noticed that several of these arms are linked to form a single unit (ref. fig. 10.2). In the hard disk drive, the read-write head and the disk pack form a closed enclosure. Thus the read-write head are made to move on a surrounding which seems like an air top. When the computer system is off, the read-write head is located on one edge or the other of the disk. This area of the disk is known as the **landing or parking zone**. (The reasons for such names will be obvious when the discussion is complete). When the system is turned on, the disks start rotating and slowly attain the required rpm. During this process of gaining momentum, the air in the enclosure between the platters stirs up. This stirred up air causes the head to rise. The atitude of the head from the platter is an important factor determining the ultimate storage capacity. The greater the seperation, the larger the magnetic flux spreads, decreasing storage capacity. Thus for best results it would be theoretically desired to have an zero altitude. But zero altitude results in more disk damage, eventually resulting in hard disk failure. Thus most hard disks keep an altitude in the range of 5 to 20 microinches. What happens when the system is shut down ? The disks slowly lose momentum causing the air in the sealed enclosure to also settle down slowly. During this process it is undesirable to land the head on the disk area used for storing information, as this could be a **head crash**. Head crash refers to the head touching the recording media resulting in disk damage. So an area is reserved for landing or parking the head, known as the landing or parking zone. No information storage is allowed in this zone. The landing is almost like an aeroplane landing on the runway and being parked in the hanger.

Recent hard disks have gone for lubrication of the disk surfaces as a preventive measure for head crashes.

The movement of the head assembly accross the disk is carried out by a mechanism known as the **head-actuator**. The precision movement generated by the head actuator can increase disk capacity, by allowing higher density of recording information. The head actuator is an electro-mechanical system. On the basis of the electronic system used in the underlying electronics of the head actuator it is classified as closed and open loop actuator.

Most hard disks using the open loop actuators use the stepper motor technology. This technology is similar to the FDD's stepper motor. Here track O is reference point, and a specific number of steps are generated by the stepper motor to move to the required track. This new position is remembered with respect to track O. When a command to move to another track is received the number of steps required is generated relative to the present track position. But this method does not allow any feedback mechanism, and hence is not fool proof.

The closed loop systems mostly use the servo voice coil mechanism. In the voice coil mechanism the head assembly is moved by pure electromagnetic force. The construction of this is analogous to an audio speaker. The audio speaker uses a stationary magnet surrounded by a voice coil (hence the name) which is connected to the paper cone.

When the coil is energised, it moves the cone resulting in production of sound. Typically, a hard disk voice coil consists of a coil mounted on a track surrounded by a stationary magnet. The coil mechanism is connected to the head assembly. When the coil is energised, it either attracts or repels the stationary magnet, causing the head assembly to move forward or backwards. This enables fast, quick and accurate operation when compared with the stepper motor mechanism. Since the movement generated here is not in predetermined steps, dictated by the track position to be achieved, some unique method must be used to determine accurate access of the tracks. This involves, allocating one surface of a platter (only one platter) as the **servo surface**. This servo surface is created by the manufacturer. The tracks on this surface are recorded with index signals to represent cylinders. The head coil on this surface can only detect these signals as shown in PLATE 10. They cannot write. This head is called the servo head giving feedback to

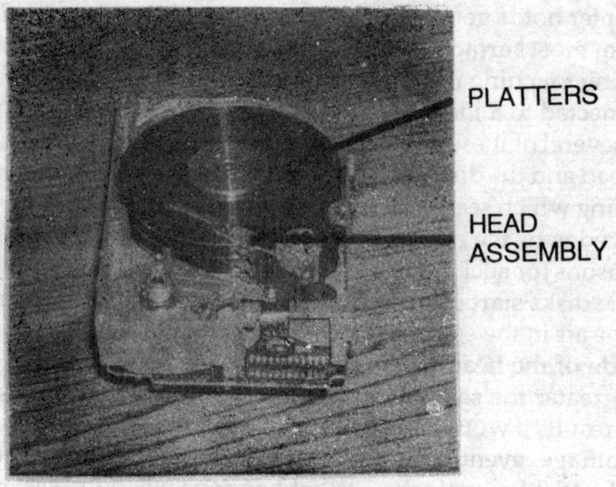

PLATE 10 : "INSIDE THE HARD DISK DRIVE"

the servo circuitry, which determine and controls the position of the head over each track thus enabling access to every cylinder on the disk. Since the feedback mechanism is provided this type of determining track positions is called closed loop configuration.

Next we need to understand what tracks and cylinders mean. Whenever read/write operations have to be taken up, the head is essentially maintained stationary. Under this constant radius it encompasses a full circle of the disk. Such full circles are called **tracks**. Previously it was mentioned that all the head assemblies are connected to form a single unit, which in turn is connected to the head actuator. Thus the motion of the head actuator moves all the head simultaneously to the same track number on their respective disk surfaces. At a particular position of the head actuator, a set of concentric tracks are traced, which collectively form the outline of a solid cylinder. This collection of concentric tracks is thus described as **cylinder**. A glance at figure 10.1 will make the discussion clearer.

Every hard disk drive is controlled by a disk controller card. The function of the disk controller card is to interpret the computer command and direct the hard disk driveaccordingly. Whenever a read/write operation is to be accomplished the controller card send the signals specifying the drive number, cylinder number, surface number and sector number. The head assembly is then positioned in accordance to the information provided by the controller card. The time taken by the head assembly to reach the head to the particular cylinder after a read-write command is received by the controller card is known as **seek time**.The seek time is generally of the order of 20 milli seconds, but is implementation dependent.

Once the required cylinder has been reached, the head correponding to the surface in consideration is activated. This delay is usually negligible. After this the time taken by the head to reach the specified sector is known as the **latency time**.

The average latency time is equal to half the time taken by the disk to rotate once. At 3600 rpm, the average latencyis 0.5/3600 or 8.3 milliseconds. With higher speeds, lower average latency is attainable. The sum of average latency and seek time is defined as the average **access time**.

10.2 HARD DISK SPECIFICATION

Hard disks are available in standard 5.25" format. Lately, we also find 3.5" hard disk also. Disk drives are available in full height or half height, e.g. the space covered in a drive bay of the system cabinet (2 half height drives can occupy one full height drive). Various storage capacity drives are also available e.g. 10Mb, 20Mb, 40Mb, etc.

10.3 HARD DISK CONTROLLER CARDS

The communication between the hard disk and the computer system (excluding the Hard Disk) is carried out by a controller card. The data coming from the disk drive is in analog form. Thus the controller should convert the analog data to digital data. This process is known as **data seperation**. Four different types of controller cards are considered in the discussion to follow.

(1) The ST506 Controller:

ST506 controller card, manufactured by Seagate Technologies for its original 5 Mb disk remains the most popular type of hard disk controller. The ST506 controller can be classified into three more types namely :

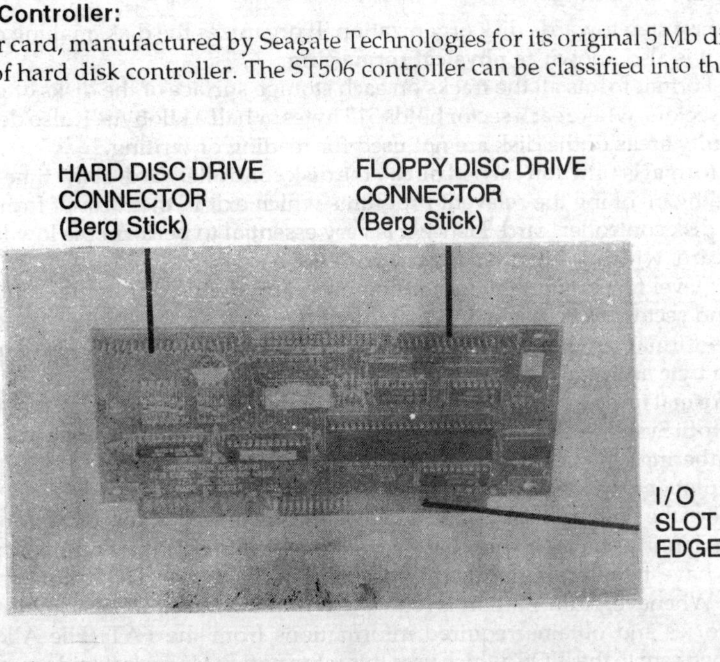

PLATE 11 : "IDE CONTROLLER CARD"

(i) The MFM (Modified Frequency Modulated) controller
(ii) The RLL (Run Length Limited) controller
(iii) The ARLL (Advanced Run Length Limited) controller

The details of the sub types mentioned above are outside the scope of the present discussion, but it should be worth noting that RLL allows 1.5 times more recording than MFM, while ARLL allows two times more information recording when compared with MFM. The RLL and ARLL controllers should be used only when a thin film magnetic hard disk is available.

(2) The ESDI Controllers :

The ESDI, or Enhanced Small Drive Interface, is another popular interface used. The major difference between these controllers and the ST506 is that, a disk using the EDSI interface does its own data seperate and thus sends digital code to the controller card. This enhances the speed of information retrieval.

(3) The SCSI Contollers :

The SCSI, or Small Computer System Interface, is another popular interface. It allows upto seven hard disk to be connected in a daisy-chain fashion. It is predominantly a system level interface and gives high speed performance. Details are not considered here.

(4) IDE Controller :

The IDE, or Integrated Drive Electronics is the most popular type of hard disks interfaces these days. The hard disk is generally 3.25" in size.The IDE drives are considered in a later section. **PLATE 11**.

10.4 DISK ORGANIZATION

After considering the hardware aspects of the hard disk subsystem, we are in a position to understand the hard disk's logical structure. Before a hard disk is made useable it has to undergo the following three procedures :

(i) Low Level Formatting
(ii) Partitioning
(iii) High Level Formatting

10.4.1 Low Level Formatting

This is the first step towards disk organization. It organizes the disk, making disk data retrievable. For this reason it is also known as **physical formatting**.

Low Level Format forms all the tracks on each storage surface of the disks of platters. Each track is divided into 17 sectors, where each sector holds 512 bytes or half a kilobyte. It also defines the bad sectors, so that these faulty areas of the disk are not used for reading or writing.

Low Level format is function carried out by the disk controller card, at the time of initialisation. This is accomplished by invoking the relevent programs which exit in the form of firmware in the EPROM residing on the disk controller card. Hence it is very essential to perform the low level formatting with that controller card, which is intended for use with the hard disk.

During low level formatting, the formatting programs are read from the controller cards ROM. It causes tracks and sectors to be formed. It then identifies each sector uniquely according to the format specified by the format programs. Each sector is given a sector address, also known as sector ID, a synchronisation byte and a gap byte.

Low level format imposes a sector numbering scheme, based on the information stored in the BIOS (Basic Input Output System). This scheme specifies each sector by the coordinates of its side, cylinder and sector. This numbering scheme is referred to as **absolute**. Thus reference to the fifth sector of the second side of the first platter is made as sector 1,1,5.

Next the use of the synchronisation and gap bytes is considered. As explained above, it is crystal clear that BIOS uses a definite scheme to number the sectors. A different sector numbering scheme is used by DOS. Thus we have two sector numbering schemes to deal with DOS numbering scheme will be explained later. Whenever, information is requested from the DISK, DOS searches for the required file from the directories and obtains required informations from the FAT (File Allocation Table). This information is then sent to the BIOS, which uses this information to generate side number, a track number and sector number for each sector required to make up the file. This process is known as data location function. The data obtained from the disk is in analog form. This necessitates the need of the synchronisation byte. The synchronisation byte is written for each sector on a **timing track**. Timing tracks run parallel to the data track and are created by the low level format program loaded in the ROM of the controller card. But how is the process of data seperation occuring ? This is precisely what is explained next. Suppose that the head reads a binary one from the data track. The head continues to read till it encounters a different binary digit, which in the case of this specific example will be a binary zero. Here the timing clock comes in use. The timing track is now used to determine how many bits have been read before a different binary digit is encountered. This changing point eg. point of transition is known as the **transition**. What the R/W head actually reads is the length of time between these transition points. This information is converted by the controller card into the required form. This process in known as **data seperation**.

The gap byte is used to enable the R/W head to access each sector distinctly.It essentially provides a time delay to enable sector determination.

The popular low level formatting utilities are:

(1) Speedstor's Hardprep
(2) Seagate's Diskmanager
(3) QA Plus Utilities
(4) Some times computers Bios itself provides such utilities.

10.4.2 Partitioning Of The Disk

After low level formatting is done, the next phase of initialization is partitioning of the hard disk. This is generally carried out by the DOS FDISK program. Partitions can be thought to be separate - logical volumes of the hard disk used to load seperate operating systems. For example, if one intends to use both DOS and UNIX, he need to create two partitions, one for each operating system. DOS 3.3 and later versions allow upto four partitions.

The FDISK program can be used to make one or more logical volumes, or partitions. It gives these logical volumes a drive name, and uses the first sector of the partition as the boot sector, DOS 3.3 onwards allow the user to declare an extended partition also. The primary partition is that partition of the disk, which generally contains DOS, or as a matter of fact any operating system that is used to boot up the system. The extended DOS partition is another separate partition, which cannot be used for booting but can be subsequently divided into further logical volumes. The primary partition is designated by the drive letter C, while all the sub-partitions of the extended partition will be designated by the drive letter D,E,F.....etc. From this discussion it must be very clear that the extended partition can be considered as a seperate hard disk to which partitioning can be applied.If only DOS is being used, users generally work with a single partition, i.e. the whole disk being denoted to the DOS. Mind it, that even when the whole disk is devoted to only one operating system, partitioning is very much essential. What happens when more than one operating system is to be loaded into the hard disk? Well, here is the answer. First a DOS portion is created using the FDISK command, ensuring that sufficient space for the other operating system to be loaded. Then using the partition program for the other operating system, we create the required partition. Every system has a primary partition, but only one of these primary partition can be designated as active. The active partition is that which takes up after the computer boots up. Most users use the DOS partition as the active partition.

A disk has to be partitioned, even through the entire disk space is used as a single logical volume. The partitioning process creates a partition table, containing informations regarding the disk structure. This table is located in the master record of the disk. The first physical sector of the disk contains this master record. Partitioning defines the first sector in the partition as the boot sector. However the entire track 0 is reserved for partition data. When more than one partitions is made on a disk, each partitions first sector is defined as the boot sector. When a system has to boot up, it reads the master record to determine which partition is active. Then it reads boot records from that partition and executes the boot function. As already mentioned, only one partition can be termed as active partition.

DOS 3.x addressed a sector by 16 bits. As a sector equals 512 bytes, or half a kilobyte, thus DOS 3.x versions could address 2^{16} sectors i.e 65536 sectors. Hence the maximum partition size is 65536 x 0.5 kb = 32 MB.

DOS 4 onwards, each sector is addressed by 32 bits. Thus DOS 4.0 and above can address 2^{32} sectors. This makes almost unlimited volume. Presently DOS 6.0 also uses 32 bits to address a sector. To have larger partition sizes we have to wait and watch out for the coming DOS versions.

10.4.3 High Level Format

The third phase of initialization of the disk, involves high level formatting, also called logical format or DOS format or soft format. The disk must be formatted using the utility provided,which should be compatible to the operating system used. This function is invoked using DOS FORMAT command. DOS uses relative numbering scheme for sector identification, sequentially. The sector numbering starts at 0 for the first sector of the first logical cylinder of the volume. It reserves certain number of sectors to be used by DOS FAT(File Allocation Table). The remaining unreserved sectors are made into groups known as clusters. The size of the clusters depends on DOS version and size of the logical volume. High Level Formatting verifies each sector before undertaking a read/write operation. If read-write operation is unsuccessful, it marks the entire track as bad.

The number of sectors reserved for DOS depends on the version of DOS used.

The disk operating system's logical volumes are divided into several fixed size control areas and file areas. The size of control area depends on several factors. These factors are:

i - the size of volume
ii - the version of format (DOS).

10.4.4 Boot sector

Logical sector 0 is known as boot sector. It contains al the critical information regarding the disk medium's characteristics.

Offset	Field	
00	JMP XXXX	
03	OEM NAME AND VERSION 8 bytes	
OB	Byte per sector (2 bytes)	BPB: BIOS PARAMETER BLOCK
OD	Sector per allocation unit (1 bytes)	
EO	Reserved sector starting at 0 (2bytes)	
10	Number of FATs (1 byte)	
11	Number of root directory entry (2 byte)	MSDOS 2.0
13	Total sector in logical volume (2 byte)	
15	Media descriptor byte	
16	No. of sector per FAT (2 bytes)	
18	Sectors per track (2 bytes)	3.0 V
1A	No. of heads (2 bytes)	
1C	No. of hidden sectors (4bytes)	
20	Total sector in logical volumes CDPS 4.0 version and above	4.0 V
24	Physical drive number	
25		

Offset	Field	
	Reserved	Additional 4.0 V information
26	Extended boot record (29 h)	
27	32 bit binary volume ID	
2B	Volume lable (11 bytes)	
36	Reserved (8 bytes)	
3E	Boot strap	

The first bytes in the sector is always a jump instruction. It may be either a jump followed by 16 bit displacement or a short jump followed by 8 bit displacement and a NOP. If either of these were are not present the disk has been not formatted or was not formatted for the use of DOS.

Following the intitial jump instruction is an 8 byte field which is reserved for OEM identification. The third major component of boot sector is BIOS Parameter Block (BPB). This structure describes the physical disk characteristics and allows the device drive to calculate the proper physical disk address for a given logical structure number. It also contains the information that is used by MS-DOS and various system utilities to calculate the address and size of each disk control area . The next element is the disk boot strap. It is usually read into the memory by the ROM boot strap which is executed automatically when the computer is turned on. The ROM bootstrap moves the head to track 00, read the first physical sector into RAM at a pre determined location.This disk bootstrap calculates the disk address of the beginning of the area read files containing the operating system into the memory and transfers the control to the BIOS module at location 0070:0000 H.

10.4.5 File Allocation Table

File allocation table gives the location of the file. The FAT works by keeping an address for each disk cluster i.e.. specific groups of bits in the FAT represents the specific cluster on the disk. The FAT takes the form of a series of linked lists i.e., if a cluster is Part of file, its address in the FAT contains the address of the next cluster that is part of the file. The address of the last cluster in the file contains a notation that the cluster is end of file. This coding is important because DOS often does not write files to clusters that are not consecutive on the disk.

Here is one entry in the FAT for each cluster in the file area. Thus if there is a bad cluster, it should be marked in AT, because value in the FAT entry itself indicates the next cluster. The FAT can formatted with either 12 bit or 16 bit entries. This is depending on the DOS version and volume of disk. DOS 3.0 and above may have either 12 bit or 16 bit entry. If the number of cluster are more than 4087, entry will be of 16 bits. The first 2 entries in the FAT are reserved for the use of DOS. The first byte of the FAT contains the same media descriptor value that apperas in the BPB in the boot sector. The remaining byte of the first 2 entries are filled with OFFH. This is because the first two clusters (0 and 1) are reserved, the cluster no.2 corresponds to the first cluster of available disk space in the file area.

10.4.6 Root Directory

Following the FAT is an area known as root directory. The root directory contains 32 bytes entry that describes files, other directories, and the optional volume label. An entry beginning with E5 represents erased file and is available for use. An entry beginning with a 00 byte is the logical end of the directory, that entry and subsequent entries have never been used.

Offset	Field	Note
00	File Name	Note 1
08	Extension	
0B	File attribute	Note 2
0C	Reserved	
16	Time created or updated	Note 3
18	Date created or updated	Note 4
1A	Starting cluster	
1C	File size (4 bytes)	Note 5
20		

Format of single entry in a disk directory.

3. Time field Bits Contents
   - 00-04 Binary numbers of 2-second increments corresponding to 0 - 59 sec.
   - 05-0A Binary number minutes (0-59)
   - 0A-0F Binary number of hours (0-23)
4. Date field.
   - Bits Contents
   - 00-04 Day of month (1-31)
   - 05-08 Month (1-12)
   - 09-0F Year (relative to 1980)
5. The file size is interpreted as a 4 byte interger, with the low order 2 bytes of the number stored first.

10.4.7 File Area

The remainder of the volume after the root directory is known as the file area or data area. Cluster are numbered beginning with 2. There are no clusters numbered 0 or 1.

The files are written to the disk beginning at the first available cluster. The one cluster is not sufficient for the file then DOS searches for the next cluster. It may be either contiguous or not. In the case of modified data files, normally sectors are non contiguous.

10.5 INTEGRATED DRIVE ELECTONICS

Integrated Drive Electonics or IDE in short, is a hard disk drive interface in which all the controller electonics is integrated into the compact 3.5 inch disk drive.

The origin of the IDE entrtface dates back to the mid eightes. In 1984 Compaq had approached Western Digital to develop a ST 506 type controller card that could be mounted directly on the hard disk drive. This started the development of the ID (Integrated Drives). But it was the Japanese electronic giant Matsushita Corporation to give the first ID's to the users in early 1985. This integrated drive had a modest storage capacity of 10 megabytes, and since its first inceptions, this technology has never looked back. Seeing this overwhelming response a group of drive, system and software manufactures formed an association known as CAM (Common Access Method) in an attempt to standardize the integrated drives use. CAM started its work around 1988 and introduced the ATA (Advanced Technology Attachment) interface, the new name for IDE, in the late 1989. This documented was then forwarded to the ANSI group for acceptance as the ANSI standard for drive interface.

Before IDE drive involved the in the hard disk market, ST 506, ESDI and SCSI hard disk interfaces were available. IDE drives blended the goodies of all its predecessor to produce a tastier product, something like making pudding from egg and milk. Originally the IBM AT used the ST 506 interface. Due to its slow speed new drives interfaces gained ground. The ESDI and SCSI, although are faster than the ST 506, are much more costlier. What the IDE drive interface did that is kept the speed of SCSI and ESDI and blended it with the price of ST 506. This is the primary reason for their place being consolidated at the top of the hill.

The Interface

The controller card is integrated to the 3.5" disk drive. This controller has a 32-64 Kb cache memory, which enables data access at RAM speed, thus increasing the speed of data retrieval. The interface has a higher number of sectors per track, some times equalling 34, just double of the original ST506 interface. As the entire controller circuit is integrated into the drive's electronics board, the entire ST506 controller card is eliminated. Thus the cost of such drives effectively come down.

The Working

The Interface maintains backward compatiblity with the ST506 interface. This results in a problem. The ROM BIOS of an AT system allows the cylinder addressing scheme to use 10 bits, thus 10limiting the total number of cylinders to 2^{10}, or 1024 cylinders.

But the IDE allows more than 1024 cylinders and around 39 sectors / track, as it uses the RLL encoding format. To overcome this problem, the IDE uses a method known as sector translation. Suppose that a drive has 2048 cylinders and 3 heads. Then the BIOS is fooled to believe that the disk has 1024 cylinders and 6 heads.

A bit of caution is required while using integrated disk drives. Due to the problem discussed above, manufacturers have ruled out low level formatting by the users. Some hard disks just don't allow the user to low format it, while other allow, resulting in disk damage. Low level formatting is done before hand by the disk manufacturer using the FDISK program.

Bad sector translation is done by the IDE. When a disk error develops, the controller detects the error and corrects it. If it can't correct it, disk failure results. The modern IDE disks brought out by Seagate INC and Connors allow low level formatting. With low level formatting one can access and format the partition table sectors and thus destroy all possible virus infections in this area.

Chapter Eleven
SERIAL PORTS

11.0 INTRODUCTION

A wide variety of peripheral devices are used with the PC to enhance their performance and utility. To use the peripheral devices, Input-Output (I/O) should be possible between them. I/O to peripheral devices involve passing the data through the hostile outside environment. As the characteristics of the signal being transmitted depend on the characteristics of the cable and the environment as a whole, data loss is eminently possible during such I/O. To communicate between two dissimilar environments (the accomodating computer environment and the hostile outside environment) an interface is required. The interface provides the point of contact between the dissimilar environments and is called a **port.**

The transfer of data can be accomplished in serial or parallel. Serial transfer consists of passing data bits one by one, while parallel transfer consists of passing all the data bits simultaneously. When the port uses the serial data transfer method, we call the interface a serial port. All IBM personal computers till recently used the serial port for bidirectional communications. Officially this serial port was termed as **the Asynchronous Data Communication Port**. Over the years, personal computer users played with the official name and chipped off most of the words describing the serial port. It is now almost universally described as the **comm port** in the personal computer jargon.

11.1 SERIAL DATA TRANSFER

As mentioned in the previous section, parallel data transfer mode involves passing all the data bits simultaneously. This mode requires more hardware in terms of cables. On the other hand, serial data transfer provides the cheaper alternative in communication. We need only a single cable as the bits are transported one by one, and there is lesser probability of data loss. The reason for the latter is given below.

When a digital signal travels through a wire, there is a considerable voltage drop due to the distributed resistance of the wire. This phenomenon is known as attenuation of the digital signal. The signal faces distortion due to the distributed capacitance and inductance of the transmitted cable. So, when we want to transmit a signal to a distant place, direct communication is outwardly rejected. The only plausible solution lies in using a device known a **MODEM**, the name being derived from the terms **MOD**ulator-**DEM**odulator.

11.1.1 Asynchronous and Synchronous Communication

Serial communication generally use either Asynchronous or Synchronous Communication Scheme. These two methods employ different techniques for synchronizing the circuits at the sending end with that of the receiving end.

In synchronous communication the data is sent in groups called blocks. Each block is followed by a special synchronizing character. Error checking is done automatically on the entire block, and if error is detected the entire block is retransmitted.

In asynchronous communication each character is sent with start and stop bits. Since asynchronous communication doesnot use a CLOCK signal, the data byte move from the transmitter to receiver with no regular time gaps. To differentiate one data byte from the other, start and stop bits are placed at the begining and end respectively. A parity bit is sometimes placed between the end of data and the stop bits. The stop bit can be 1,1.5 or 2.0 times the duration of a data bit pulse. The parity bit is either odd or even. The receiver end has a circuit which tests whether the parity bit confirms to the standard adopted. If it doesnot, then there is an error in the transmitted data. This form of error detection is not perfect because if more than one bit is lost then this method will become a prey of the data loss and will be unable to detect it.

11.1.2 Baud Rate.

The rate at which data bits are sent is called the baud rate or BPS (bits per second) and can be selected to suit the device communicating with the computer. Standard rates are 300,600,900,1200,2400,9600 etc.

11.2 RS-232 INTERFACE.

RS-232 stands for **R**ecommmend **S**tandard number **232** and was given by the EIA (Electronic Industry Association), Bell Laboratories and major communication equipment manufacturers in the year

1969. The purpose of the standard was to provide an **Interface Between Data Terminal Equipment (DTE) and Data communication Equipment (DCE) employing serial data transfer.** The RS-232 standard requires a modem to be connected between the receiving and transmitting ends. The requirment for the modem already has been mentioned. The modem is the DCE and the computer, terminal and printers with which the modem is interfaced are all DTE. IBM lays down that all IBM machines are DTE.

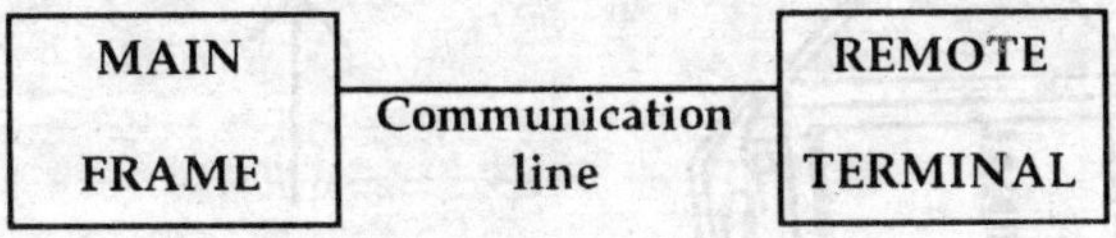

Fig. 11.1 : Remote Communication.

The protocol laid down by the RS-232 standard is briefly outlined below :-

1. Data Transfer is done serially.
2. The DCE has a receptacle, which is actually a female port, and the connection is established with a 25 pin D connector.
   The DTE has a 25 pin male connector.
3. The RS-232 uses negative logic, i.e. a positive voltage pulse is interpreted as a binary zero and a negative voltage pulse is interpreted as a binary one. The input and output logic on the RS-232 interface differ slightly and can be seen in the logic level diagrams given below :

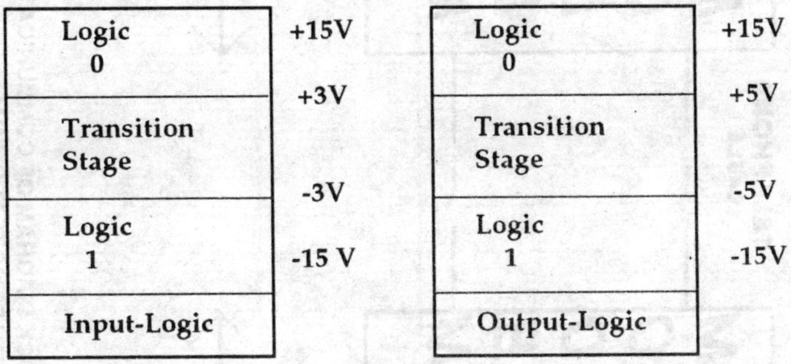

Fig.11.2 : Logic Level Diagram.

   The transition stage represents that voltage band for which logic levels are not defined. A voltage in this zone might be ambiguously interpreted as logic zero/one. For most practicle purpose the circuit uses +12V (Logic 0) and -12V (Logic 1).
4. The least significant Bit (LSB) is transmitted first, followed by all other bits in the reverse order of their significane.
5. During the dormant state (i.e. when no data transmission is occuring) a fixed current, known as the quiscent current flows. This dormant state is assigned the logic level 1 and is called **MARK Condition**. The State in which actual data transfer occurs results in a stoppage in current flow and is assigned the logic level 0. This condition is called **SPACE**.
6. The connection (cable) between DTE and DCE should not exceed 50 feet.
   Now the expanded block diagram of the MAIN computer and the Remote terminal connection is given in fig.11.3

11.2.1 RS-232 Connection

In the above block diagram, the arrow head marks the destination of the signal under consideration.

The transmitted data (TxD) is used by modem for modulation. The received data (RxD) is generated by the modem after demodulation of the signal received.

Before sending data to DCE, the DTE request for permissions form the DCE by using the Request To Send (RTS) signal. The modem has the ability to check whether the line for transmission is free and the other end modem and DTE are free. If transmission line and the other requirments are fullfilled, a signal called Clear To Send (CTS) is sent by the DCE.

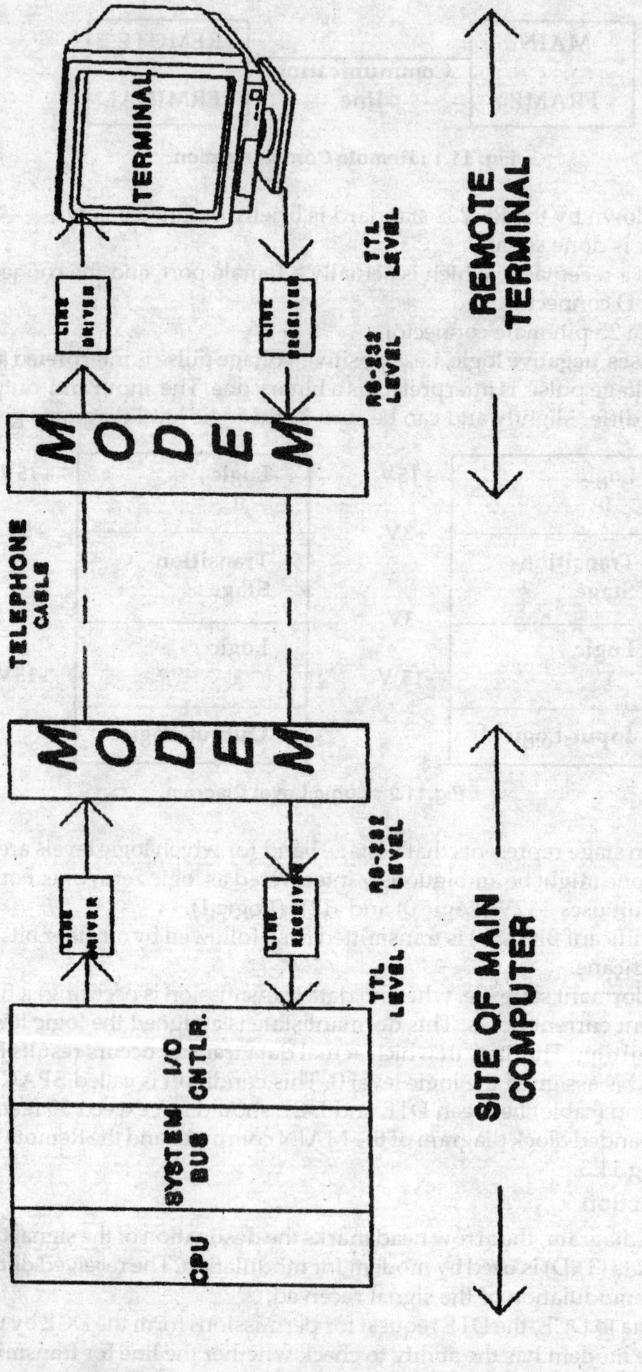

Fig. 11.3 : BLOCK DIAGRAM OF COMMUNICATION WITH REMOTE TERMINAL

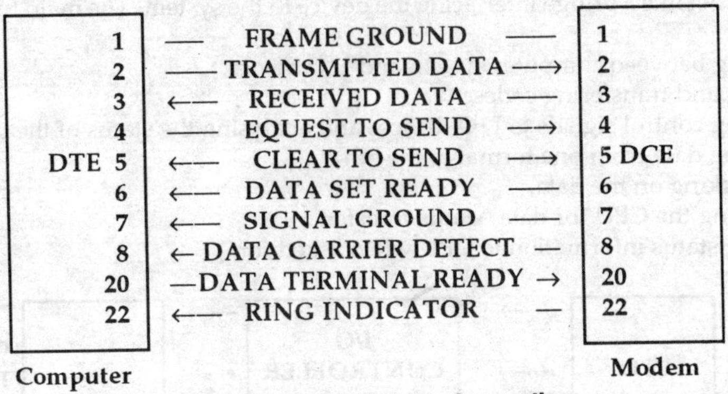

Fig. 11.5 : Null Modem Connection.

When the DTE is turned on a Data Terminal Ready (DTR) is sent by the DTE. When the corresponding DCE on it acknowledges the DTR by sending a Data Set Ready (DSR) signal.

The Ring Indicator (RI) signal and Carrier Detect (CD) signal is used with modems and telephone lines. In this case a telephone set is connected with the modem. Thus the DTE wishing to communicate has to dial a number. A dial tone (analog signal) is sent on the telephone line to the receiving end. The modem at the receiving end sends the RI signal to the calling DTE as an indication of the DTE trying to establish connection with a distant DTE. Then the called modem sends a carrier Detect (CD) signal to the called DTE as an indication that you are being called.

Pin number 1 is the frame ground. Frame Ground is that connector which connets to the chasis of the equipment. This pin is analogous to the third pin of a three pin A.C. plug. The Pin works as the ground for the system, and prevents damage of the equipment due to shock. The signal ground (pin no. 7) provides the necessary return path for both data signals and handshaking signals. But what is handshaking? It is simply a method of controlling the flow of data in a asynchronous data transfer mode.

11.2.2 The Null Modem Connection

Most often we are concerned with connecting devices like printer, mouse, bar code reader and optical scaner etc to our computer/terminal. It is also noticed that the devices being interfaced are not very for off from each other. So we rule out using modems and telephone lines as we did in our remote connection scheme. Since the devices mentioned above are all DTE's and have identical modem interface, we provide a method of connection in which no modem is used and call it the null modem connection. Actually we fool the DTE's by the null modem connection, and make them feel that they are connected to modems (this occurs due to the identical modem interface between them).

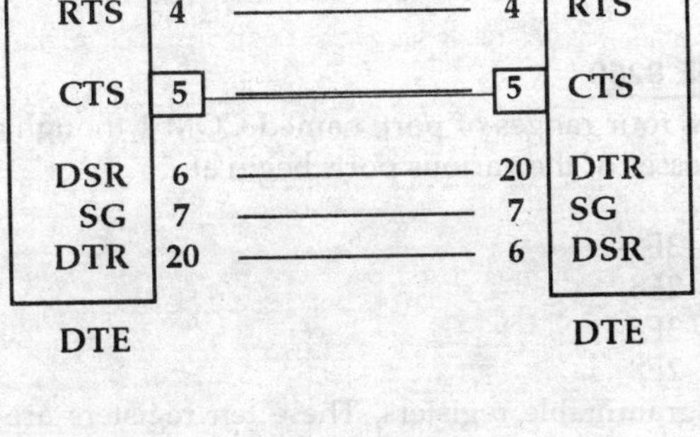

Fig 11.5 : Null Modem Connection.

11.3 I/O CONTROLLERS

The controllers act like a bridge interfacing the device to the system. The main functions of the I/O controller are :-

1. Interfacing between computer system and I/O device.
2. Receiving and transfering codes.
3. Generating control signals to I/O devices and analysing the status of the device.
4. Converting data from one format to the other.
5. Error checking on the data.
6. Interrupting the CPU for data/status transfer
7. Providing status information to CPU when asked for.

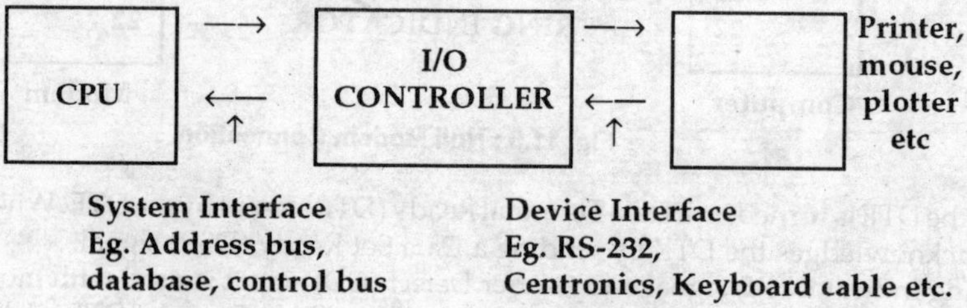

Fig 11.6 : Input-Output Device Interfacing.

11.3.1 8250 and UART

Data transfer inside the computer system is done in parallel mode. Who converts the parallel data to a serial data when the serial port is used ? It is the UART (Universal Asynchronous Receiver/ Transmitter). The UART is the workstation responsible for converting the parallel out going bits to serial and serial incoming bits to parallel.

The 8250 is a programmable LSI. It converts serial data to parallel and vice-versa. It controls data flow and sets the speed of data exchange. The data speed is set by dividing the 1.8432 MHZ CLOCK supplied with the PC with a number loaded in the chips register. The 8250 can be used to set word length, parity bits, the no. of stop and start bits etc. It allows the user direct control of all its 8 bit registers. The major disadvantage of the 8250 chip was its slow speed.

The computer users demand for speed has always provided a major thrust to computer manufacturers to provide chips with faster performance rating. In 1983-84 Intel introduced the 16450. It was fully compatible with the 8250 and had 16 bit registers. Further enhancements were brought in with the 16550 and 16550A chips.

11.3.2 UART

The UART comprises of three sections namely the TRANSMITTER, RECEIVER and CONTROL LOGIC. Fig. 11.7 gives the block diagram of a UART. The transmitter section converts the parallel data I/P to serial O/P, while the receiver converts the serial I/P to parallel O/P. It should be noted that the parallel I/P and parallel O/P occur on a shared bus, and the right choice of path is done under the action of the control logic.

11.4 PROGRAMMING THE 8250

IBM standard specifies four ranges of port, named COM 1 though COM 4. Each range has eight contiguous port. The addresses of the various ports begin at:

COM 1	3F8
COM 2	2F8
COM 3	3E8
COM4	2E8

The 8250 has ten programmable registers. These ten registers are addressed using seven port addresses. The registers are mainly concerned with intializing the serial port, set the baud rate, control the flow of data and monitoring status. The various registers are accessed through the port address. In the table given below the register are mentioned with their respective port addresses and conditions if any.

Register	Port Address	Condition	Function
1. Transmitter Holding Register (THR) LCR	3F8H i.e.	D7 = 0 at 3FBH D7 = 0 in	Holdsthe data byte to be transmitted
2. Reveiver Data Register (RD)	3F8H	D7 = 0 at 3FBH	Holds the data received
3. Baud Rate divisor (Low Byte)	3F8H	D7 = 1 at 3FB8	The clock of the system is divided by the number represented
4. Baud Rate divisor (High Byte)	3F9H	D7 = 1 at 3FBH	by these two Registers.
5. Interrupt Enable Register (IER)	3F9H	D7 = 0 at 3F9H	It is a register used to generate interrupt signals depending upon the 4 interrupt bits
6. Interrupt Identification Register	3FAH	-	Represents the status of the interrupt priority controller of the 8250
7. Line control Register (LCR)	3F8H	-	Loads the desired character format into it.
8. Modem Control Register (MCR)	3FCH	-	Controls the output signal to Modem
9. Line status Register (LSR)	3FDH	-	Keeps trackof the various status conditions of receiver/transmitter
10. Modem Status Register (MSR)	3FEH	-	Keeps the modem status

Table 11.1 : Registers Port Address and Functions

When we take up initialization of the serial port, all parameters like word lenght, the parity bit, number of stop bits and baud rate are set.

1. Baud Rate Initialization :

The baud rate register is set by making bit 7 (D7) of the line control register equal to 1. After setting the baud rate registers, D7 is set back to zero in the LCR. The baud rate divisor is a 16 bit binary number formed from the number loaded at registers 3F9H and 3F8H. The baud rate divisor so formed divide the system clock speed (1.19 MHZ). The larger the baud rate divisor, slower is the baud rate. The baud rate registers have to be adequately set to obtain the required baud rate.

2. Control Registers :

The various bit setting for the line control registers are given below :

bit 1-O Character lenght: 00 = 5 bits, 01 = 6 bits, 10 = 7bits,11 = 8 bits
2 No.of stop bits: 0=1 or 1.5 if character lenght is 5 otherwise no. of stop bits are two
3 Parity: 1= parity bit generated
4 Parity Type: 0= odd, 1= even
5 Stick parity:decides the polarity of parity bit.If bit
4 is 1 and bit 5 is 1,then parity bit follows negative logic. If bit
5 is 1 and bit 4 is 0, the positive logic is used.

6 Set break:if bit 6 = 1 then the serial output is forced to line spacing level

7 Divisor latch: set to 1 by programme before accessing registers 3F8H and 3F9H to obtain baud-divisor, set to 0 to access RD, THR etc.

3. Interrupt Enable register is used to enable different interrupts.

4. Line Status Register

This register is used by the receiver/transmitter section of the 8250 to indicate status and error conditions during communication activities.

The various bit configaration are given below :-

bit 0 = 1 implies a byte of data is received.
1 = 1 implies a data has been overrun.
2 = 1 implies parity error.
3 = 1 implies framing error.
4 = 1 implies break interrupt.
5 = 1 implies THR is empty.
6 = 1 implies transmitter shift register is empty.
7 is not used and always set to zero. it ifis1 it indicates time-out.

11.5 LIMITATIONS OF THE RS-232.

Limitations of the RS-232 are

1. Distance limitations
2. Speed limitations
3. Ground limitations

11.5.1 Distance Limitations

The principal problem with RS-232 is its distance limitation of about 50 feet. With lower data rates, much longer cable runs is possible, but they never seen to be long enough. The distance limitation is not of much concern in the modem and telephone line condition as the modem is usually close enough to the computer or terminal (DTE).

11.5.2 Speed Limitations

A second disadvantage is the maximum transmission speed of 9,600 bps, although this is not a trouble for data transfer between computers and terminals. The speed is reduced as the data cannot even travel at 9,600 bps over telephone lines, as high speed of data transfer causes data loss (inductive and capacitive loss).

11.5.3 Ground Limitation

The third disadvantage of RS-232 is the ground signal. All data and control signals are measured with the ground signal as the reference. However if there is a difference in ground potential between the two ends of the cable, then transition state becomes narrow, transition state is mentioned before. When the transition state narrows, the possibility of signal misinterpretation arises. This causes data errors.

Chapter Twelve
PARALLEL PORTS

12.0 INTRODUCTION

The parallel ports was introduced by the IBM to serve its printer. Over the years since its inception, parallel port have seen many other peripherals being interfaced in parallel. It would be worth while to note that a port is nothing but an interface, so a parallel port is essentially an interface that allows parallel data transfer to occur. By parallel data transfer we mean to exemplify that all data bits (the byte) is transmitted at the same time, unlike the serial transfer. Lets leave the method of data transfer for the present. As already mentioned, the IBM brought out the parallel port with the idea of connecting printers. So the parallel port is even known as the **Printer Port** or **Printer Adapter**. The name printer port may sound proper, but how come did the name printer adapter arise? Again we see that the name has its origin in the past - we use the 25 pin D type connector on the PC side and a 36 pin Amphenol connector on the printer side. Thus the cable used for connection has to some what work like an adapter, with some of the 36 pins not being used or shifted around.

One of the biggest advantage of the parallel port is its method of transfering data. In this respect it allows 8 times faster data transfer theoritically. With so much being said about the parallel port in the introduction itself, we should definately mention how to distinguish a serial and parallel port. Simple enough, all parallel ports are female ports while all serial ports are male ports. Now we turn our attention to the standard followed. The serial port uses the RS-232 standard, while the parallel port uses the Centronics Standard. The Centronics standard evolved from the once famous printer manufacturer, Centronics quest for a printer that could be interfaced in parallel to the IBM machine. The Centronics standard is dealth in detail next.

12.1 THE CENTRONICS STANDARD

The parallel port standard is due to the famous printer manufacturer Centronics. This standard provides the interface between a computer and printer. The printer side of the interface has a 36 pin Amphenol connector and the PC side has a 25 pin D type connector. The cable used is a 36 wire flat cable in which every alternate wire is a ground. The signals are of TTL level and are measured with respect to the reference signal (reffered to as ground).

The pin numbers of the 25 D type connector do not equal that of the 36 pin Amphenol connector. Thus proper connection between the two ends is necessary. The cross over of the cables are shown in the table below :

25 pin D Type Connector	Amphenol Connector
1	1
2	2
3	3
4	4
5	5
6	6
7	7
8	8
9	9
10	10
11	11
12	12
13	13
14	14
15	32
16	31
17	36
18	33
19	19
20	21
21	23
22	25
23	27
24	29
25	30

TABLE 12.1 : IBM Parallel Printer Cable.

Next we give the IBM parallel port pinout with the function carried out by each pin mentioned :

25 pin D type Connector Pin Number	Function
1	Strobe
2	Data bit 0
3	Data bit 1
4	Data bit 2
5	Data bit 3
6	Data bit 4
7	Data bit 5
8	Data bit 6
9	Data bit 7
10	Acknowledge
11	Busy
12	Paper End (out of paper)
13	Select
14	Auto Feed
15	Error
16	Initialize Printer
17	Select Input
18—25	Ground

TABLE 12.2 : IBM Parallel Port Pinout and Function.

Now we move on to the various port signals.

1. Datalines :

Pin no. 2—9 are laid down with the purpose of carrying the data bits, which make up the byte. They are all TTL level signals, and a high indicates a binary 1 and a low indicates a binary 0. The transfer of data bits is undirectional, in contrast with the Rs. 232 standard. Each data read has a corresponding reference level (ground lead). Here is another difference. In the Rs. 232 standard, all the signals were measured with reference to the same ground signal which was pin no. 7. Here pin numbers 19—27 are used as the reference level or ground signals. The various data lines and their corresponding ground levels are given on Table 12.3.

PC to Printer

Pin No.	Function	Ground lead
2	Data bit 0	20
3	Data bit 1	21
4	Data bit 2	22
5	Data bit 3	23
6	Data bit 4	24
7	Data bit 5	25
8	Data bit 6	26
9	Data bit 7	27

TABLE 12.3 : Data Lines and Corresponding Ground.

2. Strobe Line :

How does the printer realize that a byte of data is available for printing? The strobe lines is actually meant for this purpose. It is a CLOCK signal which becomes active only when a byte of data is available to the printer. In the Centronics standard, the clock is low when data is to be transmitted (active) and high when no data is to be read. The strobe should be active (low) for at least one microsecond for the printer to realize that data is available. A minimum gap of half a microsecond is specified by the Centronics protocol before the strobe signal is made active again. The data signals are also required to persist for another half a microsecond after the negative edge of the active strobe by the protocol. This ensures that overlapping of data signals do not occur.

3. Busy Line :

This signal enables the computer to know that the printer is busy printing and cannot except any more data. When the busy line is high, the computer understands that the printer is busy. Various conditions can cause the busy line to become high. Besides the strobe active and printing conditions, the busy line may become high due to errors in printing operation. Error conditions that can cause the busy line to become high are :

1. Ribbon jam
2. Improper printer initialization
3. Printer buffer becoming full.

4. Acknowledge Line :

This is an output signal from the printer to the computer indicating to the computer that the printer is ready to receive data. It also confirms that the preceding data has been printed. Pin no. 10 is the output signal from the printer and pin no. 28 is corresponding signal ground. Acknowledge remains high and shifts to low to indicate that printer is ready to accept the next data.

5. Paper End :

If the printer runs short of paper during the printing operation, the printer sends a signal called paper end, paper out or paper empty to the computer. After receiving this signal, the PC stops pouring data to the printer to avoid data loss. This signal is transmitted through pin no. 12. When this lead goes high the computer halts the process of sending data.

6. Select :

This is a signal sent by the printer telling the computer that it has been selected for use. It confirms that the printer is on-line. Pin no. 13 is the select line and when it is high it indicates the selected condition.

7. Auto Feed :

If the auto feed signal is low, the printer provides a line feed automatically after printing every line.

8. Error :

It is a signal that indicates a printer fault. It is normally high in the no-error condition, and becomes low on detection of an error. Many reasons can be attributed to the Error signal becoming active. The important ones are

1. Jamming of printer head
2. Drive belt broken
3. Printer in off-line state
4. Paper-end condition.

9. Initialize Printer :

Initialize Printer is an alternative means of switch on/off. With this signal it is possible to set fonts, character pitch etc. The printer always starts with a predetermined set of parameters. this signal works like a reset button, and on this line the printer runs through its own boot-up operation.

10. Select Input :

This is an interface controller. When this signal is low, the printer accepts data; when high the interface is disabled and the printer doesnot accept data.

After discussing all the signals, we are in a position to produce the whole PC to printer cable and signal configuration :

Sl.No.	SIGNAL NAME	SIGNAL SOURCE	PC SIDE CONNECTION	PRINTER SIDE CONNECTION
1	STROBE	PC	1	1
2	STROBE REFERENCE	—	19	19
3	DATA BIT 0	PC	2	2
4	DATA 0 REFERENCE	—	—	20
5	DATA BIT 1	PC	3	3
6	DATA 1 REFERENCE	—	20	21
7	DATA BIT 2	PC	4	4
8	DATA 2 REFERENCE	—	—	22
9	DATA BIT 3	PC	5	5
10	DATA 3 REFERENCE	—	21	23
11	DATA BIT 4	PC	6	6
12	DATA 4 REFERENCE	—	—	24
13	DATA BIT 5	PC	7	7
14	DATA 5 REFERENCE	—	22	25
15	DATA BIT 6	PC	8	8
16	DATA 6 REFERENCE	—	—	26
17	DATA BIT 7	PC	9	9
18	DATA 7 REFERENCE	—	23	27
19	ACKNOWLEDGE	PTR	10	10
20	ACKNOWLEDGE REFERENCE	—	—	28
21	BUSY	PTR	11	11
22	BUSY REFERENCE	—	24	29
23	PAPER END	PTR	12	12
24	PAPER END REFERENCE	—	25	30
25	SELECT	PTR	13	13
26	AUTOFEED	PC	14	14
27	ERROR	PTR	15	32
28	INITIALIZE	PC	16	31
29	SELECT INPUT	PC	17	36
30	(NO CONNECTION)	—	—	15

31	LOGIC GROUND	—	—	16
32	CHASSIS GROUND	PTR	—	17
33	(NO CONNECTION)	—	—	18
34	GROUND	—	—	33
35	(NO CONNECTION)	—	—	34
36	+ 5 Volts DC	PTR	—	35

TABLE 12.4 : PC To Printer Cable And Corresponding Configration

12.2 PORT ASSIGNMENTS AND REGISTERS

The IBM standard assigns three input - output registers to communicate with its parallel port. The original PC design was suppose to handle upto three parallel ports. This means that the PC should be able to handle three devices which can be interfaced using the centronics standard. In other words, the PC should be able to handle three parallel devices. Each of these devices are controlled using the three input **- output registers namely data output register, status register and control register.** Three ranges of ports (corresponding to each parallel port) are available, begining at the base addresses 03BC (Hex), 0378 (Hex) and 0278 (Hex). In any system, these addresses should be addressed uniquely. Thus two parallel ports cannot have the same base address.

In the IBM configuration, the special device names LPT1, LPT2 and LPT3 are reserved for the three parallel devices that can be supported. The abbreviation LPT is derived from the word Line PrinTer. These logical names donot necessarily match with a given set of I/O port addresses, however during boot-up the system searches for parallel ports at each of these base addresses. The search is always performed in the order listed below : First 03BC (Hex), then 0378 (Hex) and then 0278 (Hex).

The first parallel port that is found in the search is assigned the name LPT 1, the second being assigned the name LPT 2 and the third LPT 3. It should be noted that a base address is initialized to zero when no corresponding parallel device is found.

The data output register is simply that port address at which all the data bits are sent while transfer of data is to be made to the printer. The status register reports the status of the printer. The CPU of the computer monitors the status register to determine whether all conditions are error free or not. The control register is concerned with controlling the out-put of data. The bit pattern for control and status registers is given below :

Control Register :

Address 3BE (Example address for the first parallel port)

bit 0 0 = normal setting; 1 = causes output of data
1 0 = normal setting; 1 = automatic line feed
2 0 = initialize printer port; 1 = normal setting
3 0 = remove printer link; 1 = normal setting
4 0 = printer interrupt disabled;1= interrupt enabled
5-7 unused

Status Register :

Address 3BD (Example address for the second parallel port)

bit0 - 2 unused
3 0 = printer error; 1 = no error
4 0 = printer not online; 1 = printer on-line
5 0 = sufficient paper; 1 = paper out
6 0 = acknowledge; 1 = normal setting
7 0 = printer busy; 1 = printer not busy

Originally the IBM PC used to have parallel ports which were built using discrete logic. Nowadays with the advent of LSI technology, the circuit has been intregated and a single parallel port controller chip is used. UM 82C11 is generally used to design the parallel port.

12.3 PRINTER CLASSES

Upto this point, we have covered the parallel port, that too in some what detailed manner. Why do we use the parallel interface ? Obviously to interface a printer in parallel ! So is it not adequate to devote some time to understand the different popular printers.

Printers are generally classified into two types, namely the impact and non impact printers.

(1) **Impact Printers :** These printers utilize a typing head which hits the ribbon to leave an impression on the paper. They are very similar to the TYPEWRITERS in action, and are called Impact printers due to their hammering action. Examples of such printers are dot matrix printers and full-character impact printers. By far the dot matrix impact printer, also known as the dot matrix printer seems to be the most popular type of printer.

(2) **Non-Impact Printers :** These printers donot strike the paper at all. They use different technologies to create an impression on paper. Examples of popular non impact printers are thermal printers, inkjet printers, laser printers and dye diffusion printer. Now we explain some of the popular printers used these days.

12.4 MATRIX PRINTERS

In these printers, the characters are formed using dots and hence the name. The printer head consists of an array of pins, which move accross the lenght of the paper, and hit the ribbon to create the character, by squeezing ink from the ribbon. Refer Plate 12.

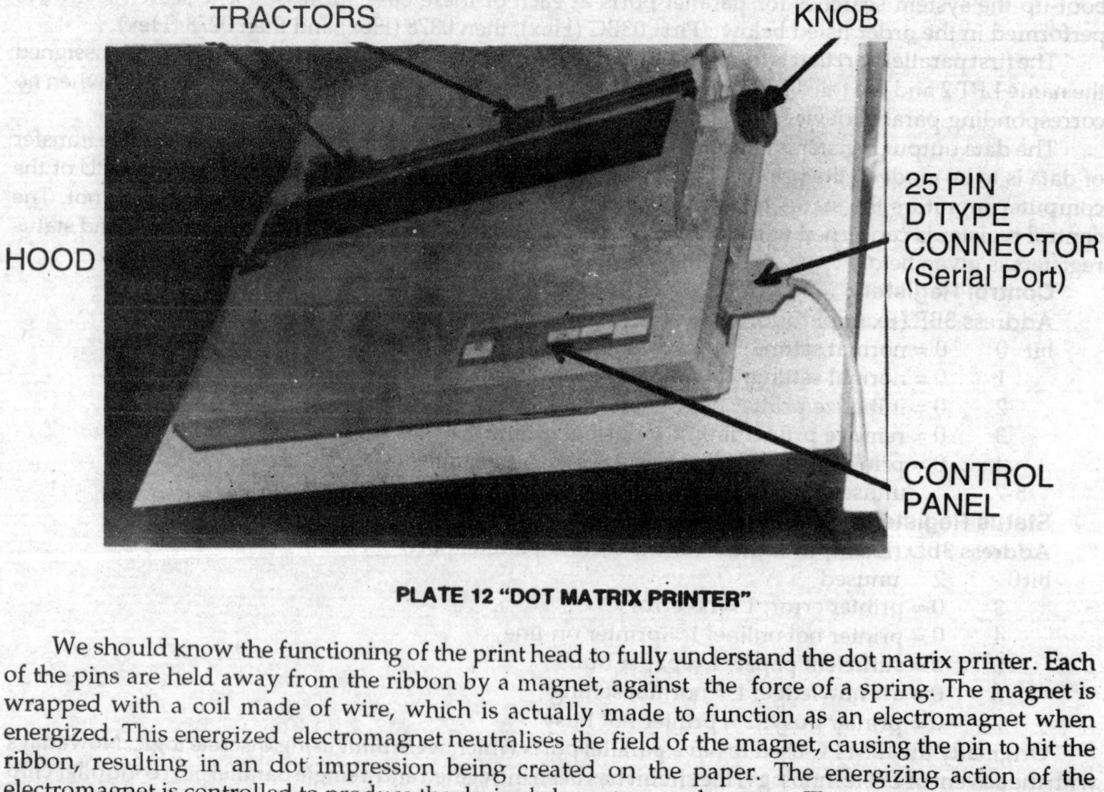

PLATE 12 "DOT MATRIX PRINTER"

We should know the functioning of the print head to fully understand the dot matrix printer. Each of the pins are held away from the ribbon by a magnet, against the force of a spring. The magnet is wrapped with a coil made of wire, which is actually made to function as an electromagnet when energized. This energized electromagnet neutralises the field of the magnet, causing the pin to hit the ribbon, resulting in an dot impression being created on the paper. The energizing action of the electromagnet is controlled to produce the desired characters on the paper. The control of the printer is rests with the computer itself.

Most printers print in both directions, that is from left to right, and then right to left. To enable this the printer has to remember the whole line, so that right to left printing is possible. This speeds up the printer speed but calls for memory to store the line.

Two feature essentially determine the quality of our printers. The first one is the printer resolution.

This is normally measured in dots per inch, or dpi. Typically, these days printers are available with dpi ranging from 300-600. The other factor is the number of printouts available in terms of pages per minute, abbreviated as ppm. Printer with ppm of 3-4 are generally used. A third feature known as CPS, or Characters Per Second is also specified with most printer. A good blend of all these features determines the quality of the printer.

12.5 INKJET PRINTERS

This is an example of the non-impact printer class. Actually the inkjet printers are some how similar to the dot impact printer, as they use similar printing pattern eg. dots forming the characters. They have tiny nozzles in the head, which flies the ink to the page in the form of a dot. The head movement is more or less similar.

In the dot matrix range of printers, Epson is the market leader. But it couldn't make a place at the top as far as inkjet printers are concerned, a place held by Hewlett-Packard for quite a long time. Hewlett-Packard have become leaders in the inkjet market.

We give certain specification of the HP Deskjet 1200 C printer :-

1. It has a top speed of 7 ppm for black text and 2 ppm for color. It uses a RISC Processor, high speed centronics parallel port and colour PCL5 Language.
2. It uses HP colour smart technology to ensure vivid colour printing every time, and improved memory management for printing of complex documents.
   It has the capability of generating 45 scalable typefaces.
3. It has a 300 dpi resolution.
4. It allows centronics, local talk (macintosh), and serial interfacing also.

12.6 LASER PRINTERS

We need to understand the underlying technology first. Here the image to be printed is made out by focussing an optical image on a photoconductive drum, which was statically charged before focussing the laser beam. Charge drains away from the focussed part, leaving charge on the unfocussed port. A pigment is applied to the drum, and the pigment sticks on the charged area. This pigment is then pasted on the paper by some fusing technique.

We give certains specification of the Epson EPL - 3000 printer.

1. Type : 300 dpc A-4 laser printer.
2. Speed : 4 ppm
3. Memory : 1MB, which is expandable to 5 MB
4. Power : 450 W.
5. Interface : Bidirectional parallel port with serial port option.
6. Rated life : 5 Years/100,000 sheets.

The Epson range of printers are obtainable from vendors Wipro peripherals Ltd, Banglore.

12.7 THERMAL TRANSFER USING DYE SUBLIMATION

This is the printer, for near photo-quality output. These printers generally use low resolutions (around 200) but give stunning continuous colour printouts almost like a photograph. This is the precise reason for its high appreciation in the market.

How does this technology work? This is what we see next. In a dye-sublimation unit, solid ink is heated. The solid-ink sublimes, that is changes directly to vapour state from the solid state, and the vapours formed percolate into the paper, and fixes itself up in the papers minute air gaps. A special coated paper has to be used for such printouts. This diffusion process results in dull text and line art, but extraordinarily good photographs. Generally special polyester paper is used.

The technology being new and uses special paper for printouts, makes such printers a costly investment. But if high quality photographs is the requirement, this is the type of printers you need.

12.8 PRINTER INTERNALS

By just saying that the whole art of printing is a smart technology, may not quench the thirst of many inquisitive readers. They want to know the how's and what's of the smart technology. This section is precisely for then. Never mind if you aren't among these thirsty readers. Just have a look down the section, and you will definitely read through.

12.8.1 Printer Overview

Our discussions in this and the coming sections are primarily centered around the dot matrix printer which we have tried to generalize when ever possible. This discussion tells you about some of the features of the printer externally visible. Throughout this discussion we encourage you to refer to fig. 1 to understand better.

On the right side of the printer we have the interface connector. Generally, this connector is a D shaped female port, to which the 36 pin Amphenol connector is connected. It is through this interface connector the PC - Printer communication is possible.

A switch bank is also provided on the right side of the printer. These are generally provided to allow the user to control the printers behaviour. As an example, lets consider the TVS 155 Dot Matrix Printers (fig 1). We provide a table showing the various functions performed in the off and on conditions of the various switches as an illustration.

SWITCH	OFF Condition	ON Condition
1	Skip perforation off	Skip Perforation On
2	Automatic line feed disabled	Automatiac line feed enabled
3	Automatic Paper loading and paper park on	Automatic paper loading and paper park off
4	Unidirectional NLQ	Bidirectional NLQ
5	Epson Emulation	IBM Emulation
6	Normal print	Compressed print
7	11" Page print	12" Page print
8	Unslashed zero	Slashed zero

TABLE 12.5 : Switch Functions.

Next we consider the top cover, also known as **dust cover**. As the name implies, its main function is to stop dust from entering the interiors of the printer. It covers the printer head, head carriage and the roller.

You are surely going to notice the two sprockets which are movable on the carriage at the rear end **of the printer. These are called tractors. They are resposinble for continuously feeding fan folded paper** into the printer and keeping the paper ALIGNED. On the right side we have a round cylindrical plastic knob, **which is used for manually feeding paper. This knob is known as the Platten knob.**

On the left side of the printer we have the power switch and power adapter conectors. In the next section we go into the details of printer head and internal layout of the printer.

12.8.2. Inside the Printer Case

After removal the dust cover we can immediately see the printer head mounted on a head carriage. Some how, the looks of the printer head resembles that of a transformer. The head has a magnet which is wound around with copper coils to function as an electromagnet. Inside the printer head we have spring mechanism attached to the peripherally visible head. All this have been explained previously. What is of our interest at present is the printers head pins. Many printer heads have 9 pins, while others have 24 pins. The number of head pins on the printer head is generally implementation dependent. The head is mounted on a carriage, known as the head carriage which allows too and fro head movement on it. The paper is fixed on a roller and the printer hits the papers portion fixed on the roller. After a line is printed, the paper advances, and the next portion is used for printing. This is how the whole job of printing is done. A head cable can be noticed to be moving down from the printer head to the logic board of the printer.

Almost every printer comes with atleast two sensors. One is the line position sensor which uses hall effect/optical sensors, while the other is the paper entry sensor. The line position sensor determines the left most position of the printer head white the paper entry sensor determines whether or not a paper is being supplied to the printer. Generally paper entry sensors are mechanical in nature.

Every printer has a control panel on the printer to control the printers action. It consists of a paper out indicator, online indicator, on line switch, line feed switch, form feed switch, draft and NLQ (Near

Letter Quality) switches. A controller card controls these switches.

On unscrewing the top panel of the printer case, the various logic cards and panel supply units become visible. We just mention the components which make up the printer. A ribbon motor is provided to rotate the ribbon while the head is busy printing. This enables even use of all parts of the ribbon, thus yeildings maximum use of the ribbon. A stepper motor is provided for carriage movement and form feed movement respectively. Generally most stepper motors inside the printers use a 24 V dc supply. A power supply unit is provided to change the 220/240 V.A. C. supply to the respective d.c voltages required by the motors and logic boards laid down with the task of electronically controlling all the components of the printer. The printer has a driver transistor responsible for the driving the head of the printer. Interface card is provided to provide the necessary interface. Most commonly the interface used is centronics parallel interfaces, but the user can change the interface to suit his needs by changing this card. Some printers provide multiple options of interfacing with their interface cards. A RAM is provided to store the incoming data from the PC. The information obtained is in ASCII code. The printer has to convert the ASCII code of a particular character to its matrix format. To complish this a ROM is provided, which has the necessary dot matrix character representation of each ASCII code. Also seen is the control panel card, which controls the control panel.

With this overview of the printer internals and functioning, we conclude the chapter on parallel ports.

Chapter Thirteen
MASS STORAGE

13.0 INTRODUCTION

Information storage is an essential feature of computing. Computer's memory is limited in size and hence there is a need for other devices which can be used to keep valuable data for use later. The mass storage devices available can be classified into two types : Serial and Random. This classification is on the basis of the method used by the devices to access data. The serial storage devices access data serially. We have to transverse through the data to reach our desired location. Random storage devices allow random access of data. Thus we can reach the portion of data under consideration, almost instantaneously. We have already covered two storage devices - Floppy disk and Hard Disk. Both are examples of random storage devices. In this chapter we consider some other types of storage devices and mention their class (eg. serial/random).

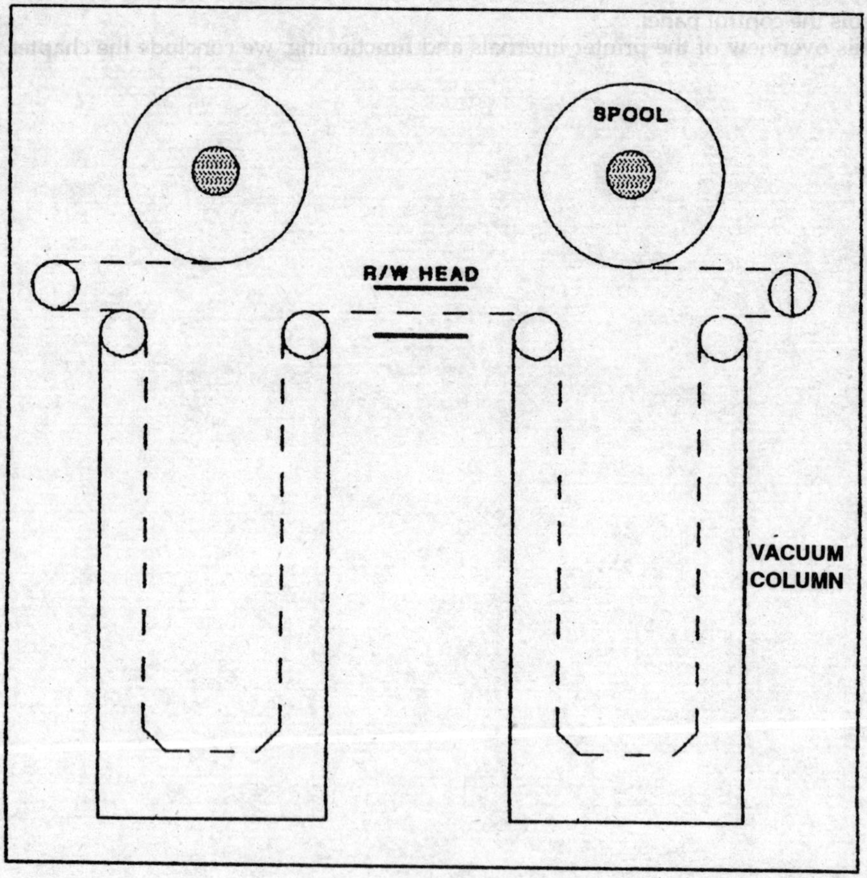

Fig. 13.1 : A MAGNETIC TAPE DRIVE

13.1 MAGNETIC TAPE.

Magnetic tapes provide serial access of data. The magnetic tape used for recording information has an iron-oxide coating on it. Magnetization of this iron-oxide coating is done to form magnetized and non-magnetized spots. Magnetized spots represent a binary one while non-magnetized spots represent binary zero. The magnetized and non-magnetized spots are arranged in tracks, which run along the length of the tape. Normally the tape is divided into nine tracks, all running parallel to the tape's edge. Varying densities of recording is possible. Typically 1600 bits per inch (bpi) density tapes are used, but it is possible to locate 6250 bpi tapes in the market. The capacity of a tape depends on the recording density, measured in bpi, length of the reel and the total length of the tape actually used for information recording.

Fig 13.1 shows a typical magnetic drive. Two tape spools are shown in the figure. One spool supplies the tape, while the other collects it. The operation is very much similar to that of an audio or video cassette. Two vacuum columns are used to keep the tape in a released condition, thus preventing accidental snapping of the tape, when the tape starts or stops moving. A electromagnetic head is used to read or write information to the tape. The standard tape width is half an inch.

Magnetic tape is used when a large amount of data must be stored and processed sequentially, as in payroll processing. It is commonly used to back up data and software and to transport data from one location to the other.

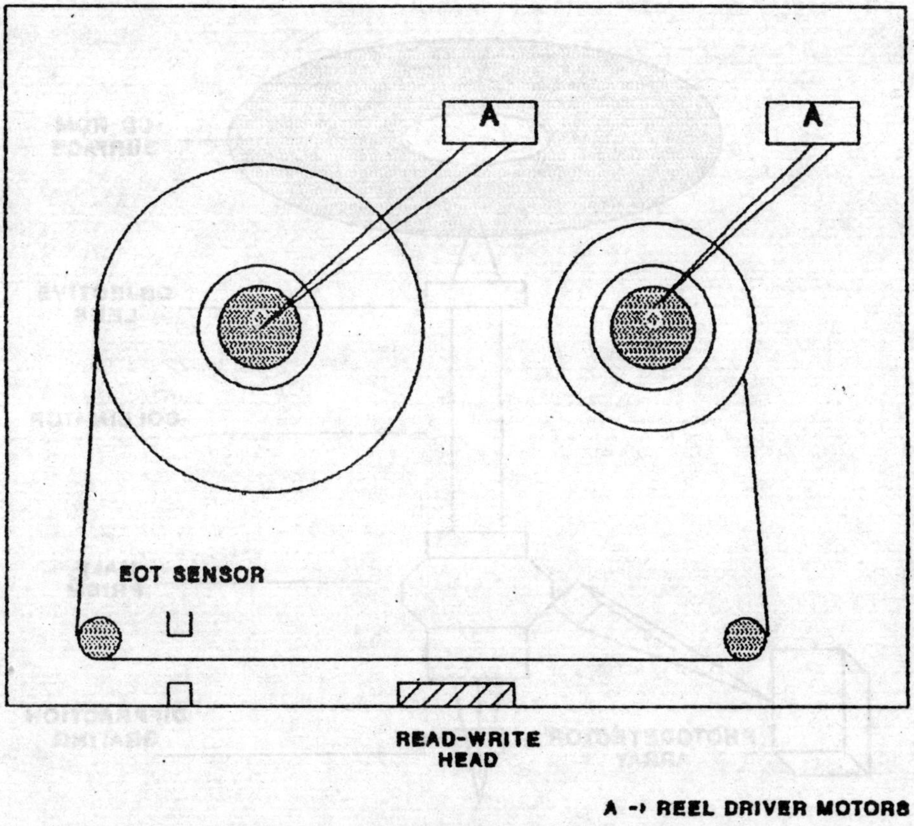

Fig. 13.2 : A MAGNETIC CARTRIDGE DRIVE

13.2 MAGNETIC CARTIDGE

The cartridge can be regarded as a compact version of the magnetic tape drives, inspired by the design of audio cassettes. The tape is half an inch wide and generally four tracks are provided. A reasonable high recording density of about 1600 bpi (bits per inch) is possible. Fig.13.2 shows a magnetic cartridge drive. Most cartidge manufacturers put a uniform "clock track" on the reverse side of the tape. This clock track is used to control the hub drive motor to give the tape a constant speed. This track is solely responsible for speed control and nothing else. Data is recorded on the other side only. A EOT sensor is used to determine the end of tape.

A hole is made in the tape towards the end of the ribbon. When this hole coincides with the EOT sensor light passes through it. This causes the control electronics to stop the reel drive motor. Had this feature not been incorporated, the chances of the tape being torn apart would have been bright !

13.3 OPTICAL DISK

This is a new family of storage devices, which uses optical technology to read information or to control the read-write head. The various types of optical disks now available are Compact Disk Read only Memory (CD-ROM), Write Once Read Memory (WORM), Flopticals and Magneto Opticals. Let us start our discussion with CD-ROM and WORM.

13.3.1 CD-ROM and WORM

A single silvery plastic disk, commonly known as platter is used to store data. CD-ROM uses the same coated, plastic platters as used for digital audio recording. Laser/Optical disk technology is used

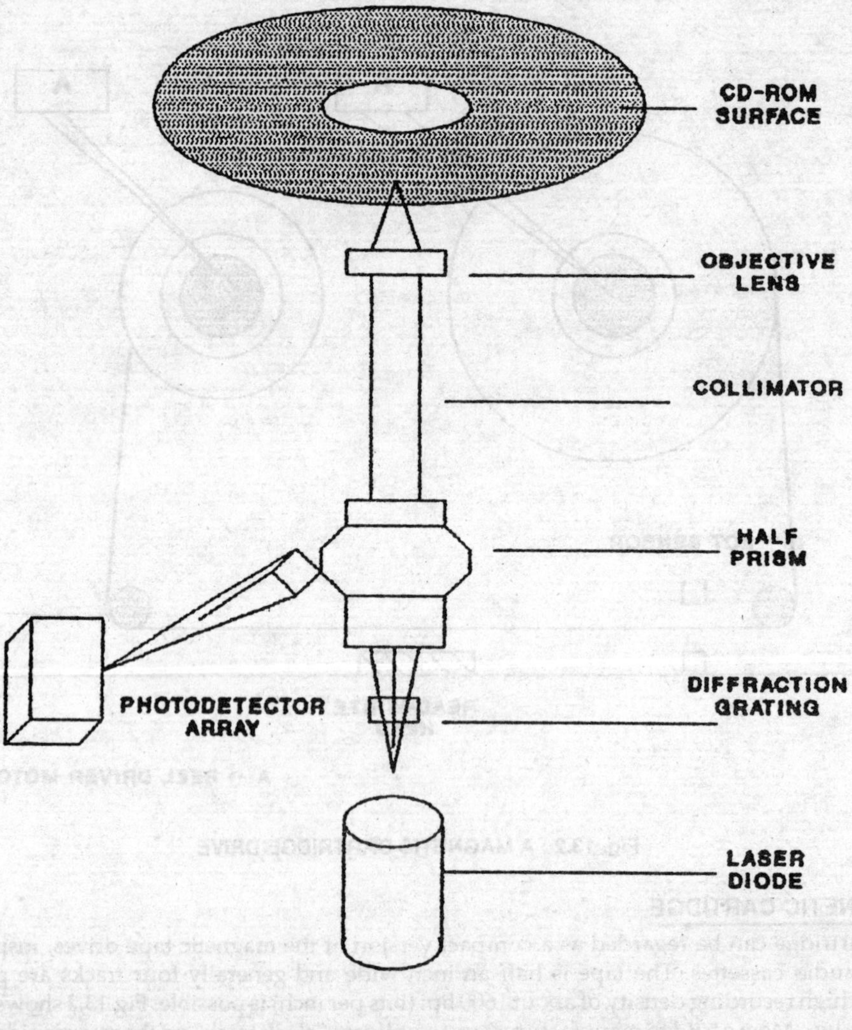

Fig. 13.3 : RECORDING ON CD-ROM SURFACE

to store information on the platters. A laser beam is used to burn tiny spots onto the disk coating. The playing surface is coated with a thin aluminium film, and this reflects the scanning laser beams of the CD-ROM disk drive, while reading the disk.

Let us now go into the details of reading the disk. A semiconductor laser diode acts as a source of the laser beam. Since the CD is tightly packed with data, the laser has to focus precisely on the pits, which represent a binary one. To ensure precise focusing the laser is passed through a diffraction grating, which splits the laser beam into three separate beams-a primary beam and two secondary beams. The three beams pass through a half prism, then a collimator and then through the objective lens which ultimately converges the rays to a tiny spot. To compensate for the vertical fluctuations and abberations of the disk, the objective lens is always vibrating. A part of the beam which strikes the CD surface, is reflected back. The reflected beam passes through objective lens, collimator and half prism, to reach the photo detector array, where appropriate electrical signals are generated. Fig.13.3 illustrates this process.

CD-ROM allows the user to only read data. No provision for erasing and recording of data is given. But the computer industry is a very promising and agile one. It always works out the needs of the potential users. As a result we are now hearing about Erasable Compact Disk. If this happens, there will be a large scale change in the mass storage scenario.

13.3.2 Magneto Optical Disk

Magneto Opticals (M O) are a type of optical technology based disks, which offer multiple writing on the disk. These disks are coated with special magnetic materials, which are unaffected by magnetism at low temperatures but polarize at high temperatures. To record data, laser beam is used to heat the MOs surface, and magnetism is used to polarize it. This represents the binary one. To read the MO, a weaker laser beam is used, which does not cause enough heating to polarize the magnetic particles, thus preventing erasure of recorded material during reading of the disk. Two configurations are available: internal configuration which plugs to the bus or to the SCSI host and the external configuration which is connected to the parallel port. They are now slowly becoming popular.

13.3.3 Flopticals

These disks use Barium Ferrite based magnetic coating to record information. The read/write head unit is magnetic, but optical servo head positioning is done. This results in larger number of track accesses, almost as high as 1245 TPI. These can store as much as 21MB of data. The biggest plus point of floptical drives, is their backward compatibility with traditional drives. They are now becoming a standard for mass data storage.

14.0 INTRODUCTION

As the utility power or the main input available to us is 220V AC, and almost all the electronic circuits operate with a DC supply of ±12V or ±5V, which means that the AC voltage has to be stepped down and converted into DC voltage of required value. The above said requirements are met by the POWER SUPPLY UNITS.

The POWER SUPPLIES are basically of two types i.e.,

1. LINEAR POWER SUPPLY
2. SWITCHED MODE POWER SUPPLY

14.1 LINEAR POWER SUPPLY

It consists of a transformer which is used to step-up or step-down the voltage, in addition, it also provides the input/output isolation for safety purposes. Two rectifiers rectify the AC into pulsating DC. A filter capacitor smooths out the pulsating DC into pure DC. A series pass element Q1 (transistor) operates in linear mode (hence the name LINEAR POWER SUPPLY) and the linear control circuit which compares a sample of the output with the fixed reference provides the power biasing to the series pass element, which in turn down steps the differential voltage of input and output to maintain a constant output voltage. Another capacitor is used to smooth the output.

14.2 SWITCHED MODE POWER SUPPLY (SMPS)

It consists of a bridge rectifier which rectifies the AC into pulsating DC,a filter capacitor which smooths out the pulsating DC into pure DC, a switching element (transistor / MOSFET) which operates in saturation or cut off mode (Hence the name Switched Mode Power Supply), a pulse width modulator (PWM) which compares the sampled output with a fixed reference and in turn adjusts the pulse width of the Switching element to get a fixed output, an inductor and a capacitor to form the filter to provide the pure DC output and a diode which provides the free wheeling path for the inductor current.

In a linear power supply, the series pass element has to dissipate the power equal to the product of the voltage drop across it (input output) and the output currrent, which is in the form of power loss. Because of this power loss, it has a very poor efficiency and as the frequency of operation is the line frequency, the size of the filter is large and also the loss in the devices calls for a fairly large heat sink, which means that the power supply is going to be very bulky and costly. Using Switching element at higher frequency makes the SMPS very compact and highly efficient.

14.2.1 Functional Description

The O/P voltage is controlled by either varying the duty cycle or frequency of the oscillator or both. The signals turn the switching transistor ON or OFF.

The Oscillator allows the control element to be switched ON and OFF. The control element usually consists of a transistor switch an inductor and a diode.

For each switching ON, the energy is pumped into the magnetic field associated with the inductor. This energy is released to the load at a desired voltage. By varying the duty cycle or frequency of switching, we can vary the stored energy in each cycle and thus control the output voltage. The switch can be only ON or OFF, thus it allows either energy to pass or stops it, but does not dissipate energy in itself. The switching cycle will be in order of 15 to 40 KHz. This reduces the size of the transformer.

Regulation

A switching power supply is regulated essentially by changing either the "Switch-ON" period or the repetition rate of switching or both.

When the power is switched ON, power is pumped into coil and thus induces energy into it. This energy is released to the O/P via a fast recovery diode into the capacitor. The O/P voltage is smooth DC. As the load varies the O/P, voltage drops. This is compensated by increasing the pulse width during which the current increases in the coil. More width means more time for current to rise to a greater value causing increased storage of magnetic energy and at that time O/P voltage becomes higher than normal value. It can be decreased quickly by fully cutting OFF or reducing the pulse width depending upon the O/P voltage requirement.

14.2.2 Specification

AT SMPS

INPUT AC VOLTAGE 180-260V 50Hz WATTAGE 200W OUTPUT

1)	+5V	20A	-RED
2)	+12V	7.5A	-YELLOW
3)	-5V	.5A	-WHITE
4)	-12V	.5A	-BROWN
5)	P.G.	-	-ORANGE

XT SMPS

INPUT AC VOLTAGE 180-260V 50Hz WATTAGE 135W OUTPUTS

1)	+5V	15A	-RED
2)	+12V	4.5A	-YELLOW
3)	-5V	.5A	-BLUE
4)	-12V	.5A	-BROWN
5)	P.G.	-	-WHITE

14.3 INSTALLATION INSTRUCTIONS

1. Fix the SMPS to the system properly.
2. Connect the power supply to the system motherboard using two Burndy connectors.
3. The connector details are as shown below.

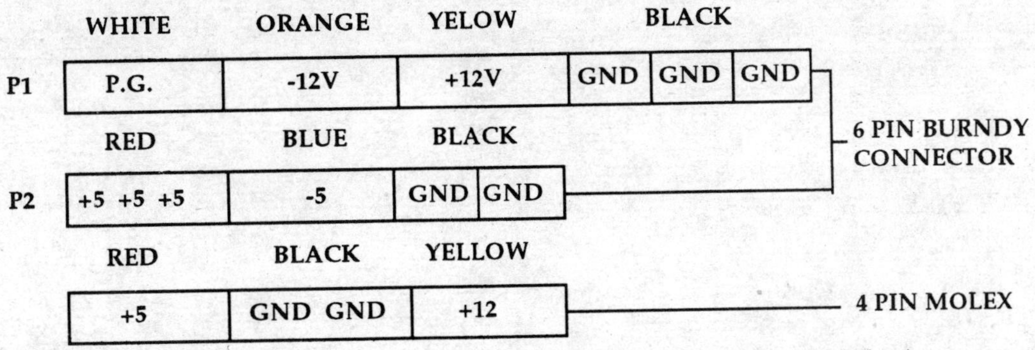

4. Connect the P1 Burndy connector in such a way that the Power Good Signal (White) comes near the keyboard connector side.
5. Connect the P2 Burndy connector so that the three +5V signals come as the last (10, 11, 12).
6. Then make sure that the four Ground wires (Black) are coming in a sequential order.
7. Connect the four pin Molex connector to the Hard disk, Floppy drive etc. This connector will go in only one way.
8. Confirm all the connections are correct and switch on the SMPS.

14.4 PROTECTION CIRCUITS

Soft start :

When AC power is initially applied the DC bus filter and capacitors have no charge and very high rise in current would result if current limiters is not used.

In addition to rush current limiting, it is vitally important to limit the collector current of the power switching transistors to be within their capability, both during initial charging of the output filter and during normal over loads of the output voltage.

This is done by a control circuit which limits the rate of increase of pulse width during start up and senses the primary current of the power transistors.

Current limiting :

A current transformer continuously monitors the current in the power switch and at a pre-determined peak level triggers the soft starting circuit. This crowbars the DC bias to the timing circuit of the one shot thus removing drive pulsing the power switches. A reset circuit then unlatches allowing the power supply to restart normally with the soft start circuit if an overload condition is once again detected. The shut down and restart procedure is repeated. This occurs with a repetition rate of around once per second until the over load condition ceases.

Auxiliary Supply :

This has got one step down transformer form 23V AC to 12V and ordinary full wave rectifier and a capacitor filter. This is the supply for control IC (more than 12V DC).

PROJECTS

Computer Network - What is that !

Connecting two or more computers for information flow is networking. Computers are networked using communication media, like ordinary twisted wires that we use for our telephone sets or coaxial cables, which are also used for Cable Television connections or fibre optics. Even radio or satellite channels can be used for networking. The hardware involved in networking are the media and a network interface unit which is to be present in each computer that is in the network.Practically these NIUS often come as separate adapter cards and control the flow of electric signals (logical bits) to or from the network media. Almost in all computer networks there is a network operating system which supervises the function of the network and provides to the network users a set of services for utilisation of the network facilities. The NOS is in addition to the computers own operating system.

Computer Networks have been broadly classified into LANs (Local Area Network). and WANs (wide Area Networks). LANs are generally owned by a single organisation and confine within a room, a building or a campus. They provide a high data transmission speed.

WANs are realised by connecting the computer to the telephone line using a device called MODEM (Modulator demodulator), since the data transmission is over the telephone network. A computer can access another computer in any corner of the world provided the other computer is also hooked to telephone line.

As already discussed media is connected to the computer through an NIU. Popular NIUs have been Ethernet Cards, ArcNet cards, serial ports and very lately parallel ports.

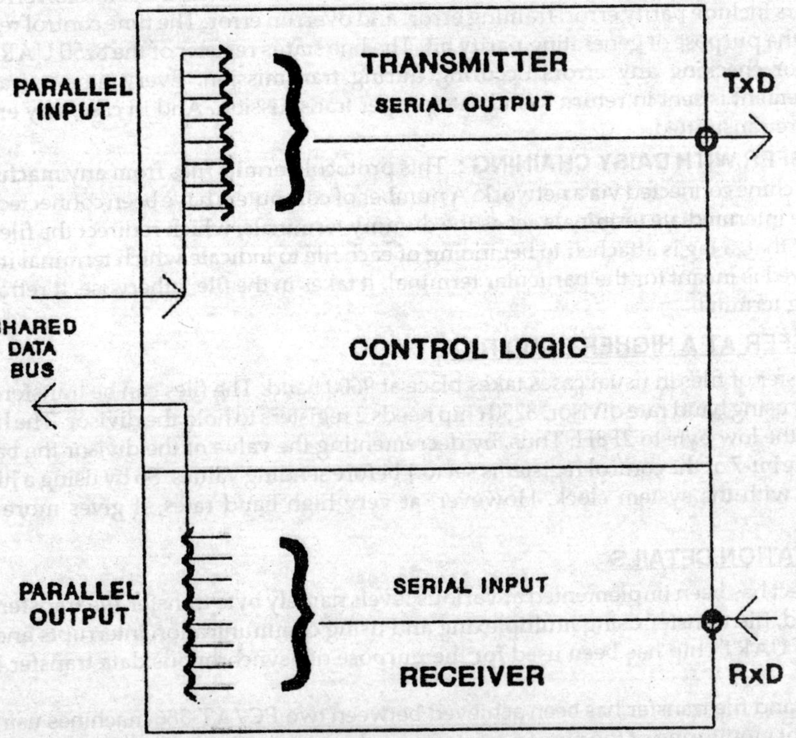

Fig. BLOCK DIAGRAM OF AN UART

In the next section we have provided four project reports, three out of what are based on networking. These projects have been carried in our Institute and have been successful.The reader will be benefitted by the hardware, software and communication aspects of these projects.

PROJECT NUMBER ONE - Development of a File Transfer system over serial ports.

PROJECT OVERVIEW

In this project, a high speed local area network has been developed using the serial ports of the connected machines. A number of protocols have been developed for the above purpose. These includes

BYTE TRANSFER PROTOCOL : This is a bidirectional protocol which permits data transfer in either direction simultaneously. Data is sent in form of bytes one after the other. Continous monitoring of the serial port status has been done for the above purpose.

REMOTE LOGIN : This protocol permits a user on a PC to login to an UNIX based system. The PC can access and share the resources of the UNIX system namely memory and processor time for doing its operation. In that respect, it can serve as a dumb terminal to a larger mainframe along with its usual functions.

FILE TRANSFER PROTOCOL :

This permits files to be transferred from one machine to another machine, as and when requested. One of the PC which is sender uses the sender protocol for sending the file and the other (receiver PC) uses the receiver protocol for receiving the same. The data present in the file is transferred in form of bytes, one after the other serially, till the end of the file is reached.

An error checking routine has been provided to take care of various transmission errors. The various kinds of errors include parity error, framing error, and overrun error. The time control register has its bit 3 set to 1 for the purpose of generating parity bit. The line status register of the 8250 UART chip has been monitored for checking any errors occuring during transmission. Every time a frame is sent, an acknowledgement is sent in return to indicate proper transmission. And in case, any error is detected, the frame is retransmitted.

FILE TRANSFER WITH DAISY CHAINING : This protocol permits files from any machine to be sent to any other machine connected via a network. A number of computers have been connected for the desired purpose. The intermediate terminals act as the dummy terminals, which redirect the files to the desired terminal. For that, a tag is attached to beginning of each file to indicate which terminal it is meant for. If the file received is meant for the particular terminal, it takes in the file, otherwise, it retransmits it to the neighbouring terminal.

FILE TRANSFER AT A HIGHER BAUD RATE :

The transfer of files in usual cases takes place at 9600 baud. The files can be transferred at different baud rates by using baud rate divisor. 8250 chip needs 2 registers to hold the divisor. The high byte is sent to 2F9H and the low byte to 2F8H. Thus, by decrementing the value of the divisor the baud rate can be increased. The bit-7 of the control register is set to 1 before sending values. So by using a higher baud rate it can match with the system clock. However, at very high baud rates, it gives more errors in data transmission.

IMPLEMENTATION DETAILS

The project has been implemented at various levels namely byte transfer,file transfer,file transfer at a higher speed, file transfer using multiplexing and using communication interrupts and remote logic.

The 8250 UART chip has been used for the purpose of asynchronous data transfer (input-output) operations.

The byte and file transfer has been achieved between two PC/AT-386 machines using status check where constant monitoring of the input port status has been done. Depending on the status of input port, the sender or the receiver portions are executed. In case of file transfer, the file name stored in form of a string is sent via the communication line, followed by a control character indicating the end of filename. It is followed by file transfer routine, which transmits the file by byte serially, till the end of file is reached. The error checking is done to check for any errors taking place during transmission and allows subsequent retransmission of the error frame.

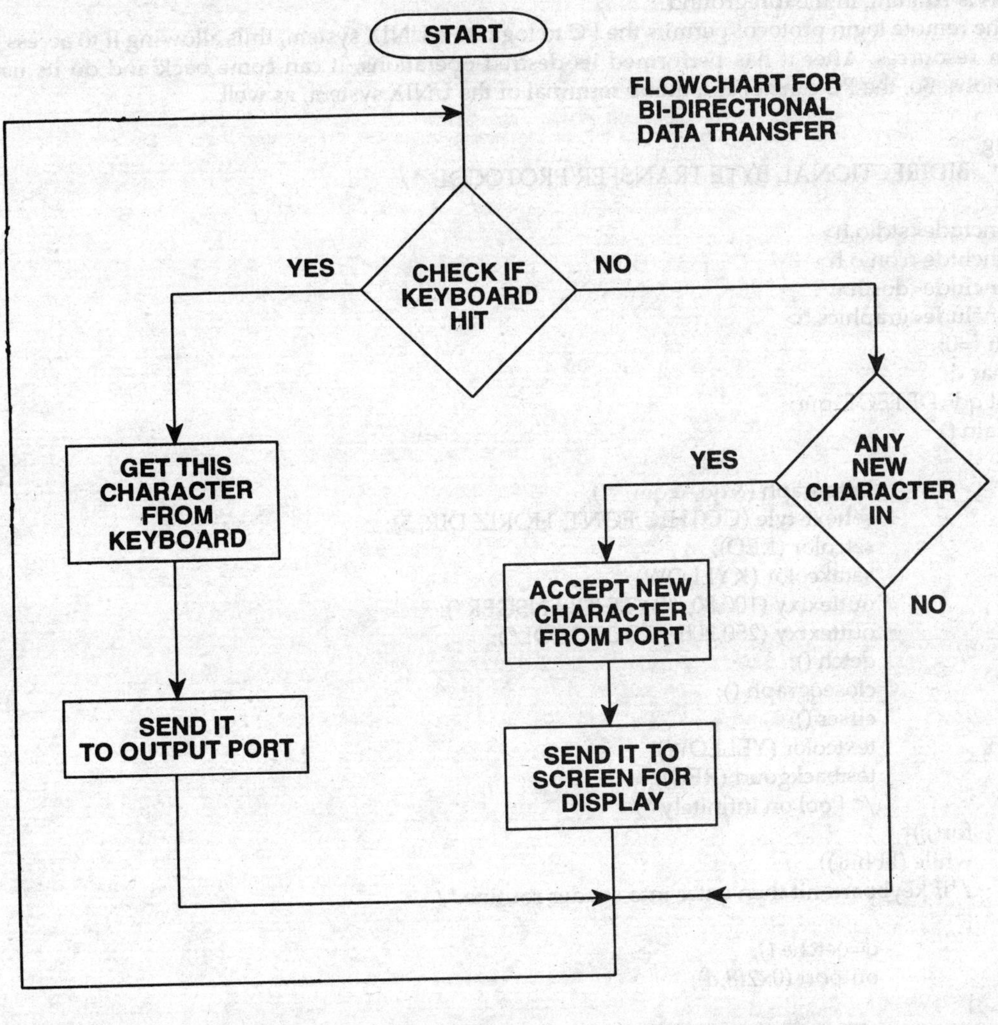

Fig. A : FLOWCHART FOR BI-DIRECTIONAL DATA TRANSFER

The file transfer protocol with multiplexing provides file to be transferred from any computer to any other computer, connected via a network, not just its immediate neighbours. The two serial ports namely COM1 and COM2 has been used for the desired purpose. Depending on the destination machine, a tag is attached to the data frame. The destination machine recognises its tag and starts storing it into its input buffer. If the file is not meant for that machine, it simply passes it on to its neighbouring machine. Here we have used point to point network topology.

File transfer at a higher speed has been achieved by modifying the baud rate by using baud rate divisor. Two registers are required for storing the baud rate divisor namely 2F8H and 2F9H. In our project, the baud rate has been adjusted to 19200 and higher. Bit 7 of the control register is set to 1 before baud rate adjustment is done.

File transfer using communication interrupt has been implemented for the purpose of facilitating better usage of computer resources such as CPU time. By setting up an interrupt, control is transferred to a data transmission routine only when the transmitter holding register is empty and control reverts to the program once a byte of data is sent, allowing the program to continue until the transmitter holding register is ready again. In this process, data transfer can take place at the background while another process is running in the foreground.

The remote login protocol permits the PC to login to a UNIX system, thus allowing it to access the system resources. After it has performed its desired operations, it can come back and do its usual operations. So, the PC can act as a dumb terminal of the UNIX system, as well.

```
Fig.
/*  BIDIRECTIONAL BYTE TRANSFER PROTOCOL  */

#include<stdio.h>
#include<conio.h>
#include<dos.h>
#include<graphics.h>
int f=0;
char d;
int qd=DETECT .qm;
main ()
{
        initqgraph (&qd, &qm,"");
        settextstyle (GOTHIC FONT, HORIZ DIR, 5);
        setcolor (RED);
        setbkcolor (KYLLOW);
        outtextxy (100,80, "BYTE TRANSGER");
        outtextxy (250,200, "PROTOCOL");
        qetch ();
        closeqgraph ();
        clrscr ();
        textcolor (YELLOW);
        testbackgoud (RED);
        /* Pool on infinitely */
    for(;;){
    while (kbhit())
    /*if keyboard hit then enter into sender routine */
    {
        d=qetche ();
        outport (0x2f8,d);
    }
        if(f==0) {
        printf ("\n");
        f=1;
      /* if not keyboard hit enter into receiver routine */
      /* prevent data duplication */
            if((inport (0x2fd) & (0x01))==1) {
            d=inport(0x2f8);
            printf("%c",d)
    }
    }
```

```
/* FILE TRANSFER PROTOCOL WITH MULTIPLEXING */
#include<stdio.h>
#include<conio.h>
#include<stdlib.h>
#include<dos.h>
#include<ctype.h>
```

```
#include<string.h>
#include<graphics.h>
main ()
{
char c, *str,ans;
int i,tno;
int qm, qd=DETECT;
FILE *fpt;
initgraph (&qd, &qm,"");
settextstyle(TRIPLEX FONT,HORIZ DIR,5);
setcolor(YELLOW);
setbkcolor (BLUE);
outtextxy(45,100,"FILE TRANSFER PROTOCOL ");
outtextxy(120,220, "WITH MULTIPLEXING" );
getch ();
closeqraph ();
clrscr();
textcolor(YELLOW);
textbackground(BLUE);
printf("Do you wanna send a file(Y/N)");
scanf("%c",&ans);
if(toupper(ans)=='Y'){
printf("Enter the terminal to which to be sent");
scanf("%d",&tno);
/* select terminal to which file is to be sent */
if(tno==1)
c='*';
else if(tno==2)
c='&';
else
c='^';
/* attach taq for the particular terminal */
outport(0x2f8.c);
printf("Enter name of file to be transferred ");
scanf("%s",str);
fpt=fopen(str, "r");
        /* file being sent to other terminal */
        do
        {
        outport(0x2f8.c=qetc(fpt));
        printf("%c".C);
        for(i=0;i<=10000;i++){}
        }while(!feof(fpt));/*continue till end of file is reached */
    /* send a taq to indicate the end of file */
    c='@' ;
    outport(0x2f8.c);
    getch();
    fclose(fpt);
    }
    else
    {
        c=inport(0x2f8);
        /*check if file is meant for that terminal */
        if(c== '!')
```

```
{
printf("Enter the file in which to be copied ");
scanf("%s",str);
fpt=fopen(str,"w");
if((inport(0x2fd)& (ox01))==1){
c=inport(0x2f8);
}
c='.';
/*copying file into the specified file name */
do{
if((inport(0x2fd)&(0x01))==1){
c=inport(0x2f8);
fprintf(fpt,"%c",c);
printf("%c,c);
}
}while(c!='@');
printf("File copied!!!");
getch();
fclose(fpt);
}
else
{
/*sending file to the other terminal if file is not meant*/
/*for that terminal */
printf("Sending to %d terminal",tno);
outport(0x2f8,c);
    do
    {
        c=inport(0x2f8);
        outport(0x2f8.c);
    while(c!='@');
}

/* SENDING FILE AT A HIGHER SPEED */
#include<stdio.h>
#include<conio.h>
#include<stdlib.h>
#include<dos.h>
#include<ctype.h>
#inclue<string.h>
#include<graphics.h>
main()
{
char c,*str,ans;
int i, qd=DETECT, qm;
FILE *fpt;
initgraph(&qd,&qm"");
settextstyle (TRIPLEX FONT, HORIZ DIR, 5);
setcolor (YELLOW);
setbkcolor (GREEN);
outtextxy(140,80,"FILE TRANSFER"); outtextxy(250,180,"PROTOCOL");
getch();
closegraph();
clrscr();
```

```
printf("Do you wants a send a file (y/N)");
scanf("%c",&ans);
/* MODIFY BAUD RATE DIVISOR REGISTER FOR 19200 BAUD */
c=0x80;
outport(0x2fb,c);
c=0x06;
outport(0x2f8,c);
c=0x00;
outport(0x2f9.c);
if(toupper(ans)=='Y'){
printf("Enter name of file to be transferred ");
scanf("%s",str);
fpt=fopen(str,"r");
/* Open the file which is to be transferred */
do
{
outport(0x2f8,c=qetc(fpt));
printf ("%c",c);
while((inport(0x2fd)&(0x20))!=1){}
/* check whether transmitter holding register is empty */
}while(!feof(fpt));
c='@';
outport(0x2f8,c);
getch();
fclose(fpt);
}
else
{
    printf("Enter the file in which to be copied ");
    scanf("%s",str);
    /* Enter the filename for transferring */
    fpt=fopen(str,"w");
    if((inport(0x2fd)&(ox01))==1){
    c=inport(0x2f8;
    }
    do{
    if((inport(0x2fd)&(0x01))==1){
    c=inport(0x2f8);
    fprintf(pft,"%c",c);
    printf("%c",c);
    }
    }while(c!='@');
    /* proceed until it receives the terminating character */
    /* from other terminal                                */
    printf("File copied!!!");
    getch();
    fclose(fpt);
    }
}

/* ERROR CHECKING DURING FILE TRANSFER */ #include<stdio.h>
#include<conio.h>
#include<stdlib.h>
#include<dos.h>
```

```
#include<ctype.h>
#include<string.h>
#include<graphics.h>
main()
{
char c,*str,ans,d;
int i,e=0;
int qd=DETECT, qm;
FILE *fpt;
/* Documentation */
initgraph (&qd,&qm,"");
settextstyle(GOTHIC FONT,HORIZ DIR,6);
setbkcolor(RED);
setcolor(YELLOW);
outtextxy(100,80,"FILE TRANSFER");
outtextxy(350,200,"PROTOCOL");
getch();
closegraph();
clrscr();
textcolor(YELLOW);
textbackground (GREEN);
printf("\n\n");
printf("\n\tDo you want a send a file(Y/N)");
scanf("%c",&ans);
printf("\n");/* FILE SENDER PROTOCOL */
if(toupper (ans)=='Y'){
printf("\tEnther name of file to be transferred ");
scanf(f"%s",str);
printf("\n");
fpt=fopen(str,"r');
/* enabling parity bit (bit 3 or 2 fbh) and sending it to port */
c=0x08;
outport(0x2fb,c);
/*SENDING FILE */
do
{
outport(0x2f8,c=qetc (fpt));
printf("%c",c);
/* check whether entire byte is recieved */
/* checks if transmitter holding req. is empty */
while((inport(0x2fd)&(0x20))!=1){}
/* if error in transmission then retransmit */
d=inport (ox2f8);
if(d==' '){
—fpt;
++e;
}
}while)!feof(fpt));
/* file transmitted */
c= '@' ;   /*taq attached end of file */
outport(0x2f8,c);
printf("\n\n\t NUMBER OF RETRANSMISSIONS ARE %d",e);
getch();
fclose(fpt);
```

```
}
else
{
/* receiver protocol */
printf("\tEnter the file in which to be copied");
scanf("%s",str);
fpt=fopen(str,"w");

/* to prevent duplication of data */
if((inport(0x2fd)&(0x01))==1){
/* error checking */
/* Bit 1-overrun error, bit 2-parity error, bit 3-framing error in line status reg */
if(((inport(0x2fd)&(0x02))!=1)&&(inport(0x2fd)&(0x04)!=1)&&(inpot
(0x2fd)&(0x08)!=1))
c=inport(0x2f8); /*inport if no error */
/*sending a frame byte back to indicate proper receiving */
d=' ';
outport(0x2fd,d);
}
else
{
/* send a frame to indicate error in data */
d=' ';
outport(0x2f8,d);
}
}
do{
        if((inport(0x2fd)&(0x01))==1){
        if (((inport(0x2fd)&(0x02))!=1)&&(inport(0x2fd)&(0x04)!=1)
        &&(inport(0x2f8 & (0x08)!=)))
        {
        c=inport(0x2f8);
        fprintf(fpt,"%c",c);
        printf("\t%c",c);
        d= '@';
        outport(0x2f8,d);
        }
else
{
do ' ';
outport(0x2f8,d);
}
  }
/* proceed until all frames have been sent */
}while(c='@');
printf("\tFile copied!!!");
getch();
fclose(fpt);
     }
}
#include<stdio.h>
#include<conio.h>
#include<stdlib.h>
#include<dos.h>
```

```
#include<ctype.h>
#include<string.h>
#include<graphics.h>
main()
{
char c,*str,d;
int i,1;
int qd=DETECT, qm;
FILE *fpt;
/* Documentation */
initgraph (&qd,&qm,"");
settextstyle (COTHIC FONT,HORIZ DIR,6);
setbkcolor (RED);
setcolor (YELLOW);
outtextxy(100,80,"FILE TRANSFER ");
outtextxy(350,200,"PROTOCOL");
getch();
closeqgraph();
clrscr();
textcolor(YELLOW);
textbackground (GREEN);
printf("\n\n");
printf("\n\tDo you wanna send a file (Y/N)");
scanf("%c",&ans);
printf("\n");
/* SPEED SETTING IN DATA TRANSFER TO 19200 (Set bit 7 to 1)*/
c=0x80;
outport(0x2fb,c);
c=0x06;      /*Divisor is 6 for baud rate 19200 */
outport(0x2f8,c);
c=0x00;
outport(0x2f9,c);
/* FILE SENDER PROTOCOL */
if(toupper(ans)=='Y'){
printf("\tEnther name of file to be transferred ");
scanf("%s",str);
1=strlen(str);
for(i=0;i<=1;++i)
{
outport(0x2f8,*(str+i);
while ((inport(0x2fd)&0x20))!=1){}
}
c='~';
outport(0x2f8,c);
printf("\n");
fpt=fopen(str,"r");
/* enabling parity bit (bit 3 of 2 fbh) and sending it to port */
c=0x08;
outport(0x2fb,c);
/* SENDING FILE */
do
{
outport(0x2f8,c=qetc(fpt));
printf("%c",c);
```

```
/* check whether entire byte is recieved */
/* checks if transmitter holding reg. is empty */
while ((inport (0x2fd)&(0x20))!=1){}
/* if error in transmission then retransmit */
d=inport(0x2f8);
if(d==' ')
fpt;
}while (!feof(fpt);
/* file transmitted */
c='@';            */ taq attached to end of file */
outport(0x2f8,c);
getch();
fclose(fpt);
}
else
{
/* reciver protocol */
i=0;
while(c=inport(0x2f8)!='~')
{
if((inport(0x2fd)&(0x01)==1){
*(str+i)=c;
i++;
}
}
fpt=fopen(str,"w");
/* to prevent duplication of data */
if((inport(0x2fd)&(0x01))==1){
/* error checking */
/* Bit 1-overrun error, bit2-parity error, bit 3-framing error in line status */
if(((inport(0x2fd)&(0x02))!=1)&&(inport(0x2fd)&0x04)!=1)&&(inport
(0x2fd)&(0x08)!=1))
c=inport(0x2fd);  /*inport if no error */
/* sending a frame byte back to indicate proper receiving */
d= ' ';
outport(0x2f8,d);
}
else
{
/*send a frame to indicate error in data */
d=' ';
outport(0x2f8,d);
}
}
do {
if((inport(0x2fd)&(0x01))==1){
if(((inport(0x2fd)&(0x02)!=1)&&(inport(0x2fd)&(0x04)!=1)&&(inport(0x2fd)
(0xo8);
{
c=inport(0x2f8);
fprintf(fpt,"%c",c);
printf("\t%c",c);
d='@' ;
outport(0x2f8,d);
```

```
}
else
{
d=' ';
outport(0x2f8,d);
}
}
/* proceed until all frames have been sent */
}while(c!='@');
printf("\tFile copied !!!");
getch();
fclose(fpt);}
}
```

ACHIEVEMENTS

In this project, we have been able to implement a high speed cost effective LAN data transmission at a higher speed has been achieved by using the baud rate divisor present in the 8250 chip. No extra hardware has been used for the above purpose. Error free data transmission has been made possible by use of acknowledgement frames for each of the correct data frame being sent. The cost effectiveness has been achieved by use of serial ports present in the computer. No special hardware devices such as interface cards has been used for the desired purpose. The cost of data transmission media has been reduced drastically by the use of networking ribbon. This is comparatively much cheaper than coaxial cable optical fibre and like.

FUTURE SCOPE OF PROJECT

Although the 8250 chip can be used for achieving a baud rate of 19200 and higher, errors start cruping in when the data transmission is at a higher baud rate.

To eliminate this effectively, we can use the chip 16550.This chip can transmit data without errors at a speed upto 1Mbps.

The change also implemented the daisy-chain networking of terminals. However this makes the terminals a dedicated one, which prohibits them exempting a foreground process. To avoid this, we can run the program in background via interrupts which can facilitate the file transfer and other communication between the terminals in the background, while the computer is executing a program in the foreground.

This makes the network more efficient and data transfer more error free.

PROJECT NUMBER TWO - Development of a non-dedicated server over parallel ports

COMMUNICATION USING PARALLEL PORTS

Communication - can be explicitly defined as the transfer of signals over a channel. In Asynchronous Communication, the machine sends or receives bytes of information/data one bit at a time. Here the timing between the bytes of data is not important, but the timing of the sequence of bits that make up the byte is critical. The signal on the line goes high or low corresponding to the logical 'Ones' and 'Zero' and the line is said to be marking (in transfer mode) when the level is high (= 1) and to be spacing when the level is low (= 0).

The line is held in the marking condition whenever it is not transfering data. At the onset of the transmission of a byte of data, the signal drops to 0 during the start bit. Then the eight bits of data (sometimes fewer) follow as a pattern of highs and lows. The last data bit is optionally followed by a parity bit used in error detection, and then the sequence concludes with 1 or more stop bits, which comprise of a high signals.

In addition to the above restrictions both the transmitting and receiving station must be using

* the — same protocols
* and — same transmission speed (baud rate).

The serial hardware offers a variety of status information both for the port and the modem for error detection. The modem converts the signal generated by the serial port into an analog form for transmission across phone lines.

Chips used for forming and timing the strings of bits that comprise the serial data are referred to as Universal asynchronous receiver transmitter or UART. The IBM microcomputers uses the INTEL 8250 (UART). DOS supports two communication ports and hence two UARTS. Their base addresses are kept at 0040:0000 for COM1 and 0040:0002 for COM2. The serial interface is compatible to the RS 232 C specification.

Compared to just two serial ports DOS can handle 3 parallel devices (LPT1, LPT2 and LPT3). The parallel interface is called the printer adapter or parallel port (centronics Interface). It may be physically present as a seperate printer adapter board or as a port in the

- MDA BOARD
- Multiple Input/Output Board
- Mother Board
- CGP/MGP.

Each parallel device has its own adapter. An adapter is manipulated through three input/output registers and the port addresses of these registers are different for each adapter as specified in the table below :

Port Name	Decoded Signal	Port Address (MDA Board)	Port Address (Printer Address Main)	Port Address (Printer Adapter Additional)
Data Out	WPA	3BC	378	278
Command Out	WPC	3BE	37A	27A
Status In	RPB	3BD	379	279
Data In	RPA	3BC	378	278
Command In	RPC	3BE	37A	27A

Fig. Port Address Summary

The BIOS data area contains the lowest address of the group of 3 port addresses. The base address for the ports are :

i) LPT1 — 0040:0008
ii) LPT2 — 0040:000A
iii) LPT2 — 0040:000C

The base address is initialized to 0 when no corresponding adapter is installed.

The system software recognises three different parallel interfaces LPT1, LPT2, LPT3. Usually the parallel interface in MDA board is the primary parallel port, LPT1. The parallel interfaces present in multiple-I/O board or in the printer adapter board become secondary ports LPT2,

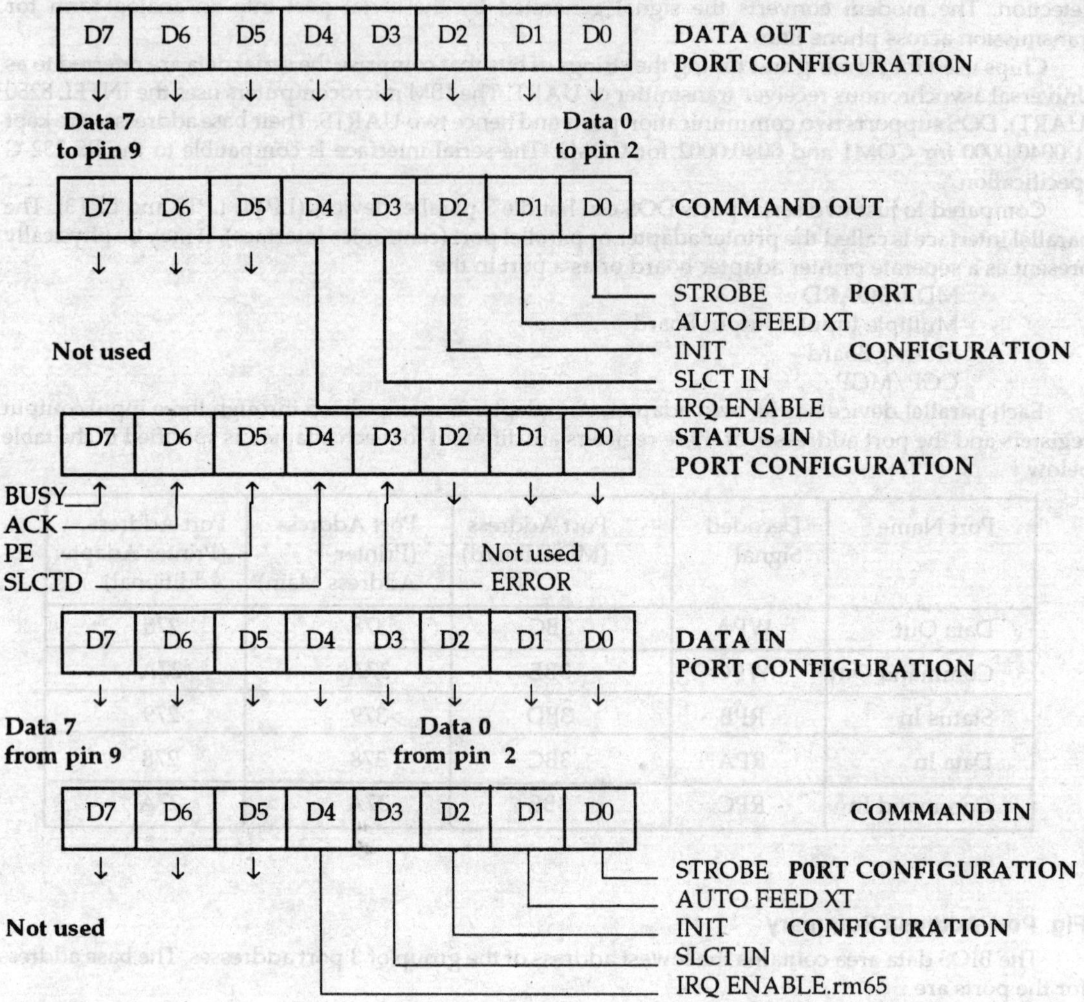

LPT3, etc. If the MDA board is not present in a PC, the BIOS assigns one of the secondary parallel ports as LPT1. Jumpers are provided in the multi I/O board and printer adapter so that different port addresses can be set.

Centronics Interface:

The centronics Interface provides a handshake protocol between a computer and a printer and supports a maximum data transfer rate of about 100 kbytes per second which can be modified to suit the users need.

The printer side of the interface is a 36 pin connector and the PC side is a 25 pin D type connector. (Reference Fig. next page).

Input/Output port configurations:

The different registers used are

* Data Output Register is the port address to which each byte of data is sent on its way out.
* Status Register is the input register used for receiving data. In this,bit 0-2 are unused. CPU may monitor it continuously (in polling) to sense the signals of handshaking.

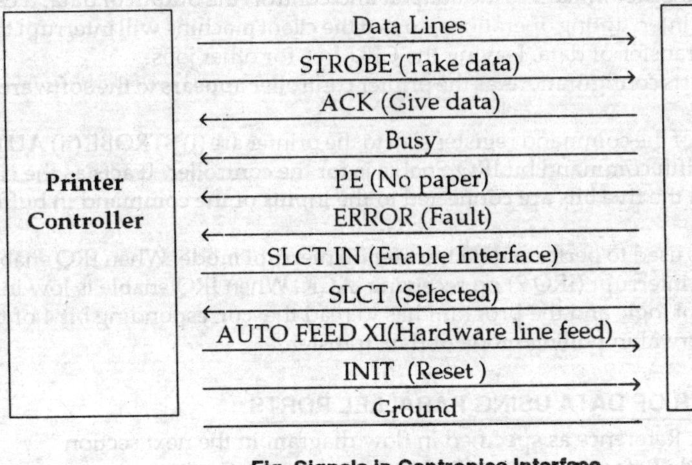

Fig. Signals in Centronics Interface

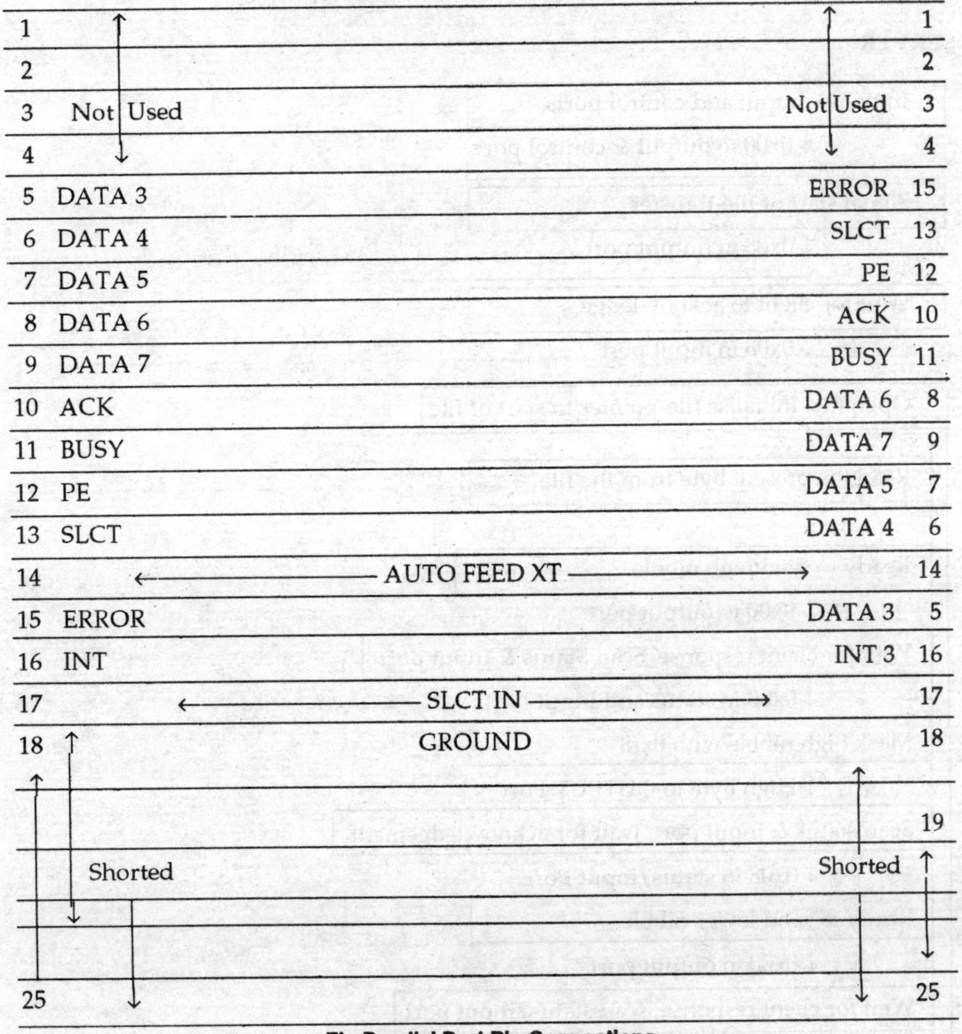

Fig Parallel Port Pin Connections

* control Register initializes the adapter and controls the output of data. It can also set the parallel Port for interrupting operations, so that the client machine will interrupt the CPU when it is ready for transfer of data, leaving the CPU free for other jobs.

The different I/O ports configurations as the printer controller appears to the software are specified in figure next page.

The four output bits of the command register sent to the printer are (i) STROBE (ii) AUTO FD XT (iii) INIT (iv) SLCT IN. The fifth command bit IRQ Enable is for the controller. It acts as the enabling input to the interrupt logic. All the five bits are connected to the inputs of the command in buffer in order to loop back the command.

The interrupt logic is used to perform data transfer in interrupt mode. When IRQ enable is high, the interrupt logic generates interrupt (IRQ 7) on receiving ACK. When IRQ enable is low interrupt is not generated by the interrupt logic and the program has to read the corresponding bit 4 of the (status in-port) to check for data arrival in polling mode of data transfer.

METHOD OF TRANSFER OF DATA USING PARALLEL PORTS

1) Polling Method : Reference as specified in flow diagram in the next section
2) Interrupt Method : Reference as specified in Server Design Section.

SERVER

Initialise output and control ports

↓ 0x00 to output & control port

Signal start of file-transfer

↓ 0x08 to output port

Wait for client to acknowledge

↓ 0x08 in input port

Open file, Initialise file-pointer to start of file

↓

Read the present byte from the file

↓

Ready to send high nibble

↓ 0x00 to output port

Wait for client response; Scan Status & Input port

↓ 0x00 in status and Input Port

Mask high nibble with 0xf8

↓ High byte to OUTPUT Port

Scan status & input port; wait for acknowledgement

↓ 0x08 in status/input Port

Ready to send lower nibble

↓ 0x00 to output port

Wait for client response; scan status/input port

↓ 0x00 in status/input Port

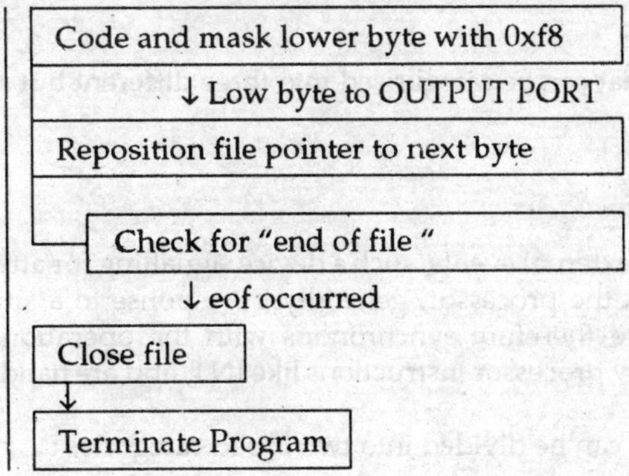

Fig. Logical flow sequence in Server Design

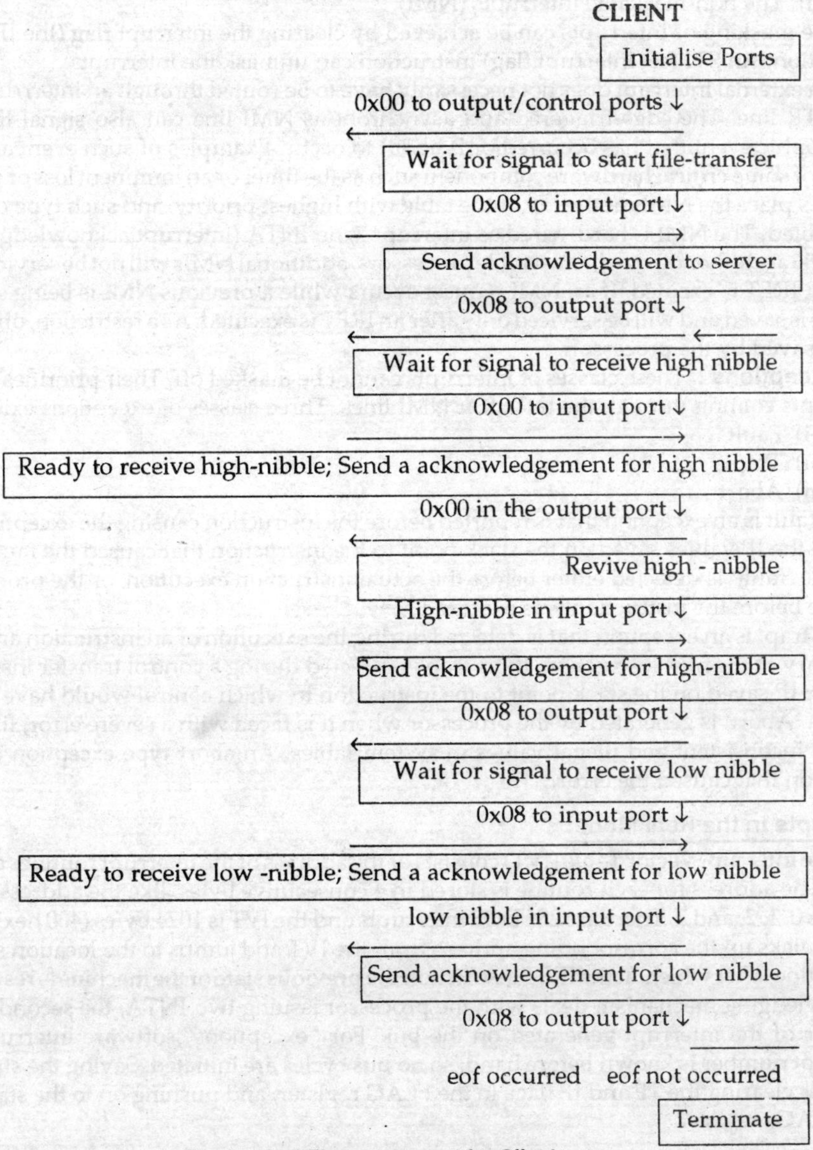

Fig. Logical Flow-sequence for Client

INTERRUPTS : AN OVERVIEW

Interrupts are control transfer mechanisms that can be categorised into three different but related types of events :-

i) the external interrupts,
ii) the exceptions,
iii) and the software interrupts.

The external interrupts are those triggered by external events, such a device signalling for attention. An exception on the other hand originate within the processor, generally in response to a situation detected while executing an instruction, and are therefore synchronous with the operations of a processor. The software interrupts are generated by processor instructions like INT, and are handled by the processors as if they were exceptions.

External Interrupts : The external interrupts can be divided into two broad categories :

i) The maskable interrupts
ii) The non-maskable interrupts (NMI).

The masking of interrupts can be achieved by clearing the interrupt flag (the IF flag) with the CLI instruction. An STI (set interrupt flag) instruction can unmask the interrupts.

An external interrupt does not necessarily have to be routed through an interrrupt controller or use the INTR line. The edge-triggered and asynchronous NMI line can also signal the processor, for a catastrophic event that has occurred or is about to occur. Examples of such event are bus parity error, failure of some critical hardware component such as the timer or an imminent loss of power. The priority schemes place the NMIs at the top of the table with highest priority, and such type of interrupts cannot be disabled. The NMI is hard-wired as interrupt 2, no INTA (interrupt acknowledge) are required. On the 80286 and other upward compatible processors, additional NMIs will not be serviced by the processor until an IRET is excuted. If an NMI request occurs while a previous NMI is being serviced the second request is saved and will be serviced only after an IRET is executed. As a restriction, only one NMI request can be saved by the processor.

Exceptions : These classes of interrupts cannot be masked off. Their priorities are higher than the interrupts coming through the INTER & NMI lines. Three classes of exceptions exist :

i) Fault
ii) Trap
iii) Abort

A fault is an exception that is reported before the instruction causing the exception is executed. The CS and the IP values saved on the stack point to the instruction that caused the fault.

The 'fault' is detected either before the actual instruction execution, or the processor is restored to its state before the instruction was executed.

A 'trap' is an exception that is detected during the execution of an instruction and is reported at the boundary of the next instruction. If the trap is detected during a control transfer instruction, the values of CS & IP saved on the stack point to the instruction to which control would have been transferred.

An 'Abort' is generated by the processor when it is faced with a severe error, like hardware errors and by inconsistent and illegal values in system tables. An abort type exception cannot identify the operation that caused the error.

Interrupts in the Real Mode:

The interrupt Vector Table (IVT) consists of the address of the interrupt routines existing in the ROM BIOS. The address for each routine is stored in 4 consecutive bytes, like the address for INTO is stored in bytes 0, 1, 2, and 3. There are 256 DOS interrupts and the IVT is 1024 bytes (400 hex) long. An interrupt issued picks up the corresponding address from the IVT and jumps to the location specified to execute the routine, after which, at the IRET instruction the previous state of the machine is restored. The interrupt acknowledging mechanism deals with the processor issuing two INTA, the second of which puts the number of the interrupt generated on the bus. For "exceptions",software interrupts and NMIs, the interrupt number is known before hand, so no bus cycles are initiated. Saving the status of the machine includes clearing the TF and IF flags in the FLAG register, and pushing on to the stack, the values of IP and FLAGs register.

Interrupts in the protected Mode:

Handling of interrupts in the protected mode is very similar to that in the real mode, except that there are more possible processor 'exceptions' in the protected mode, e.g. those generated by protection violations, virtual memory implementations or paging systems.

Lack of proper communication channel renders a superior subordinate relationship worthless. Preventing such a situation is the concern of the 8259A chip, which connects the various pieces of hardware like the timer, the keyboard processor, the COM1, the COM2, the disk, the diskette and the printer, to the 8086/88, via one interrupt input line. Upto eight different hardware interrupts can share this input line, with only one interrupt being recognised at a time. There exist priority schemes to resolve situatior:s like simultaneity of issue of more than one interrupt. Enabling and disabling interrupts independently is another feature of the 8259A. The 8288 bus controller chip is required to complete the IBM PC interrupt hardware.

The Interrrupt Mechanism:

The masking scheme renders worthless the interrupts that have been masked off. The priority scheme gives a priority number to the interrupts on the basis of which interrupt requests may be accepted.An incoming IRQ request to the 8259A chip sends an interrrupt to the 8088 CPU, by making the INT pin go high. This interrupt will be acknowledged by the CPU only if the interrupt enable flag (The flag) is high (in the flags register). The 8088 signals the bus controller (The 8288) via the status lines S0-S2 to put an interrupt- acknowledge to the 8259A onto the INTA bar line. The mechanism then calls for another such acknowledgement which triggers the 8259A to put the interrupt-number associated with the specific interrupt line on the bus. The CPU reads the incoming interrupt number and recognises the interrrupt. It completes the execution of the current statement and prepares for executing the interrupt routine corresponding to the incoming interrupt. The flags register is pushed onto the stack to save the present status of the machine. Next, the 'if' (interrupt enable flag) and the 'if' (trap flag) are cleared to prevent intervening of interrupts and traps. Furthermore, the code segment (cs) and the instruction-pointer (ip) are pushed on to the stack. The program counter (pc) then loads the 'cs' and 'ip' corrosponding to the Interrupt Service Routine (ISR) in question. The ISR is then executed till the 'iret' statement at the end of the ISR, after which the old status of the machine is restored by popping from the stack, the corresponding values of 'ip', and 'flags, and enabling the 'if' and the 'tf' flags.

The status of the 8259A is kept in three registers :

i) The Interrupt Request Register (IRR)
ii) The In-service Register (ISR)
iii) The Interrupt Mask Register (IMR)

The IRR keeps track of which interrupt input lines are requesting for service. The ISR contains a record of interrupts that are currently being processed. The IMR contains a record of which interrupts are turned-on (0 in the corresponding bit) or turned-off (1 in the corresponding bit). The 'priority-resolver logic' decides which lines requesting service will receive service. It takes into account, the IMR and the relative priorities of other inputs either requesting service or being serviced. Here, the highest priority-interrupts is chosen the CPU is informed via the control logic section, and when the INTA bar is received, the corresponding bit is set in the ISR. The read/write logic analyses input to the 8259A recognising various commands for initialising or changing the state of the processor. The cascade buffer/comparator is used when a number of 8259A, are cascaded in order to allow more than eight interrupts.

Features of the 8259A :

Interrupt Masking : Setting and resetting the bits in the IMR can turn individual interrupts off and on respectively. Turning an interrupt off, refers to ignoring the incoming interrupt whose corrosponding bit in the IMR register has been turned off. The IMR register can be accesed for reading or writing at the PCs I/O port 0x21. Moreover, to turn all interrupts off and on, the assembly language commands 'cli' (clear interrupt) and 'sti' (set interrupt) are sufficient. There also exists a 'Special mask mode' where the interrupt in service is disabled while all the other interrupts, irrespective of their priority level are disabled. On resetting the 'Special Mask', the operation reverts to its previous mode.

Interrupt Status Interrogation :

The status of the interrupt registers can be interrogated by two methods :

a) Reading the interrupt registers ISR, IRR, IMR b) Polling.

Reading the ISR and IRR are done in two steps involving the specification of the register (ISR, or IRR) in the first step and the value of the register in the second step.

Reading of the IMR is done from the port 0x21 directly. In case of polling, the CPU s/w issues a poll command to the 8259A. In case, interrupt requests are pending, the next read command from the CPU will cause the 8259A to put the interrupt no. of highest level interrupt into the data bus. The s/w running in the CPU must read this number and perform the transfer of control.

The Fully Nested Mode :

The priority levels of the hardware interrupts range from 0 to 7, 0 being the highest priority interrupt and others decreasing in priority in the reverse numerical order. For an incoming interrupt, the first check is made to see if any other interrupt with a priority higher than that of the incoming interrupt is in service or not. If so, then the incoming interrupt is ignored, otherwise the execution of the previous lower priority interrupt is suspended and the incoming interrupt is attended to. Also, only the interrupts having priority more than the incoming one are enabled.

SIMULATION OF A NON DEDICATED SERVER

The various aspects to be taken into consideration for the above have been mentioned clearly under subheadings, with the final proposed server design in form of a flow chart for ease in understanding and implementation.

Terminate yet Stay Resident programs :

There are basically 2 types of TSR's

1. Passive TSR's
2. Active TSR's

"Passive TSR's" often replace existing Software interrupt like the "BIC\Video Service". In this the TSR intercepts the calls that read or write to the screen, and access the video buffer directly thus increasing the display speed. Passive TSR's allow limited access since they can be invoked only by another program. They have the advantage of executing within the context of the calling program and run no risk of interfering with another process.

"Active TSR" is a program which is loaded into memory and is continually on the look out for the start up signal. The obvious advantage lies in its accessibility. The interrupt handlers in the ACTIVE TSR's actually service the interrupt routine as and when required along with the handling of all the exception conditions.

It is often required that one should explicitly take care in

1) Understanding how MSDOS uses stack
2) Determining when MSDOS is active
3) Determining whether a TSR can safely interrupt an active MSDOS function.
4) Monitoring the CRITICAL ERROR FLAG before actually invoking a TSR.

This is all due to the non re-enterant nature of MSDOS.

MSDOS Stacks :

The 8086 requires the permanent existence of a stack during its normal operations. The stack is requred to save the present status of the machine during interrupts and for implementing nested procedure calls. Instructions like, PUSH, POP CALL, RET and INT make exclusive use of the stack. The stacks are implemented in the normal memory space (mostly in the higher memory). The system may have unlimited number of stacks out of which only one can be the current stack, pointed to by the SS:SP register pair.

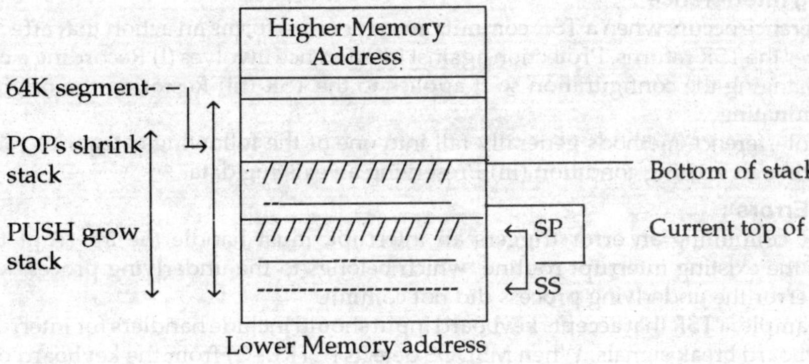

Fig. 8086 Stack Model.

Stack grows from higher memory to lower memory. Stack operations in the 80286 move 16-bit operands to the stack, while on the 80386 double word operation are available. They operate by adding or removing one word at a time in a LIFO (last in first out) basis. This is done by updating the stack pointer, never by moving or increasing stack entries.

MSDOS functions sets up their own stack which makes them Non-reenterant. MSDOS versions 2.0 or later uses 3 internal stacks namely (i) I/O stack (ii) Disk (iii) Auxillary stack.

MSDOS Activity :

The activity of MSDOS can be determined by the TSR's handler by consulting a 1-byte flag called the in DOS flag. Every MS-DOS function sets this flag upon entry and clears it upon termination. During installation a TSR locates the flag through function 34H (Get Address of InDOS flag), which returns the address as ES:BX flag without again calling function 34H.

Theoretically, a TSR can wait to execute until the InDOS flag is clear, thus side stepping the entire issue of interrupting MSDOS. However several low functions such as OAH (Get buffered Keyboard Input) wait idle for an expected key stroke before they terminate. If a TSR were allowed to execute after MSDOS returned, it too would have to wait for the terminating event. The solution lies in determining when the low order functions 01H through 0CH are active. MSDOS provides a mother service for this purpose the INT 28H (The idle interrupt).

Interrupting MSDOS functions

MSDOS continually calls interrupt 28H from the low order polling functions as they wait for keyboard input. This signal implies that MSDOS is idle and that a TSR may interrupt provided it does not overwrite the I/O stack or a TDR can safely interrupt MSDOS functions 01H through CH provided it does not call them.

An active TSR that calls MSDOS must monitor interrupt 28H, with a handler. When the handler gains control, it checks the TSR request flag. If the flag indicates the TSR has been requested and if system hardware is inactive, the handler executes the TSR. Since the control must eventually return to the idle MSDOS function which has stored data on the I/O stack, the TSR in this case must not call any MSDOS function that also uses the I/O stack. TSR's that perform tasks of long or indefinite duration, should themselves call interrupt 28H.

Monitoring the Critical Error Flag

MSDOS sets the critical error flag to a non zero value when it detects a critical error. It then invokes interrupt 24h (Critical Error Handle) and clears the flag when interrupt 24H returns. MSDOS functions higher than 0CH are illegal during the CRITICAL error processing. Therefore TSR that calls MSDOS must not execute while the CRITICAL error flag is set.

MSDOS versions 3.1 and later locate the critical error flag in the byte preceding the In DOS flag. A single call to 24H thus effectively returns the address of both flag. The operand field in the first instruction gives the flags offset. The value in the ES determines the segment address.

Preventing Interference :

Interference occurs when a TSR commits an error or performs an action that affects the interrupted process after the TSR returns. Protection against interference involves (i) Recording a current configuration (ii) Changing the configuration so it applies to the TSR (iii) Restoring the original configuration before terminating.

Non interference methods generally fall into one of the following categories : (i) trapping errors (ii) preserving an existing condition (iii) Preserving an existing data.

Trapping Errors :

A TSR commiting an error triggers an interrupt, must handle the interrupt to trap the error. Otherwise the existing interrupt routine, which belongs to the underlying process would attempt to service an error the underlying process did not commit.

For example, a TSR that accepts keyboard input should include handlers for interrupts 23H and 1BH to trap keyboard break signals. When MSDOS detects (CTRL+C) from the keyboard or input stream, it transfers control to interrupt 23H (CTRL+C) Handler. Similarly the BIOS keyboard routine calls interrupt 1BH (CTRL+BREAK) Handler when it detects CTRL + BREAK key combination. Both routines normally terminate the current process.

A TSR that calls MSDOS should also trap critical errors through interrrupt 24H (critical error handler) MSDOS functions call interrupt 24H when they encounter certain Hardware errors. A TSR must not allow the existing interrupt routine to service the error, since the routine might allow the user to abort service and return control to MSDOS. This would terminate both the TSR and the underlying process. By handling Int 24H the TSR returns control if a critical error occurs.

An error trapping handler differs in 2 ways from a TSR's other handlers.

1) It is temporary, in service only while the TSR executes. At start up the TSR copies the handler's address to the IVT, it then restores the original vector before returning.
2) It provides complete service for the interrupt, it does not pass control on to the original routine.

Error trapping handlers often set a flag to let the TSR know the error has occured.

Preserving an existing condition :

A TSR and its interrupt handlers must preserve register values so that all registers are returned intact to the interrupted process. The is usually done by pushing the registers onto the stack before changing them, then popping the original values before returning.

Setting up a new stack is another important safe gaurd against interference. A TSR should usually provide its own stack to avoid the possibility of over running the current stack.

Example - A TSR that alters the video configuration should return the configuration to its original state upon return. Video configuration includes the cursor position, cursor position, cursor shape, and video mode. The services provided through interrupt 10H enable a TSR to determine the existing configuration and alter it if necessary.

However some applications set video parameters by directly programming the video controller. When this happens BIOS remains unaware of the new configuration and consequently returns inaccurate information to the TSR. Unfortunately there is no solution to this problem if the controllers data registers provide write only access and thus cannot be querried directly.

Preserving Existing Data :

A TSR requires its own DTA if it calls MSDOS functions that access the DTA. These include file control block functions and functions 11, 12, 4E, 4FH. The TSR must switch to a new DTA to avoid overwriting the one belonging to the interrupted process. On becoming active, the TSR calls Function 2FH to obtain the address of the current DTA. The TSR stores the address and then calls function 1AH to establish a new DTA. Before returning the TSR again calls function 1AH to restore the address of the original DTA.

MSDOS versions 3.1 and later allow a TSR to preserve extended error information. This prevents the TSR from destroying the original information if it commits an MSDOS error. The TSR retrieves the current extended error data by calling MSDOS function 59H. It then copies registers AX, BX, DX, SI, DI, DS, ES, to a parallel word data structure in the order given.MSDOS reserves the last three words of the structure, which should each be set to zero. Before returning, the TSR calls function 5DH. With AL = 0AH and DS:DX pointing to the data structure. This call restores the extended error data to their original state.

Communication Through the Multiplex Interrupt :

The multiplex interrupt (2Fh) provides the microsoft approved way for a program to verify the presence of an installed TSR and to exchange information with it. MSDOS version 2.x uses INTERRUPT 2Fh only as an interface for the resident print spooler utility PRINT.COM. Later MSDOS versions standardised calling conventions so that multiple TSR's can share the interrupt. A TSR chains to the multiplex interrupt by setting up a handler. The TSR's installation code records the interrupt 2Fh vector and then replaces it with the address of the new multiplex handler.

A program communicates with a multiplex Handler by calling interrupt 2Fh with a unique identity number in the Ah register. As each handler in the chain gains control, it compares the value in Ah with its own id-no. If the handler finds that it is not the intended recipient of the call, it passes control to the previous handler. This process continues till control reaches the target handler. When the target handler finishes its tasks, it returns via an IRET instruction to terminate the interrupt.The target handler determines its tasks from the function number in AL. Conventionally Function 0 is used as a request for installation status. A multiplex handler must respond to Function 0 by setting AL to OFFh, to inform the caller of the handlers presence in memory. The handler should also return other information to provide completely reliable identification. For example it might return in ES:BX a far pointer to the TSR's copy right notice. This assures the caller it has located the intended TSR and not another TSR that has already claimed the id-no. in AH.

Identify numbers range from 192 to 255, since MSDOS reserves values for its own use. During installation a TSR must verify the uniqueness of its number and must not set up a multiplex handler identified by a number already in use.

SERVER DESIGN :

The proposed Non Dedicated Server can be implemented as shown in flow chart.

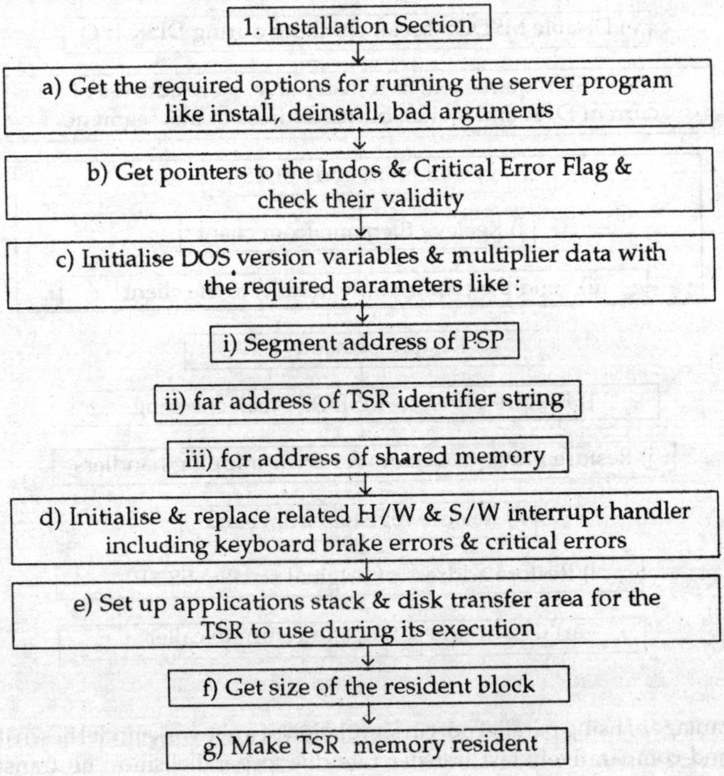

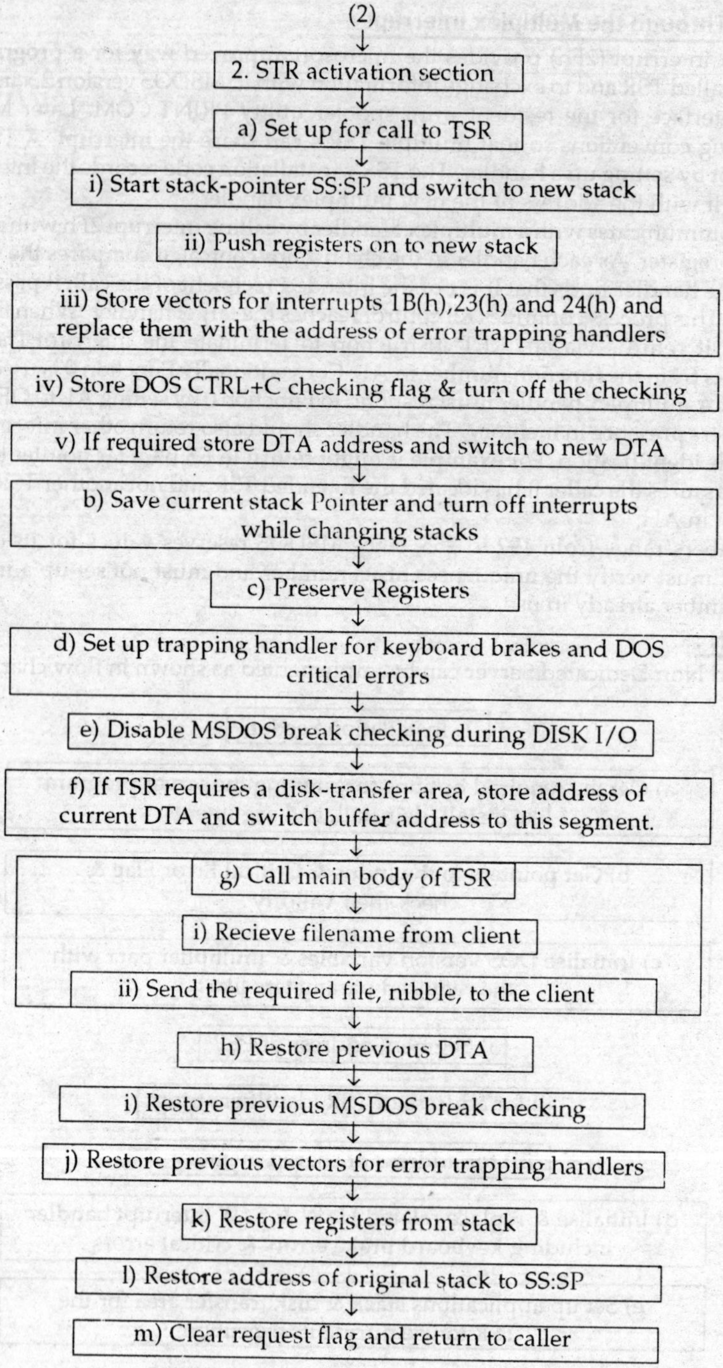

CONCLUSION

The basic advantage of using parallel port in simulation of a network model lies in its simplicity, ease of use, low cost and comparatively fast transfer rate due to parallelism in bit transfer. The network topology used consists of a dedicated, full duplex, point-to point wire connections between the system to be networked. Due to the modular design features of the program, modification and further enhancements can be incorporated in realising a full-fledged LAN, as specified in the figure below.

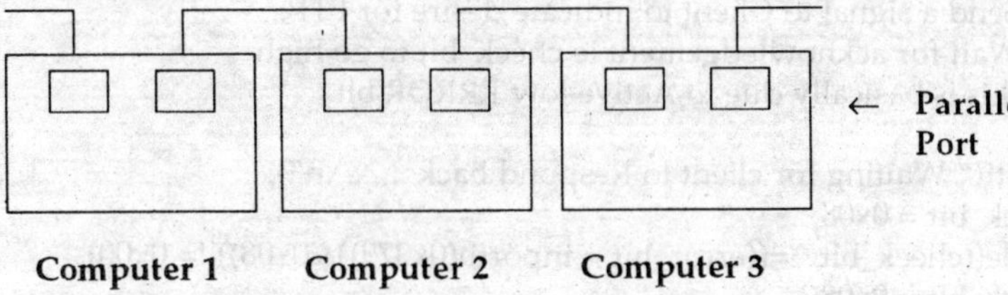

Fig. : LAN using parallel ports

It is clearly evident that the above figure is a typical example of LAN implementing "Daisy-Chaining". The proposed model of the non-dedicated server can be altered as per the needs of the user for a variety of handware interrupts compatible to the IBM PC AT.

Polling method of file transfer using parallel port. programs :

i) SERVER.C : The server program sends the file to the client using handshaking.
ii) CLIENT.C : The client program receives the file from the server using handshaking.

Interrupt mode of file transfer using parallel port. Programs :

i) SERV_CLI.ASM : Installs, Deinstalls and Services the printer interrupt IRQ7 generated by the Client.
ii) SERV_HAN.ASM : Contains all the hardware/Software initiated interrupt handlers for servicing the varied requests with the TSR loaded into memory.
iii) INSTALL.ASM : Multiplexing, Making a program resident and handling all critical errors and traps during installation phase of the TSR.
iv) SERV_TSR.INC : Header file containing all declarations & SERV_DEM.INC of variables and routines for proper functioning of the TSR.
v) SERVER_C.ASM : Runs at server end to send a file on request.

/* PROGRAM NAME - SERVER.C */

```
# include <stdio.h>
# include <conio.h>
# include <dos.h>
void InitiaLize_ports(void);
void main(void)
{
        //Program to send a file to the CLIENT
        FILE *f_send;
        unsigned char ch_temp,c; // Temp-Variable to which the input is transfered
        unsigned char ch;     // Variable used to read from the input file
        int par_port= 0x378; // Address of the parallel outport
        unsigned char error_bit ; // Check for the acknowledgement
    // from the receiver before sending data
        unsigned char check_bit = 0x08; // Value of check_bit for handshaking
        long i=0;
        int true = 1; // To exit finally from file transfer routine.
        int count = 0; // To check for end of file count

        clrscr();
        printf(" This program is to send data to the parallel port \n");

        // Initializing Output Parallel port
        InitiaLize_ports();
        // To start communication send a signal 0x08 in output port
```

```
outportb(0x378,0x08);
// Send a signal to Client to indicate desire for FTP...
// Wait for acknowledgement ie check_bit to go high
// this is basically due to Active low ERROR bit.

printf(" Waiting for client to Respond back .......\n");
check_bit = 0x08;
while((check_bit ^=((error_bit = inportb(0x379))&0x08)) != 0x00)
check_bit = 0x08;
printf(" First response from client ....\n");

// Received an acknowledgement . Now wait for the Triggering Edge.

f_send = fopen("bgidemo.c","r");
// Received an acknowledgement for starting FTP.
do
{  i++;
ch = fgetc(f_send);
// Read first byte from the file
// To inform the Client that Upper Nibble is to arrive.
// Send a 0x00 to the Client Input port or Server Data
// Output port.
outportb(0x378,0x00);
// Wait for Client to respond that it is ready to receive
// the upper nibble.

check_bit = 0x08;
while ((check_bit ^=((error_bit=inportb(0x379))&0x08)) == 0)
check_bit = 0x08;

// Received response from client to send Upper nibble.
// Sending Upper nibble.

ch_temp = ((ch & 0xf0) | 0x08);

// The byte is 'Nded with 0xf0 and Or'es with 0x08
// as the 4th bit has to be HIGH for signifying the
// arrival of new data bit to the parallel STATUS
// INPUT port to the client .

outportb(par_port,ch_temp);

// initializing char for testing end of file
c = ch_temp;
if((((int)c)&0x00f0) >= 0x00f0){
count += 1;
}
// Wait for acknowledgement for sending second
// half of the nibble. It waits for the value to go high
// as it acts as the triggering edge.

check_bit = 0x08;
while ((check_bit ^=((error_bit=inportb(0x379))&0x08)) != 0)
check_bit = 0x08;
```

```
// Received an acknowledgement
// Send a triggering pulse to inform the client that
// LOWER half of the nibble is to be send.
outportb(0x378,0x00);

// Now wait for client to respond back to your call

check_bit = 0x08;
while ((check_bit ^=((error_bit=inportb(0x379))&0x08)) == 0)
check_bit = 0x08;

// Received acknowledgment to send Lower nibble
// Sending the LOWER NIBBLE.

ch_temp = (((ch <<= 4)&0xf0) | 0x08);

outportb(0x378,ch_temp);


c = ch_temp;
if (count == 1){ count++;
  if ((((int)c)&0x00ff) >= 0x00f0)
     {
printf("%c : with count 2 \n",c);
// End of file detected
        // Send signal to client ....
break;
  }
 else
          count =0;
  }
  // Wait for acknowledgement for sending the consequitive
  // characters
  check_bit = 0x08;
  while ((check_bit ^=((error_bit=inportb(0x379))&0x08)) != 0)
  check_bit = 0x08;
  } while (true==1);

  printf(" completion of file transfer ..... \n");
  printf(" The size of file transfered is %ul \n",i);
  fclose(f_send);
  getch();
  }
  void InitiaLize_ports()
  {
  printf(" Initializing ports ...... \n");
  outportb(0x378,0x00);
  printf(" Initializing ports Complete ... \n");
}
/* PROGRAM NAME CLIENT.C */


# include <stdio.h>
```

```
# include <conio.h>
# include <stdlib.h>
# include <dos.h>
void Initialize_ports(void);
void main(void)
{
unsigned char error_bit;// Character in which input is received from
    // parallel inport.
unsigned char t_e_bit;// Character in which input is copied for checking
   // it's validity and decoding.
unsigned char tt_e_bit;// ———————— do ————————
unsigned char check_bit = 0x08;// This variable is used for checking
   // of the arrival of new byte.
int end_of_file ,count=0;
FILE *f_recv;// Pointer to Receiving file.
unsigned long n_bytes_recvd =0 ;

clrscr();
printf(" This program is to read from the PARALLEL INPORT \n");
printf("————————————————————————————————————————————————\n");

// INITIALIZATION OF Parallel output PORT
InitiaLize_ports();

// client waits for signal from server to start file transfer....

while ((check_bit ^= ((error_bit = inportb(0x379))&0x08)) != 0x00)
check_bit = 0x08;

printf(" Received signal for permission to start FTP ... \n");

f_recv = fopen("jon.dat","w");
// Received signal for permission to start FTP....
// Send 0x08 in outport to signal server the receive of REQUEST

outportb(0x378,0x08);
// Wait for check bit to go high for indication of arrival of byte
// Reinitialization of check_bit before entering loop for
// overcoming any modifications made to it earlier.

for(;;){
      n_bytes_recvd++;
      check_bit = 0x08;
      while ((check_bit ^=((error_bit=inportb(0x379))&0x08)) == 0)
      check_bit = 0x08;
// Respond to server that CLient is ready to receive UPPER
// BYTE (NIBBLE) by making the server STATUS PORT LOW.

outportb(0x378,0x00);

// Wait for the Arrival of UPPER BYTE .
      check_bit = 0x08;
      while ((check_bit ^=((error_bit=inportb(0x379))&0x08)) != 0)
      check_bit = 0x08;
```

```
// Arrival of UPPER BYTE .
// Decoding of byte received
// printf(" The first byte received is %x \n",(error_bit));
// The byte transferred by the Server is having it's
// D7th bit inverted .
// Thus we have to check for it and decode the byte
// accordingly. The following is used .....
//      1. The byte is copied to t_e_bit.
//      2. The t_e_bit is and'ed with 0x80
//      3. The result is checked with 0x00
//      4. If it is 0x00 it implies that D7th was a '1'
//      5. Thus it is ored with 0x80.
//      6. Accordingly the change is made for D7th being a 0

t_e_bit = error_bit&0xff;
if ((t_e_bit &=0x80) == 0x00) {
   error_bit |= 0x80;
}
else {
   error_bit &= 0x70;
}

t_e_bit = error_bit&0xf0;
//     Decoding of byte complete .
//---------------------------------------------------

//     Send back Signal to server to indicate completion of
//     decoding and to send next byte .

outportb(0x378,0x08);

//     Send acknowledgement  to server .......
//     Wait for server to send signal for DATA TRANSFER

          check_bit = 0x08;
          while ((check_bit ^=((error_bit=inportb(0x379))&0x08)) == 0)
          check_bit = 0x08;
//     Received signal and Inform server that Client is
//     ready to receive LOWER BYTE.

outportb(0x378,0x00);

//     Wait for LOWER byte to arrive.

          check_bit = 0x08;
          while ((check_bit ^=((error_bit=inportb(0x379))&0x08)) != 0)
          check_bit = 0x08;

//     Arrival of LOWER BYTE.
//     Decoding of lower byte ........
tt_e_bit = error_bit&0xff;
if (( tt_e_bit &=0x80) == 0x00) {
   error_bit |= 0x80;
```

```
}
else {
  error_bit &= 0x70;
}

 // Decoding of byte complete.
 // To process the nibbles and decode the BYTE received.

      error_bit >>= 4;
      t_e_bit |= ((error_bit &=0x0f));
 putc((((int)t_e_bit)&0x00ff),f_recv);

 // Checking for EOF.......
 if (((((int)(t_e_bit))&0x00ff) == 0x00ff ) || (count == 1))
 {
    count +=1;
    printf(" Inside first if loop count is : %d :\n",count);
    break;
  }
  // Send back Signal to server to indicate completion of
  // decoding and to send next byte .
  outportb(0x378,0x08);

  // Send acknowledgement
  // Wait for receiving data from the server
  // Waiting complete signifying arrival of new byte.

}

printf("\nNo. of bytes recved : %ul\n",n_bytes_recvd);

fclose(f_recv);

printf(" File receiving complete ..... \n");
getch();
}
void InitiaLize_ports()
{
printf(" Initializing ports ...... \n");
outportb(0x378,0x00);
printf(" Initializing ports Complete .... \n");
}
/* PROGRAM SERV_CLI.ASM */

.MODEL  small, pascal
.DOSSEG
INCLUDE SERV_DEMO.INC
INCLUDE SERV_TSR.INC

.STACK
.DATA
EXTRN BUFFER:DWORD
EXTRN FILE_PTR:BYTE
EXTRN INT_CNT :BYTE
```

```
EXTRN BYTE_CNT:BYTE

HOT_SCAN EQU 00h          ; For hot key and install process
HOT_SHIFT EQU 00h
HOT_MASK EQU 00h
ZERO EQU 00h


COUNT_PAR_PORT BYTE ZERO ; Shared variable ....
Handle         WORD   ?;Handle for file
FILEZ  BYTE 'c:\junk.jun',0;Name of file to read data from ..
.CODE

FILENAMERECV PROC FAR
push ax
push bx
push dx
push cx

;************ INITIALIZING CLIENT PORTS *****************

mov al,00h
mov dx,0378h
out dx,al
; Receiving the nibbles and decoding as in pooling method
.IF (INT_CNT >= 00h )
.IF (INT_CNT <= 016h )
;* To receive the file name for the next 22 int's
add int_cnt,01h
in al,0379h
.IF ( byte_cnt == 00h)
mov temp_high,al
and al,080h
.IF ( al == 080h)
and temp_high,070h
.ELSE
.IF (al == 00h)
and temp_high,0F0h
.ENDIF
.ENDIF
.ELSE
mov temp_low,al
and al,080h
.IF( al == 080h)
and temp_low,070h
.ELSE
.IF ( al == 00h)
and temp_low,0f0h
.ENDIF
.ENDIF
.ENDIF

.IF (byte_cnt == 01h)
mov cx,04h
```

```
mov al,temp
rar
or temp,temp1
mov name_of_file[int_cnt],temp
mov byte_cnt,00h
jmp just_exit
.ENDIF
jmp file_trns_exit
.ENDIF
.ENDIF
.IF (INT_CNT == 0FFh)
mov file_ptr,00h
mov int_cnt ,00h
pushf
mov al,0f8h
mov dx,0378h
out dx,al
popf

jmp file_trns_exit
.ENDIF


;*************************************************

.IF (byte_cnt < 1)
call OpenfileCopy ; Open File And Set Pointer to next byte

.IF !carry?

call ReadFile ; If no error proceed for byte transfer...

.ENDIF
add byte_cnt,01h
jmp file_trns_exit

.ENDIF


.IF(byte_cnt > 3)
mov byte_cnt,00h
.ENDIF

.IF (BYTE_CNT == 01h)
mov al,BYTE PTR buffer[01h]
and al,0F8h
mov dx,0378h
out dx,al
jmp file_trns_exit
.ENDIF

.IF (BYTE_CNT == 02h)
mov al,BYTE PTR buffer[02h]
and al,0F8h
```

```
mov dx,0378h
out dx,al
jmp file_trns_exit
.ENDIF

.IF (BYTE_CNT == 03h)
mov al,BYTE PTR buffer[03h]
and al,0F8h
mov dx,0378h
out dx,al
jmp file_trns_exit
.ENDIF


file_trns_exit:
add byte_cnt,01h

just_exit:
pop cx
pop dx
pop bx
pop ax

retf

FILE NAME RECV ENDP

;**************************************************************************

Open File Copy PROC

mov   ax,3D00h        ;  Request DOS to open file to read from
mov   dx,OFFSET name_of_file ; DS:DX points to file specification
int   21h             ;  Open File

.IF   carry?          ;  If it doesn't exist,

mov   ah, 3Ch         ;  request create file
sub   cx,cx           ;  with normal attributes
int   21h             ;  Create File

.ENDIF

; .IF !carry?
pushf
mov   Handle, ax      ;  store file handle
mov   bx, ax
mov   ax, 4200h       ;  Request DOS to reset file pointer
sub   cx, cx          ;   to next byte of file
sub   dx, dx
mov   dl,FILE_PTR
add   FILE_PTR,04h
int   21h
popf
```

```
; .ENDIF

ret

OpenFileCopy ENDP

;***************************************************************************
; This procedure reads the contents of the file one byte at a time and
; sends it to the Client..... after decoding .

ReadFile PROC

mov   ah, 03Fh        ;  Request DOS Function 3Fh
mov   cx, 04h         ;  CX = number of bytes to READ
mov   bx, Handle      ;  BX = file handle
mov   dx, OFFSET Buffer  ; DS:DX points to buffer
int   21h             ;  Write to file

.IF (ax == 00h)          ; If EOF is detected
     push ax
     pushf             ; Close the file
     mov ah,3Eh
     mov bx,Handle
     int 21h
     popf               ; And exit
     pop ax
     mov int_cnt,0ffh
    jmp read_exit
.ENDIF

.IF      (ax != cx)    ;    If number of bytes READ !=

stc                    ;    number requested, set carry

.ENDIF                 ;    flag to indicate failure

pushf                  ;    Save carry flag

mov     ah, 3Eh        ;    Request DOS Function 3Eh
mov     bx,Handle
int      21h           ;    Close file

popf    ;      Recover carry

;****************** SEND TO CLIENT *********************

mov al,BYTE PTR BUFFER[0h]
and al,0F8h
mov dx,0378h
out dx,al
jmp ret_exit

read_exit:
```

```
mov al,0f8h
mov dx,0378h
out dx,al

ret_exit:
ret

ReadFile ENDP

;*********************************************************************

@CurSeg ENDS

;* INSTALLATION SECTION - The following code and data are used only
;* during SNAP's installation phase. When the program terminates
;* through Function 31h, the above code and data remain resident;
;* memory occupied by the following code and data segments is returned
;* to the operating system.

DGROUP  GROUP INSTALLCODE, INSTALLDATA

INSTALLDATA SEGMENT WORD PUBLIC 'DATA2'

IDstr  BYTE   'SNAP DEMO TSR', 0      ; Multiplex identifier string
INSTALLDATA ENDS

INSTALLCODE SEGMENT PARA PUBLIC 'CODE2'
ASSUME  ds:@data

Begin  PROC  NEAR

mov    ax, DGROUP
mov    ds, ax                ; Initialize DS
; Before calling any of the TSR procedures, initialize global data

INVOKE  InitTsr,             ; Initialize data
es,               ; Segment of PSP
ADDR IDstr,              ; Far address of multiplex ID string
ADDR COUNT_PAR_PORT     ; Far address of memory shared
;   with multiplex handler
.IF    ax == WRONG_DOS        ; If DOS version less than 2.0,
jmp    exit                ;   exit with message
.ENDIF

;********************DEINSTALL ******************************


mov al,'d'
call GetOptions
cmp ax,NO_ARGUMENT
je installtsr
cmp ax,OK_ARGUMENT
```

```
je deinstalltsr
mov al,'c'
call GetOptions
cmp ax,BAD_ARGUMENT
je exit



; This section sets up the TSR's interrupt handlers and
; makes the program memory-resident

installtsr:

push    es                      ; Preserve PSP address

mov     ax, @code
mov     es, ax
mov     bx, OFFSET FILENAMERECV ; ES:BX points to Snap
mov file_ptr,00h
mov int_cnt,00h
mov byte_cnt,00h
INVOKE  Install,                ; Install handlers
HOT_SCAN,                       ; Scan code of hot key
HOT_SHIFT,                      ; Bit value of hot key
HOT_MASK,                       ; Bit mask for shift hot key
es::bx                          ; Far address of Snap procedure

pop     es                      ; Recover PSP address
or      ax, ax                  ; If nonzero return code,
jnz     exit                    ; exit with appropriate message
INVOKE  GetResidentSize,        ; Get size of resident block
es
sti
push ax
push dx
mov al,00h
out 21h,al
mov dx,037ah
mov al,10h
out dx,al
pop dx
pop ax
INVOKE  KeepTsr,                ; Make TSR memory-resident
ax                              ; AX = size of block in paragraphs

; This section deinstalls the resident TSR from memory

deinstalltsr:

INVOKE  Deinstall               ; Unchain interrupt handlers

.IF     ax > OK_ARGUMENT ; If successful,
INVOKE  FreeTsr,                ; deinstall TSR by freeing memory
```

```
                          ; Address of resident seg
ax
.ENDIF                    ; Else exit with message
exit:
INVOKE FatalError,        ; Exit to DOS with message
ax                        ; Error number

Begin ENDP

INSTALLCODE ENDS

END Begin
```

/* PROGRAM SERV_HAN.ASM */

```
.MODEL small, pascal
INCLUDE serv_tsr.inc

.CODE

; Stack buffer used by TSR. Size is determined by constant STACK_SIZ,
; declared in SERV_TSR.INC file. NewStack points to top of stack.

 EVEN
 BYTE  STACK_SIZ DUP(?)  ; Stack buffer
 NewStack LABEL BYTE     ; Pointer to top of stack

; Structures for interrupt handlers or "interrupt service routines."
; The following handlers are replaced during installation. Such routines
; usually set a flag to indicate they are active, call the original
; interrupt handler, optionally do some processing (such as detecting a
; hot key), and when finished clear the active flag.

 HandArray     LABEL  BYTE              ; Array of handler structures
;           Num  Flag   OldHand NewHand
 intClock INTR < 8h, FALSE,  NULL,  Clock>
 intKeybrd INTR < 9h, FALSE,  NULL,  Keybrd>
 intPrint INTR <0Fh, FALSE,  NULL,  Printer>
 intVideo INTR <10h, FALSE,  NULL,  Video>
 intDiskIO INTR <13h, FALSE,  NULL,  DiskIO>
 intMisc  INTR <15h, FALSE,  NULL,  SkipMiscServ>
 intIdle  INTR <28h, FALSE,  NULL,  Idle>
 intMultex INTR <2Fh, FALSE,  NULL,  Multiplex>

 CHAND  EQU   ($ - HandArray) / (SIZEOF INTR) ; Number of handlers in array

 ; Interrupt trap routines. These interrupt routines are set up
 ; temporarily to trap keyboard break errors and critical errors
 ; while the TSR is active. When the TSR finishes its tasks, it
 ; restores the old interrupts before returning.

 TrapArray     LABEL  BYTE              ; Array of trap structures
 ;          Num  Flag   OldHand NewHand
 intCtrlBk INTR <1Bh, FALSE,  NULL,  CtrlBreak>
 intCtrlC INTR <23h, FALSE,  NULL,  CtrlC>
```

```
intCritEr INTR <24h, FALSE, NULL, CritError>

CTRAP EQU ($ - TrapArray) / (SIZEOF INTR) ; Number of traps in array

; Address of application's stack. Before calling the main body of the TSR,
; the Activate procedure stores the application's stack address, then resets
; SS:SP to point to LABEL NewStack (see above). This gives the TSR its own
; stack space without making demands on the current stack. Activate restores
; the application's stack before returning.

OldStackAddr    FPVOID ?              ; SS:SP pointer to application stack

; The TSR must set up its own disk transfer area if it calls DOS functions
; that use the DTA (see section "Preserving Existing Data" in Chapter 11 of
; the Programmer's Guide). DTA_SIZ is defined in the SERV_TSR.INC include file.

IFDEF DTA_SIZ
OldDtaAddr      FPVOID ?              ; Address of application's DTA
DtaBuff         BYTE DTA_SIZ DUP(?)   ; DTA buffer
ENDIF

; Multiplex data. STR_LEN is defined in the SERV_TSR.INC include file

IDnumber        BYTE 0                ; TSR's identity number
IDstring        BYTE STR_LEN DUP (0)  ; Copy of identifier string
IDstrlen        WORD ?                ; Length of identifier string
ShareAddr       FPVOID ?              ; Address of shared memory

; Miscellaneous data

TsrRequestFlag  BYTE FALSE            ; Flag set when hot key is pressed
TsrActiveFlag   BYTE FALSE            ; Flag set when TSR executes
BreakCheckFlag  BYTE ?                ; Break-checking status of application
TsrPspSeg       WORD ?                ; Segment address of PSP
TsrAddr         FPVOID ?              ; Pointer to main part of TSR
CritErrAddr     FPVOID ?              ; Pointer to MS-DOS critical error flag
InDosAddr       FPVOID ?              ; Pointer to MS-DOS InDos flag

; Scan and shift codes for hot key. Install procedure initializes
; HotScan, HotShift, and HotMask during installation.

HotScan         BYTE ?                ; Scan code hot key
HotShift        BYTE ?                ; Shift value of hot key
HotMask         BYTE ?                ; Mask unwanted shift values

Version         LABEL WORD            ; DOS version number
minor           BYTE ?
major           BYTE ?

; Timer data, used when the TSR is activated at a preset time instead
; of activated from the keyboard.

Tick91          BYTE 91               ; Measures 91 timer ticks (5 seconds)
CountDown       WORD 0                ; Counts 5-second intervals
```

```
;* Clock - Interrupt handler for Interrupt 08 (timer). Executes at each
;* timer interrupt; these occur an average of 18.2 times per second. Clock
;* first allows the original timer service routine to execute. It then
;* checks the flag TsrRequestFlag maintained either by the keyboard handler
;* (if keyboard activated) or by this procedure (if time activated). If
;* TsrRequestFlag = TRUE and system is okay, Clock invokes the TSR by
;* calling the Activate procedure. Uses an active flag to prevent the
;* Clock procedure from being reentered while executing.
;*
;* Uses:   intClock, TsrActiveFlag, CountDown
;*
;* Params: None
;*
;* Return: None
Clock   PROC    FAR

pushf                              ;  Simulate interrupt by pushing flags,
call    cs:intClock.OldHand        ;  far calling orig Int 08 routine

.IF     cs:intClock.Flag == FALSE ;  If not already in this handler:
mov     cs:intClock.Flag, TRUE     ;  Set active flag

sti                                ;  Interrupts are okay
push    ds                         ;  Save application's DS
push    cs
pop     ds                         ;  Set DS to resident code segment
ASSUME  ds:@code

call    CheckRequest               ;  Check conditions
.IF     !carry?                    ;  If TSR requested and safe,
mov     TsrActiveFlag, TRUE        ;  activate TSR
call    Activate
mov     TsrActiveFlag, FALSE
.ENDIF                             ;  End carry flag check

cmp     CountDown, 0               ;  If CountDown = 0, TSR is not time
je      ticked                     ;  activated or has already executed
dec     Tick91                     ;  Else count down 91 timer ticks
jnz     ticked                     ;  If 91 ticks have not elapsed, exit
mov     Tick91, 91                 ;  Else reset secondary counter and
dec     CountDown                  ;  subract one 5-second interval
ja      ticked                     ;  If counter not yet drained, exit
mov     TsrRequestFlag, TRUE       ;  Else raise request flag
ticked:
mov     intClock.Flag, FALSE       ;  Clear active flag
pop     ds                         ;  Recover application's DS
ASSUME  ds:NOTHING

.ENDIF                             ;  End in-handler check
iret
```

```
Clock   ENDP


;* Keybrd - Interrupt handler for Interrupt 09 (keyboard).
;*
;* IBM PC/AT and compatibles:
;*     Gets the scan code of the current keystroke from port 60h. Then
;*     compares the scan code and shift state to the hot key. If they
;*     match, sets TsrRequestFlag to signal the handlers Clock and Idle
;*     that the TSR is requested.
;*
;* IBM PS/2 series:
;*     Only the instructions at KeybrdMonitor (see below) are installed
;*     as Interrupt 09 handler, since above method should not be used to
;*     determine current keystroke in IBM PS/2 series. In this case, the
;*     Interrupt 15h handler MiscServ takes care of checking the scan codes
;*     and setting the request flag when the hot key is pressed.
;*
;* Time-activated TSRs:
;*     If the TSR is activated by time instead of by a hotkey, KeybrdMonitor
;*     serves as the Interrupt 09 handler for both PC/AT and PS/2 systems.
;*
;* Uses:   intKeybrd, TsrRequestFlag
;*
;* Params: None
;*
;* Return: None

Keybrd  PROC    FAR

sti                              ; Interrupts are okay
push    ax                       ; Save AX register
in      al, 60h                  ; AL = scan code of current key
call    CheckHotKey              ; Check for hot key
.IF     !carry?                  ; If not hot key:

; Hot key pressed. Reset the keyboard to throw away keystroke.

cli                              ; Disable interrupts while resetting
in      al, 61h                  ; Get current port 61h state
or      al, 10000000y            ; Turn on bit 7 to signal clear keybrd
out     61h, al                  ; Send to port
and     al, 01111111y            ; Turn off bit 7 to signal break
out     61h, al                  ; Send to port
mov     al, 20h                  ; Reset interrupt controller
out     20h, al
sti                              ; Reenable interrupts

pop     ax                       ; Recover AX
mov     cs:TsrRequestFlag, TRUE  ; Raise request flag
iret                             ; Exit interrupt handler
.ENDIF                           ; End hot-key check

; No hot key was pressed, so let normal Int 09 service routine take over
```

```
pop    ax                    ; Recover AX and fall through
cli                          ; Interrupts cleared for service

KeybrdMonitor LABEL FAR             ; Installed as Int 09 handler for
;  PS/2 or for time-activated TSR
mov    cs:intKeybrd.Flag, TRUE ; Signal that interrupt is busy
pushf                    ; Simulate interrupt by pushing flags,
call   cs:intKeybrd.OldHand    ;   far calling old Int 09 routine
mov    cs:intKeybrd.Flag, FALSE
iret

Keybrd  ENDP

;*************************************************************
;*************************************************************
;******************** PRINTER ***************************
;*************************************************************
;*************************************************************


Printer   PROC FAR

pushf ; Simulate interrupt  by pushing flag
call cs:intPrint.OldHand

.IF  cs:intPrint.Flag == FALSE
    mov cs:intPrint.Flag , TRUE
sti            ; Interrupts are okay

      push ds         ; Save applications DATA SEGMENT
      push cs         ; Set DS to Resident Code SEGMENT
      pop  ds

      ASSUME ds: @code
      mov TsrRequestFlag, TRUE

      call CheckRequest   ; Check Conditions
      .IF !carry?         ; If Tsr requested is safe
  mov TsrActiveFlag,True ; Activate TSR
  call Activate
  mov TsrActiveFlag ,FALSE
  .ENDIF

  mov intPrint.Flag ,FALSE; Clear Active FLag
  pop ds              ; Recover Applications DS

  ASSUME ds:NOTHING
  .ENDIF
  iret
  Printer ENDP


;*************************************************************
```

```
;************************************************************

;* Video - Interrupt handler for Interrupt 10h (video). Allows the original
;* video service routine to execute. Maintains an active flag to prevent
;* the TSR from being called while Interrupt 10h is executing.
;*
;* Uses:   intVideo
;*
;* Params: Registers passed to Interrupt 10h
;*
;* Return: Registers returned by Interrupt 10h

Video   PROC    FAR

mov     cs:intVideo.Flag, TRUE  ; Set active flag
pushf                           ; Simulate interrupt by pushing flags,
call    cs:intVideo.OldHand     ;   far calling old Int 10h routine
mov     cs:intVideo.Flag, FALSE ; Clear active flag
iret

Video   ENDP


;* DiskIO - Interrupt handler for Interrupt 13h (disk I/O). Allows the
;* original disk I/O service routine to execute. Maintains an active flag
;* to prevent the TSR from being called while Interrupt 13h is executing.
;*
;* Uses:   intDiskIO
;*
;* Params: Registers passed to Interrupt 13h
;*
;* Return: Registers and the carry flag returned by Interrupt 13h

DiskIO  PROC    FAR

mov     cs:intDiskIO.Flag, TRUE ; Set active flag
pushf                           ; Simulate interrupt by pushing flags,
call    cs:intDiskIO.OldHand    ;   far calling old Int 13h routine
mov     cs:intDiskIO.Flag, FALSE; Clear active flag without
;   disturbing flags register
sti                             ; Enable interrupts
ret     2                       ; Simulate IRET without popping flags
;   (since services use carry flag)
DiskIO  ENDP


;* MiscServ - Interrupt handler for Interrupt 15h (Miscellaneous System
;* Services).
;*
;* IBM PC/AT and compatibles:
;*     Stub at SkipMiscServ is used as handler, bypassing all calls to
;*     Interrupt 15h. Keypresses are checked by Keybrd (Int 09 handler).
;*
```

```
;* IBM PS/2 series:
;*    This procedure handles calls to Interrupt 15h, searching for
;*    Function 4Fh (Keyboard Intercept Service). When AH = 4Fh, gets
;*    scan code of current keystroke in AL register. Then compares the
;*    scan code and shift state to the hot key. If they match, sets
;*    TsrRequestFlag to signal the handlers Clock and Idle that the
;*    TSR is requested.
;*
;* Uses:   intMisc, TsrRequestFlag
;*
;* Params: Registers passed to Interrupt 15h
;*
;* Return: Registers returned by Interrupt 15h

MiscServ PROC   FAR

sti                       ; Interrupts okay
.IF    ah == 4Fh                        ; If Keyboard Intercept Service,
push   ax                               ; preserve AX,
call   CheckHotKey                      ; check for hot key
pop    ax
.IF    !carry?                          ; If hot key,
mov    cs:TsrRequestFlag, TRUE          ; raise request flag,
clc                                     ; signal BIOS not to process the key,
ret    2                                ; simulate IRET without popping flags
.ENDIF                                  ; End carry flag check
.ENDIF                                  ; End Keyboard Intercept check

cli                                     ; Disable interrupts and fall through

SkipMiscServ LABEL FAR                  ; Interrupt 15h handler if PC/AT

jmp    cs:intMisc.OldHand

MiscServ ENDP


;* CtrlBreak - Interrupt trap for Interrupt 1Bh (CTRL+BREAK Handler).
;* Disables CTRL+BREAK processing.
;*
;* Params: None
;*
;* Return: None

CtrlBreak PROC  FAR

iret

CtrlBreak ENDP


;* CtrlC - Interrupt trap for Interrupt 23h (CTRL+C Handler).
;* Disables CTRL+C processing.
;*
```

```
;* Params: None
;*
;* Return: None

CtrlC   PROC    FAR

iret

CtrlC   ENDP


;* CritError - Interrupt trap for Interrupt 24h (Critical Error Handler).
;* Disables critical error processing.
;*
;* Params: None
;*
;* Return: AL = Stop code 0 or 3

CritError PROC  FAR

sti
sub     al, al                  ; Assume DOS 2.x
; Set AL = 0 for ignore error
.IF     cs:major != 2           ; If DOS 3.x, set AL = 3
mov     al, 3                   ; DOS call fails
.ENDIF

iret

CritError ENDP


;* Idle - Interrupt handler for Interrupt 28h (DOS Idle). Allows the
;* original Interrupt 28h service routihe to execute. Then checks the
;* request flag TsrRequestFlag maintained either by the keyboard handler
;* (keyboard-activated TSR) or by the timer handler (time-activated TSR).
;* See header comments above for Clock, Keybrd, and MiscServ procedures.
;*
;* If TsrRequestFlag = TRUE and system is in interruptable state, Idle
;* invokes the TSR by calling the Activate procedure..Uses an active flag
;* to prevent the Idle procedure from being reentered while executing.
;*
;* Uses:   intIdle and TsrActiveFlag
;*
;* Params: None
;*
;* Return: None

Idle   PROC   FAR

pushf                           ; Simulate interrupt by pushing flags,
call   cs:intIdle.OldHand       ; far-calling old Int 28h routine

.IF    cs:intIdle.Flag == FALSE ; If not already in this handler,
```

```
mov     cs:intIdle.Flag, TRUE   ; set active flag

sti                             ; Interrupts are okay
push    ds                      ; Save application's DS
push    cs
pop     ds                      ; Set DS to resident code segment
ASSUME  ds:@code

call    CheckRequest            ; Check conditions
.IF     !carry?                 ; If TSR requested and safe,
mov     TsrActiveFlag, TRUE     ; activate TSR
call    Activate
mov     TsrActiveFlag, FALSE
.ENDIF                          ; End carry flag check

mov     intIdle.Flag, FALSE     ; Clear active flag
pop     ds                      ; Recover application's DS
.ENDIF                  ; End in-handler check

iret

Idle    ENDP


;* Multiplex - Handler for Interrupt 2Fh (Multiplex Interrupt). Checks
;* AH for this TSR's identity number. If no match (indicating call is
;* not intended for this TSR), Multiplex passes control to the previous
;* Interrupt 2Fh handler.
;*
;* Params: AH = Handler identity number
;*         AL = Function number 0-2
;*
;* Return: AL    = 0FFh (function 0)
;*         ES:DI = Pointer to identifier string (function 0)
;*         ES:DI = Pointer to resident PSP segment (function 1)
;*         ES:DI = Pointer to shared memory (function 2)

Multiplex PROC  FAR

.IF     ah != cs:IDnumber       ; If this handler not requested,
jmp     cs:intMultex.OldHand    ; pass control to old Int 2Fh
.ENDIF                          ; handler

.IF     al == 0                 ; If function 0 (verify presence),
mov     al, 0FFh                ; AL = 0FFh,
push    cs                      ;   ES = resident code segment
pop     es
mov     di, OFFSET IDstring     ;   DI = offset of identifier string

.ELSEIF al == 1                 ; If function 1 (get PSP address),
mov     es, cs:TsrPspSeg        ;   ES:DI = far address of resident PSP
sub     di, di

.ELSE
```

```
les    di, cs:ShareAddr          ; If function 2 (get shared memory),
ENDIF                            ; set ES:DI = far address

NoMultiplex LABEL  FAR           ; Secondary entry for null Multiplex

iret

Multiplex ENDP


;* CheckHotKey - Checks current keystroke for hot key. Called from Keybrd
;* handler if IBM PC/AT or compatible, or from MiscServ handler if PS/2.
;*
;* Uses:   HotScan, HotShift, HotMask, and SHFT_STAT
;*
;* Params: AL = Scan code
;*
;* Return: Carry flag set = FALSE; carry flag clear = TRUE

CheckHotKey PROC NEAR

cmp    al, cs:HotScan             ; If current scan code isn't code
jne    e_exit                     ;   for hot key, exit with carry set

push   es                         ; Else look into BIOS data area
sub    ax, ax                     ;   (segment 0) to check shift state
mov    es, ax
mov    al, es:[SHFT_STAT]         ; Get SHIFT-key flags
and    al, cs:HotMask             ; AND with "don't care" mask
cmp    al, cs:HotShift            ; Compare result with hot SHIFT key
pop    es
je     exit                       ; If match, exit with carry clear

e_exit: stc                       ; Set carry if not hot key
exit:  ret

CheckHotKey ENDP


;* CheckRequest - Checks request flag and system status using the
;* following logic:
;*
;*      IF (TsrRequestFlag AND (NOT TsrActiveFlag)
;*         AND DosStatus AND HardwareStatus)
;*         return TRUE
;*      ELSE
;*         return FALSE
;*
;* Uses:   TsrRequestFlag and TsrActiveFlag
;*
;* Params: DS = Resident code segment
;*
;* Return: Carry flag set = TRUE; carry flag clear = FALSE
```

```
CheckRequest PROC NEAR

rol     TsrRequestFlag, 1           ; Rotate high bit into carry - set
;  if TRUE (-1), clear if FALSE (0)
cmc                                 ; NOT carry

.IF     !carry?                     ; If TsrRequestFlag = TRUE:
ror     TsrActiveFlag, 1            ; Rotate low bit into carry - set
;  if TRUE (-1), clear if FALSE (0)
.IF     !carry?                     ; If TsrActiveFlag = FALSE:
call    CheckDos                    ; Is DOS in interruptable state?

.IF     !carry?                     ; If so,
call    CheckHardware               ;   if hardware or BIOS unstable,
.ENDIF                              ;   set carry and exit
.ENDIF
.ENDIF
ret

CheckRequest ENDP


;* CheckDos - Checks status of MS-DOS using the following logic:
;*
;*      IF (NOT CritErr) AND ((NOT InDos) OR (Idle AND InDos))
;*          return DosStatus = TRUE
;*      ELSE
;*          return DosStatus = FALSE
;*
;* Uses:   CritErrAddr, InDosAddr, and intIdle
;*
;* Params: DS = Resident code segment
;*
;* Return: Carry flag set if MS-DOS is busy

CheckDos PROC   NEAR USES es bx ax

les     bx, CritErrAddr
mov     ah, es:[bx]                 ; AH = value of CritErr flag

les     bx, InDosAddr
mov     al, es:[bx]                 ; AL = value of InDos flag

sub     bx, bx                      ; BH = 0, BL = 0
cmp     bl, intIdle.Flag            ; Carry flag set if call is from
;  Interrupt 28h handler
rcl     bl, 1                       ; Rotate carry into BL: TRUE if Idle
cmp     bx, ax                      ; Carry flag clear if CritErr = 0
;  and InDos <= BL
ret

CheckDos ENDP
```

```
;* CheckHardware - Checks status of BIOS and hardware using the
;* following logic:
;*
;*      IF HardwareActive OR KeybrdActive OR VideoActive OR DiskIOActive
;*          return HardwareStatus = FALSE
;*      ELSE
;*          return HardwareStatus = TRUE
;*
;* Uses:  intKeybrd, intVideo, and intDiskIO
;*
;* Params: DS = Resident code segment
;*
;* Return: Carry flag set if hardware or BIOS is busy

CheckHardware PROC NEAR USES ax

; Verify hardware interrupt status by interrogating Intel 8259A
; Programmable Interrupt Controller

mov   ax, 00001011y         ; AL = 0CW3 for Intel 8259A
;  (RR = 1, RIS = 1)
out   20h, al               ; Request 8259A in-service register
jmp   delay                 ; Wait a few cycles
delay:
in    al, 20h               ; AL = hardware interrupts being
cmp   ah, al                ;   serviced (bit = 1 if in service)

.IF   !carry?               ; If no hard interrupts in service,
sub   al, al                ;   verify BIOS interrupts not active,
cmp   al, intKeybrd.Flag    ;   check Interrupt 09 handler

.IF   !carry?               ; If Int 09 not active,
cmp   al, intVideo.Flag     ;   check Interrupt 10h handler

.IF   !carry?               ; If Int 10h not active,
cmp   al, intDiskIO.Flag    ;   check Interrupt 13h handler,

.IF   !carry?               ; If Int 13h not active
cmp   al, intPrint.Flag     ;   check Interrupt 0fh handler
.ENDIF
.ENDIF                      ;   return with carry set if
.ENDIF                      ;   Interrupt 09, 10h,13h or 0Fh
.ENDIF                      ;   is active

ret

CheckHardware ENDP


;* Activate - Sets up for far call to TSR with the following steps:
;*
;*  1. Stores stack pointer SS:SP and switches to new stack
;*  2. Pushes registers onto new stack
;*  3. Stores vectors for Interrupts 1Bh, 23h, and 23h, and
```

```
;*      replaces them with addresses of error-trapping handlers
;*  4. Stores DOS CTRL+C checking flag, then turns off checking
;*  5. If required, stores DTA address and switches to new DTA
;*
;* When TSR returns, restores all the above.
;*
;* Uses:   Reads or writes the following globals:
;*         OldStackAddr, TrapArray, BreakCheckFlag, TsrRequestFlag
;*
;* Params: DS = Resident code segment
;*
;* Return: None

Activate PROC   NEAR

; Step 1.  Set up a new stack

mov     WORD PTR OldStackAddr[0], sp    ; Save current
mov     WORD PTR OldStackAddr[2], ss    ;  stack pointer

cli                                     ; Turn off interrupts while
push    cs                              ;   changing stack
pop     ss                              ; New stack begins
mov     sp, OFFSET NewStack             ;   at LABEL NewStack
sti

; Step 2.  Preserve registers (DS already saved in Clock or Idle)

push    ax
push    bx
push    cx
push    dx
push    si
push    di
push    bp
push    es

cld                                     ; Clear direction flag

; Step 3.  Set up trapping handlers for keyboard breaks and DOS
; critical errors (Interrupts 1Bh, 23h, and 24h)

mov     cx, CTRAP                       ; CX = number of handlers
mov     si, OFFSET TrapArray            ; DS:SI points to trap array

.REPEAT
mov     al, [si]                        ; AL = interrupt number
mov     ah, 35h                         ; Request DOS Function 35h
int     21h                             ; Get interrupt vector (ES:BX)
mov     WORD PTR [si].INTR.OldHand[0], bx ; Save far address of
mov     WORD PTR [si].INTR.OldHand[2], es ;   application's handler
mov     dx, WORD PTR [si].INTR.NewHand[0] ; DS:DX points to TSR's hand
mov     ah, 25h                         ; Request DOS Function 25h
int     21h                             ; Set interrupt vector
```

```
add     si, SIZEOF INTR             ; DS:SI points to next in list
.UNTILCXZ

; Step 4.  Disable MS-DOS break checking during disk I/O

mov     ax, 3300h                   ; Request DOS Function 33h
int     21h                         ; Get CTRL+BREAK flag in DL
mov     BreakCheckFlag, dl          ; Preserve it

sub     dl, dl                      ; DL = 0 to disable I/O break checking
mov     ax, 3301h                   ; Request DOS Function 33h
int     21h                         ; Set CTRL+BREAK flag from DL

; Step 5.  If TSR requires a disk transfer area, store address of current
; DTA and switch buffer address to this segment.

IFDEF   DTA_SIZ
mov     ah, 2Fh                     ; Request DOS Function 2Fh
int     21h                         ; Get DTA Address into ES:BX
mov     WORD PTR OldDtaAddr[0], bx      ; Store address
mov     WORD PTR OldDtaAddr[2], es

mov     dx, OFFSET DtaBuff          ; DS:DX points to new DTA
mov     ah, 1Ah                     ; Request DOS Function 1Ah
int     21h                         ; Set DTA Address
ENDIF

; Call main body of TSR.

mov     ax, @data
mov     ds, ax                      ; Initialize DS and ES
mov     es, ax                      ;   to data segment

call    cs:TsrAddr                  ; Call main part of TSR

push    cs
pop     ds                          ; Reset DS to this segment

; Undo step 5.  Restore previous DTA (if required)

IFDEF   DTA_SIZ
push    ds                          ; Preserve DS
lds     dx, OldDtaAddr              ; DS:DX points to application's DTA
mov     ah, 1Ah                     ; Request DOS Function 1Ah
int     21h                         ; Set DTA Address
pop     ds
ENDIF

; Undo step 4.  Restore previous MS-DOS break checking

mov     dl, BreakCheckFlag          ; DL = previous break state
mov     ax, 3301h                   ; Request DOS Function 33h
int     21h                         ; Set CTRL+BREAK flag from DL
```

```
; Undo step 3.  Restore previous vectors for error-trapping handlers

mov   cx, CTRAP
mov   di, OFFSET TrapArray
push  ds                          ; Preserve DS
push  ds                          ; ES = resident code segment
pop   es

.REPEAT
mov   al, es:[di]                 ; AL = interrupt number
lds   dx, es:[di].INTR.OldHand; DS:DX points to application's handler
mov   ah, 25h                     ; Request DOS Function 25h
int   21h                         ; Set interrupt vector from DS:DX
add   di, SIZEOF INTR             ; ES:DI points to next in list
.UNTILCXZ
pop   ds

; Undo step 2.  Restore registers from stack

pop   es
pop   bp
pop   di
pop   si
pop   dx
pop   cx
pop   bx
pop   ax

; Undo step 1.  Restore address of original stack to SS:SP

cli
mov   sp, WORD PTR OldStackAddr[0]
mov   ss, WORD PTR OldStackAddr[2]
sti

; Clear request flag and return to caller (Clock or Idle procedure)

mov   TsrRequestFlag, FALSE
ret

Activate ENDP


;* INSTALLATION SECTION - The following code is executed only during
;* the TSR's installation phase. When the program terminates through
;* Function 31h, the above code and data remain resident; memory
;* occupied by the following code segment is returned to the operating
;* system.

DGROUP  GROUP INSTALLCODE

INSTALLCODE SEGMENT PARA PUBLIC 'CODE2'
ASSUME  ds:@code
```

```
;* Install - Prepares for installation of a TSR by chaining interrupt
;* handlers and initializing pointers to DOS flags. Install does not
;* call the Terminate-and-Stay-Resident function.
;*
;* This library of routines accommodates both keyboard-activated and
;* time-activated TSRs. The latter are TSRs that activate at a preset
;* time. If the first parameter (Param1) is a valid scan code, Install
;* assumes the TSR is activated from the keyboard and sets up a keyboard
;* handler to search for the hot key. If Param1 is null, Install assumes
;* the next two parameters (Param2 and Param3) are respectively the hour
;* and minute at which the TSR is to activate. In this case, Install
;* calls GetTimeToElapse to initialize the variable CountDown and sets
;* up.KeybrdMonitor as the keyboard handler. If (Param1) ,(Param2) ,(Param3)
;* are null Install assumes that the printer interrupt is to be serviced
;* Install is callable from a high-level language.
;*
;* Uses:   InDosAddr, CritErrAddr, CHAND,
;*         HandArray, CTRAP, TrapArray
;*
;*              Keyboard-activated          Time-activated
;*              __________________          ______________
;* Params: Param1 - Scan code for hot key          0
;*         Param2 - Bit value for shift hot key    Hour to activate
;*         Param3 - Bit mask for shift hot key     Minute to activate
;*         Param4 - Far address of main TSR procedure  (same)
;*
;* Return: AX = 0 if successful, or one of the following codes:
;*         IS_INSTALLED          FLAGS_NOT_FOUND      NO_IDNUM
;*         ALREADY_INSTALLED     WRONG_DOS

Install PROC    FAR USES ds si di,
Param1:WORD, Param2:WORD, Param3:WORD, Param4:FAR PTR FAR

mov     ax, @code
mov     ds, ax                          ; Point DS to code segment

; Get and store parameters passed from main program module

mov     al, BYTE PTR Param1
mov     HotScan, al                     ; Store hot-key scan code
mov     al, BYTE PTR Param2             ;  or flag for time activate
mov     HotShift, al                    ; Store hot-key shift value
mov     al, BYTE PTR Param3             ;  or hour value
mov     HotMask, al                     ; Store hot-key shift mask
;  or minute value
mov     ax, WORD PTR Param4[0]
mov     bx, WORD PTR Param4[2]
mov     WORD PTR TsrAddr[0], ax         ; Store segment:offset of
mov     WORD PTR TsrAddr[2], bx         ;  TSR's main code

; Get addresses of DOS flags, then check for prior installation

call    GetDosFlags                     ; Find DOS service flags
```

```
or     ax, ax
jnz    exit                        ; If flags not found, quit

sub    al, al                      ; Request multiplex function 0
call   CallMultiplex               ; Invoke Interrupt 2Fh
cmp    ax, NOT_INSTALLED           ; Check for presence of resident TSR

.IF    !zero?                      ; If TSR is installed,
cmp    ax, IS_INSTALLED            ;  return with appropriate
jne    exit                        ;  error code
mov    ax, ALREADY_INSTALLED
jmp    exit
.ENDIF

; Check if TSR is to activate at the hour:minute specified by Param2:Param3.
; If so, determine the number of 5-second intervals that must elapse before
; activation, then set up the code at the far LABEL KeybrdMonitor to serve
; as the keyboard handler.

.IF    HotScan == 0            ; If valid scan code given,

.IF HotShift == 0

.IF HotMask == 0
    cmp Version ,031Eh         ; Printer interrupt to be
    jb setup                   ; serviced ......
.ENDIF
.ENDIF

mov    ah, HotShift            ;  AH = hour to activate
mov    al, HotMask             ;  AL = minute to activate
call   GetTimeToElapse         ; Get number of 5-second intervals
mov    CountDown, ax           ;  to elapse before activation

.ELSE                          ; Force use of KeybrdMonitor as
;  keyboard handler
cmp    Version, 031Eh          ; DOS Version 3.3 or higher?
jb     setup                   ; No? Skip next step

; Test for IBM PS/2 series. If not PS/2, use Keybrd and SkipMiscServ as
; handlers for Interrupts 09 and 15h respectively. If PS/2 system, set up
; KeybrdMonitor as the Interrupt 09 handler. Audit keystrokes with MiscServ
; handler, which searches for the hot key by handling calls to Interrupt 15h
; (Miscellaneous System Services).

mov    ax, 0C00h               ; Function 0Ch (Get System
int    15h                     ;  Configuration Parameters)
sti                            ; Compaq ROM may leave interrupts
; 'disabled

jc     setup                   ; If carry set,
or     ah, ah                  ;  or if AH not 0,
jnz    setup                   ;  services are not supported
```

```
test   BYTE PTR es:[bx+5], 00010000y   ; Test bit 4 to see if
jz     setup                           ;  intercept is implemented

mov    ax, OFFSET MiscServ     ; If so, set up MiscServ as
mov    WORD PTR intMisc.NewHand, ax  ;   Interrupt 15h handler
.ENDIF

mov    ax, OFFSET KeybrdMonitor        ; Set up KeybrdMonitor as
mov    WORD PTR intKeybrd.NewHand, ax  ;  Interrupt 09 handler

; Interrupt structure is now initialized for either PC/AT or PS/2 system.
; Get existing handler addresses from interrupt vector table, store in
; OldHand member, and replace with addresses of new handlers.

setup:
mov    cx, CHAND               ; CX = count of handlers
mov    si, OFFSET HandArray    ; SI = offset of handler structures

.REPEAT
mov    ah, 35h                 ; Request DOS Function 35h
mov    al, [si]                ; AL = interrupt number
int    21h                     ; Get interrupt vector in ES:BX
mov    WORD PTR [si].INTR.OldHand[0], bx ; Save far address
mov    WORD PTR [si].INTR.OldHand[2], es ;  of current handler
mov    dx, WORD PTR [si].INTR.NewHand[0] ; DS:DX points to TSR handler
mov    ah, 25h                 ; Request DOS Function 25h
int    21h                     ; Set interrupt vector from DS:DX
add    si, SIZEOF INTR         ; DS:SI points to next in list
.UNTILCXZ

sub    ax, ax                  ; Clear return code
exit:
ret                            ; Return to caller

Install ENDP


;* Deinstall - Prepares for deinstallation of a TSR. Deinstall is the
;* complement of the Install procedure. It restores to the vector table
;* the original addresses replaced during installation, thus unhooking
;* the TSR's handlers. Checks to see if another TSR has installed handlers
;* for the interrupts in array HandArray. If so, the procedure fails with
;* an appropriate error code. Callable from a high-level language.
;*
;* Params: None
;*
;* Return: AX = Segment address of resident portion's PSP or
;*         one of the following error codes:
;*         CANT_DEINSTALL        WRONG_DOS

Deinstall PROC  FAR USES ds si di

mov    ax, @code
mov    ds, ax                  ; Point DS to code segment
```

```
sub    al, al                    ; Request multiplex function 0
call   CallMultiplex             ; Get resident code segment in ES
cmp    ax, IS_INSTALLED          ; If not resident,
jne    exit                      ;   exit with error
push   es                        ; Else point DS to
pop    ds                        ;   resident code segment
mov    cx, CHAND                 ; Count of handlers
mov    si, OFFSET HandArray ; SI points to handler structures

; Read current vectors for TSR's interrupt handlers and compare with far
; addresses. If mismatch, another TSR has installed new handlers and ours
; cannot be safely deinstalled.

.REPEAT
mov    al, [si]                  ; AL = interrupt number
mov    ah, 35h                   ; Request DOS Function 35h
int    21h                       ; Get interrupt vector in ES:BX
cmp    bx, WORD PTR [si].INTR.NewHand[0] ; If offset different,
jne    e_exit                    ;   error
mov    ax, es
cmp    ax, WORD PTR [si].INTR.NewHand[2] ; If segment different,
jne    e_exit                    ;   error
add    si, SIZEOF INTR           ; DS:SI points to next in list
.UNTILCXZ

; If no interrupts replaced, call TSR's multiplex handler to locate
; address of resident portion's PSP. Although the PSP is not required
; until memory is returned to DOS, the call must be done now before
; unhooking the multiplex handler.

mov    al, 1                     ; Request multiplex function 1
call   CallMultiplex             ; Get resident code's PSP in ES
push   es                        ; Save it

; Unhook all handlers by restoring the original vectors to vector table.

mov    cx, CHAND                 ; Count of installed handlers
mov    si, OFFSET HandArray ; SI points to handler structures

.REPEAT
mov    al, [si]                  ; AL = interrupt number
push   ds                        ; Preserve DS segment
lds    dx, [si].INTR.OldHand     ; Put vector in DS:DX
mov    ah, 25h                   ; Request DOS Function 25h
int    21h                       ; Set interrupt vector from DS:DX
pop    ds
add    si, SIZEOF INTR           ; DS:SI points to next in list
.UNTILCXZ

pop    ax                        ; Return address of resident PSP
jmp    exit                      ;   to signal success
e_exit:
mov    ax, CANT_DEINSTALL
exit:
```

```
ret

Deinstall ENDP


;* GetVersion - Gets the DOS version and stores it in a global variable as
;* well as returning it in AX.
;*
;* Uses:   Version
;*
;* Params: DS = Resident code segment
;*
;* Return: AH = Major version
;*         AL = Minor version

GetVersion PROC NEAR

mov   ax, 3000h                 ; Request DOS Function 30h
int   21h                       ; Get MS-DOS version number
.IF   al < 2                    ; If Version 1.x:
mov   ax, WRONG_DOS             ; Abort with WRONG_DOS as error code
.ELSE
xchg  ah, al                    ; AH = major, AL = minor version
mov   Version, ax               ; Save in global
.ENDIF
ret

GetVersion ENDP


;* GetDosFlags - Gets pointers to the DOS InDos and Critical Error flags.
;*
;* Params: DS = Resident code segment
;*
;* Return: 0 if successful, or the following error code:
;*         FLAGS_NOT_FOUND

GetDosFlags PROC NEAR

; Get InDOS address from MS-DOS

mov   ah, 34h                   ; Request DOS Function 34h
int   21h                       ; Get Address of InDos flag
mov   WORD PTR InDosAddr[0], bx   ; Store address (ES:BX)
mov   WORD PTR InDosAddr[2], es   ;   for later access

; Determine address of Critical Error Flag

mov   ax, Version               ; AX = DOS version number

; If DOS 3.1 or greater and not OS/2 compatibility mode, Critical Error
; flag is in byte preceding InDOS flag
.IF   (ah < 10) && ((ah > 3) || ((ah == 3) && (al >= 10)))
dec   bx                        ; BX points to byte before InDos flag
```

```
.ELSE
; For earlier versions, the only reliable method is to scan through
; DOS to find an INT 28h instruction in a specific context.

mov   cx, 0FFFFh                  ; Maximum bytes to scan
sub   di, di                      ; ES:DI = start of DOS segment

INT_28  EQU    028CDh

.REPEAT
mov    ax, INT_28                 ; Load opcode for INT 28h

.REPEAT
repne  scasb                      ; Scan for first byte of opcode

.IF    !zero?
mov    ax, FLAGS_NOT_FOUND        ; Return error if not found
jmp    exit
.ENDIF
.UNTIL  ah == es:[di]             ; For each matching first byte,
;   check the second byte until match

; See if INT 28h is in this context:
;                                 ;   (-7)   (-5)
;      CMP    ss:[CritErrFlag], 0 ; 36, 80, 3E,  ?,  ?,  0
;      JNE    NearLabel           ; 75,  ?
int    28h                        ; CD, 28
;                                 ; (0) (1)
CMP_SS    EQU   3E80h
P_CMP_SS  EQU   8
P_CMP_OP  EQU   6

mov    ax, CMP_SS                 ; Load and compare opcode to CMP
.IF    ax == es:[di-P_CMP_SS]     ; If match:
mov    bx, es:[di-P_CMP_OP]       ; BX = offset of
jmp    exit                       ;   Critical Error flag
.ENDIF

; See if INT 28h is in this context:
;                                 ;   (-12)  (-10)
;      TEST    ?s:[CritErr], 0FFh ; ?6  F6, 06,  ?,  ?, FF
;      JNE     NearLabel          ; 75, ?
;      PUSH    ss:[CritErrFlag]   ; 36, FF, 36,  ?,  ?
int    28h                        ; CD, 28
;                                 ; (0) (1)
TEST_SS   EQU   06F6h
P_TEST_SS EQU   13
P_TEST_OP EQU   11

mov    ax, TEST_SS                ; Load AX = opcode for TEST
.UNTIL  ax == es:[di-P_TEST_SS]   ; If not TEST, continue scan

mov    bx, es:[di-P_TEST_OP]      ; Else load BX with offset of
```

```
.ENDIF                                ; Critical Error flag
exit:
mov   WORD PTR CritErrAddr[0], bx ; Store address of
mov   WORD PTR CritErrAddr[2], es  ;  Critical Error flag
sub   ax, ax                          ; Clear error code
ret

GetDosFlags ENDP


;* GetTimeToElapse - Determines number of 5-second intervals that
;* must elapse between specified hour:minute and current time.
;*
;* Params: AH = Hour
;*         AL = Minute
;*
;* Return: AX = Number of 5-second intervals

Get Time To Elapse PROC NEAR

push  ax                    ; Save hour:minute
mov   ah, 2Ch               ; Request DOS Function 2Ch
int   21h                   ; Get Time (CH:CL = hour:minute)
pop   bx                    ; Recover hour:minute
mov   dl, dh
sub   dh, dh
push  dx                    ; Save DX = current seconds

mov   al, 60                ; 60 minutes/hour
mul   bh                    ; Multiply by specified hour
sub   bh, bh
add   bx, ax                ; BX = minutes from midnight
;  to activation time
mov   al, 60                ; 60 minutes/hour
mul   ch                    ; Multiply by current hour
sub   ch, ch
add   ax, cx                ; AX = minutes from midnight
;  to current time
sub   bx, ax                ; BX = minutes to elapse before
.IF   carry?                ; If activation is tomorrow,
add   bx, 24 * 60           ;   add number of minutes per day
.ENDIF

mov   ax, 60
mul   bx                    ; DX:AX = minutes-to-elapse-times-60
pop   bx                    ; Recover current seconds
sub   ax, bx                ; DX:AX = seconds to elapse before
sbb   dx, 0                 ;   activation
.IF   carry?                ; If negative,
mov   ax, 5                 ;   assume 5 seconds
cwd
.ENDIF

mov   bx, 5                 ; Divide result by 5 seconds
```

```
div    bx                      ; AX = number of 5-second intervals
ret

GetTimeToElapse ENDP


;* CallMultiplex - Calls the Multiplex Interrupt (Interrupt 2Fh).
;*
;* Uses:  IDstring
;*
;* Params: AL = Function number for multiplex handler
;*
;* Return: AX   = One of the following return codes:
;*              NOT_INSTALLED     IS_INSTALLED     NO_IDNUM
;*         ES:DI = Resident code segment:identifier string (function 0)
;*         ES:DI = Resident PSP segment address (function 1)
;*         ES:DI = Far address of shared memory (function 2)

CallMultiplex PROC FAR USES ds

push   ax                      ; Save function number
mov    ax, @code
mov    ds, ax                  ; Point DS to code segment

; First, check 2Fh vector. DOS Version 2.x may leave the vector null
; if PRINT.COM is not installed. If vector is null, point it to IRET
; instruction at LABEL NoMultiplex. This allows the new multiplex
; handler to pass control, if necessary, to a proper existing routine.

mov    ax, 352Fh               ; Request DOS Function 35h
int    21h                     ; Get interrupt vector in ES:BX
mov    ax, es
or     ax, bx
.IF    zero?                   ; If Null vector,
mov    dx, OFFSET NoMultiplex      ;  set vector to IRET instruction
mov    ax, 252Fh               ;  at LABEL NoMultiplex
int    21h                     ; Set interrupt vector
.ENDIF

; Second, call Interrupt 2Fh with function 0 (presence request). Cycle
; through allowable identity numbers (192 to 255) until TSR's multiplex
; handler returns ES:DI = IDstring to verify its presence or until call
; returns AL = 0, indicating the TSR is not installed.

mov    dh, 192                 ; Start with identity number = 192

.REPEAT
mov    ah, dh                  ; Call Multiplex with AH = trial ID
sub    al, al                  ;   and AL = function 0
push   dx                      ; Save DH and DS in case call
push   ds                      ;   destroys them
int    2Fh                     ; Multiplex
pop    ds                      ; Recover DS and
pop    dx                      ;   current ID number in DH
```

```
or      al, al                  ; Does a handler claim this ID number?
jz      no                      ; If not, stop search

.IF     al == 0FFh              ; If handler ready to process calls,
mov     si, OFFSET IDstring ;   point DS:SI to ID string, compare
mov     cx, IDstrlen        ;   with string at ES:DI returned
repe    cmpsb               ;   by multiplex handler
je      yes                     ; If equal, TSR's handler is found
.ENDIF

inc     dh                      ; This handler is not the one
.UNTIL  zero?                   ; Try next identity number up to 255

mov     ax, NO_IDNUM            ; In the unlikely event that numbers
jmp     e_exit                  ;   192-255 are all taken, quit

; Third, assuming handler is found and verified, process the multiplex
; call with the requested function number.

yes:
pop     ax                      ; AL = original function number
mov     ah, dh                  ; AH = identity number
int     2Fh                     ; Multiplex
mov     ax, IS_INSTALLED        ; Signal that handler has been found
jmp     exit                    ;   and quit

; Reaching this section means multiplex handler (and TSR) not installed.
; Since the value in DH is not claimed by any handler, it will be used as
; the resident TSR's identity number.  Save the number in resident code
; segment so multiplex handler can find it.

no:
mov     IDnumber, dh            ; Save multiplex identity number
mov     ax, NOT_INSTALLED       ; Signal handler is not installed
e_exit:
pop     bx                      ; Remove function number from stack
exit:
ret

CallMultiplex ENDP


;* InitTsr - Initializes DOS.version variables and multiplex data with
;* following parameters. This procedure must execute before calling
;* either the Install, Deinstall, or CallMultiplex procedures. Callable
;* from a high-level language.
;*
;* Uses:   IDstring
;*
;* Params: PspParam - Segment address of PSP
;*         StrParam - Far address of TSR's identifier string
;*         ShrParam - Far address of shared memory
;*
;* Return: AX = WRONG_DOS if not DOS Version 2.0 or higher
```

```
InitTsr PROC    FAR USES ds es si di,
PspParam:WORD, StrParam:FPVOID, ShrParam:FPVOID

mov     ax, @code
mov     ds, ax                  ; Point DS and ES
mov     es, ax                  ;   to code segment

; Get and store parameters passed from main program module

mov     ax, PspParam
mov     TsrPspSeg, ax           ; Store PSP segment address

mov     ax, WORD PTR ShrParam[0]
mov     bx, WORD PTR ShrParam[2]
mov     WORD PTR ShareAddr[0], ax    ; Store far address of
mov     WORD PTR ShareAddr[2], bx    ;   shared memory

push    ds
mov     si, WORD PTR StrParam[0]  ; DS:SI points to multiplex
mov     ax, WORD PTR StrParam[2]  ;  identifier string
mov     ds, ax
mov     di, OFFSET IDstring       ; Copy string to IDstring
mov     cx, STR_LEN               ;  at ES:DI so multiplex
;  handler has a copy
.REPEAT
lodsb                             ; Copy STR_LEN characters
.BREAK .IF al == 0                ;  or until null terminator
stosb                             ;  found
.UNTILCXZ

pop     ds                        ; Recover DS = code segment
mov     ax, STR_LEN
sub     ax, cx
mov     IDstrlen, ax              ; Store string length

INVOKE  GetVersion                ; Return AX = version number
ret                               ;  or WRONG_DOS

InitTsr ENDP

INSTALLCODE ENDS

END
/* PROGRAM INSTALL.ASM */

.MODEL  small, pascal
INCLUDE serv_tsr.inc

;* INSTALLATION SECTION - The following code and data are used only
;* during the TSR's installation phase. When the program terminates
;* through Function 31h, memory occupied by the following code and
;* data segments is returned to the operating system.
```

```
DGROUP  GROUP INSTALLCODE, INSTALLDATA

INSTALLDATA SEGMENT WORD PUBLIC 'DATA2' ; Data segment for installation phase

FILE_PTR DB ?        ; global declaration of the variables for
PUBLIC FILE_PTR      ; keeping track of file pointer ....

BYTE_CNT DB ?        ; Keeping track of the nibble to be send HIGH/LOW
PUBLIC BYTE_CNT ; 0-> Higher nibble , 1 -> Lower nibble

BUFFER DWORD ?  ; Buffer into which data is read from the file
PUBLIC BUFFER

INT_CNT DB ?         ; Keeps track and indicates EOF if value = 0ffh
PUBLIC INT_CNT

TEMP_HIGH DB ?  ; High nibble storing variable
PUBLIC TEMP_HIGH

TEMP_LOW DB ?   ; Low nibble storing variable
PUBLIC TEMP_LOW

NAME_OF_FILE DB 11(?); Name of file var to store filename from
PUBLIC NAME_OF_FILE       ; Client.

PUBLIC  _MsgTbl

_MsgTbl WORD   Msg0      ; Deinstalled okay
WORD    Msg1             ; Installed okay
WORD    Msg2             ; Already installed
WORD    Msg3             ; Can't install
WORD    Msg4             ; Can't find flag
WORD    Msg5             ; Can't deinstall
WORD    Msg6             ; Requires DOS 2+
WORD    Msg7             ; MCB damaged
WORD    Msg8             ; Invalid ID
WORD    Msg9             ; Invalid memory block address
WORD    Msg10            ; Successful access
WORD    Msg11            ; Can't access
WORD    Msg12            ; Unrecognized option

Msg0   BYTE   CR, LF, "TSR deinstalled", CR, LF, 0
Msg1   BYTE   CR, LF, "TSR installed", CR, LF, 0
Msg2   BYTE   CR, LF, "TSR already installed", CR, LF, 0
Msg3   BYTE   CR, LF, "Can't install TSR", CR, LF, 0
Msg4   BYTE   CR, LF, "Can't find MS-DOS Critical Error Flag", CR, LF, 0
Msg5   BYTE   CR, LF, "Can't deinstall TSR", CR, LF, 0
Msg6   BYTE   CR, LF, "Requires MS-DOS 2.0 or later", CR, LF, 0
Msg7   BYTE   CR, LF, "Memory Control Block damaged", CR, LF, 0
Msg8   BYTE   CR, LF, "No ID numbers available", CR, LF, 0
Msg9   BYTE   CR, LF, "Can't free memory block:  invalid address", CR, LF,0
Msg10  BYTE   CR, LF, "TSR successfully accessed", CR, LF, 0
Msg11  BYTE   CR, LF, "Can't access:  TSR not installed", CR, LF, 0
```

```
Msg12   BYTE   CR, LF, "Unrecognized option", CR, LF, 0

INSTALLDATA ENDS


INSTALLCODE SEGMENT PARA PUBLIC 'CODE2'

ASSUME ds:@data

;* GetOptions - Scans command line for argument of form /X or -X
;* where X = specified ASCII character. Presumes that argument is
;* preceded by either '/' or '-'. Comparisons are case insensitive.
;* Designed to be callable only from an assembly-language program.
;*
;* Params: ES = Segment address of Program Segment Prefix
;*         AL = Argument character for which to scan
;*
;* Return: AX    =  One of the following codes:
;*                  NO_ARGUMENT  if empty command line
;*                  OK_ARGUMENT  if argument found
;*                  BAD_ARGUMENT if argument not as specified
;*         ES:DI =  Pointer to found argument

GetOptions PROC NEAR

and   al, 11011111y             ; Make character upper case
mov   ah, NO_ARGUMENT           ; Assume no argument
mov   di, 80h                   ; Point to command line
sub   ch, ch
mov   cl, BYTE PTR es:[di]      ; Command-line count
jcxz  exit                      ; If none, quit
sub   bx, bx                    ; Initialize flag

; Find start of argument

loop1:
inc   di                        ; Point to next character
mov   dl, es:[di]               ; Get character from argument list
cmp   dl, '/'                   ; Find option prefix '/'
je    analyze
cmp   dl, '-'                   ;   or option prefix '-'
je    analyze
.IF   (dl != ' ') && (dl != TAB ) ; If not white space,
inc   bx                        ; Set flag if command line not empty
.ENDIF

loop  loop1

or    bx, bx                    ; Empty command line?
jz    exit                      ; Yes? Normal exit
jmp   SHORT e_exit              ; Error if no argument is preceded
;  by '-' or '/' prefixes

; '/' or '-' prefix found. Compare command-line character
```

```
; with character specified in AL.
analyze:
mov   ah, OK_ARGUMENT   ; Assume argument is okay
inc   di
mov   dl, es:[di]
and   dl, 11011111y     ; Convert to upper-case
cmp   dl, al            ; Argument as specified?
je    exit              ; If so, normal exit
mov   ah, BAD_ARGUMENT  ; Else signal bad argument,
inc   bx                ;   raise flag, and
jmp.  loop1             ;   continue scan

e_exit:
mov   ah, BAD_ARGUMENT
exit:
mov   al, ah
cbw                     ; AX = return code
ret

GetOptions ENDP


;* FatalError - Displays an error message and exits to DOS.
;* Callable from a high-level language.
;*
;* Params: Err = Error number
;*
;* Return: AL = Error number returned to DOS (except DOS 1.x)

FatalError PROC FAR,
Err:WORD

mov   ax, Err
push  ax
mov   bx, @data
mov   ds, bx            ; DS points to DGROUP
mov   bx, OFFSET _MsgTbl
shl   ax, 1             ; Double to get offset into _MsgTbl
add   bx, ax            ; BX = table index
mov   si, [bx]          ; DS:SI points to message
sub   bx, bx            ; BH = page 0

.WHILE 1
lodsb                   ; Get character from ASCII string
.BREAK .IF al == 0      ; Break if null terminator
mov   ah, 0Eh           ; Request video Function 0Eh
int   10h               ; Display text, advance cursor
.ENDW

pop   ax                ; Recover original error code

.IF   ax == WRONG_DOS   ; If DOS error,
int   20h               ;   terminate Program (Version 1.x)
.ELSE                   ; Else,
```

```
mov   ah, 4Ch                    ;  request DOS Function 4Ch
int   21h                        ;  terminate Program (2.x and later)
.ENDIF

FatalError ENDP


;* GetResidentSize - Returns the number of paragraphs between Program
;* Segment Prefix (PSP) and beginning of INSTALLDATA. This is the size of
;* the program less the now-unneeded installation code and data — in other
;* words, the size of the resident TSR block. The return value can serve as
;* the argument for the routine KeepTsr.
;*
;* Params: PspSeg - PSP segment address
;*
;* Return: AX = Number of paragraphs

GetResidentSize PROC FAR,
PspSeg:WORD

mov   ax, INSTALLDATA            ; Bottom of installation section
inc   ax                         ; plus one paragraph
sub   ax, PspSeg                 ; AX = number of paragraphs in
ret                              ; block to be made resident

GetResidentSize ENDP


;* KeepTsr -  Calls Terminate-and-Stay-Resident function to
;* make TSR resident. Callable from a high-level language.
;*
;* Params:  ParaNum - Number of paragraphs in resident block
;*
;* Return:  DOS return code = 0

KeepTsr PROC    FAR,
ParaNum:WORD

mov   ax, @data
mov   ds, ax                     ; DS:SI points to "Program
mov   si, OFFSET Msg1            ; installed" message
sub   bx, bx                     ; BH = page 0

.WHILE 1
lodsb                            ; Get character from ASCII string
.BREAK .IF al == 0               ; Break if null terminator
mov   ah, 0Eh                    ; Request video Function 0Eh
int   10h                        ; Display text, advance cursor
.ENDW

mov   dx, ParaNum                ; DX = number of paragraphs
mov   ax, 3100h                  ; Request Function 31h, err code = 0
int   21h                        ; Terminate-and-Stay-Resident
ret
```

```
KeepTsr ENDP


;* FreeTsr - Deinstalls TSR by freeing its two memory blocks: program
;* block (located at PSP) and environment block (located from address
;* at offset 2Ch of PSP). Callable from a high-level language.
;*
;* Params:  PspSeg - Segment address of TSR's Program Segment Prefix
;*
;* Return:  AX = 0 if successful, or one of the following error codes:
;*         MCB_DESTROYED  if Memory Control Block damaged
;*         INVALID_ADDR  if invalid block address

FreeTsr PROC    FAR,
PspSeg:WORD

mov     es, PspSeg            ; ES = address of resident PSP
mov     ah, 49h               ; Request DOS Function 49h
int     21h                   ; Release memory in program block

.IF     !carry?               ; If no error:
mov     es, es:[2Ch]          ; ES = address of environment block
mov     ah, 49h               ; Request DOS Function 49h
int     21h                   ; Release Memory in environment block
.IF     !carry?               ; If no error:
sub     ax, ax                ; Return AX = 0
.ENDIF                        ; Else exit with AX = error code
.ENDIF

ret

FreeTsr ENDP


;* CallMultiplexC - Interface for CallMultiplex procedure to make it
;* callable from a high-level language. Separating this ability from
;* the original CallMultiplex procedure keeps assembly-language calls
;* to CallMultiplex neater and more concise.
;*
;* Params: FuncNum - Function number for multiplex handler
;*         RecvPtr - Far address to recieve ES:DI pointer
;*
;* Return: One of the following return codes:
;*           NOT_INSTALLED    IS_INSTALLED    NO_IDNUM
;*         ES:DI pointer written to address in RecvPtr

CallMultiplexC PROC FAR USES ds si di,
FuncNum:WORD, RecvPtr:FPVOID

mov     al, BYTE PTR FuncNum  ; AL = function number
call    CallMultiplex         ; Multiplex

lds     si, RecvPtr           ; DS:SI = far address of pointer
```

```
mov    [si], di              ; Return ES:DI pointer for the
mov    [si+2], es            ; benefit of high-level callers
ret

CallMultiplexC ENDP


INSTALLCODE ENDS

END
/* SERV_TSR.INC */


COMMENT +

To force TSR to set up its own disk transfer area, define the equate
constant DTA_SIZ with the desired buffer size in bytes.
DTA_SIZ               EQU    40     ; DTA size in bytes
+
STACK_SIZ             EQU    400h   ; Stack size in bytes
STR_LEN               EQU    20     ; Max length of multiplex ID string

TRUE                  EQU    -1
FALSE                 EQU    0
NULL                  EQU    0
TAB                   EQU    09     ; ASCII code for TAB key
LF                    EQU    10     ; ASCII code for line feed
CR                    EQU    13     ; ASCII code for ENTER key
ESCAPE                EQU    27     ; ASCII code for ESCAPE key
SHFT_STAT             EQU    417h   ; Offset of shift-key status mask at
;  0:417h in the ROM BIOS data area

; Return codes used by procedures in HANDLERS and INSTALL modules
NOT_INSTALLED         EQU    0      ; TSR not installed
IS_INSTALLED          EQU    1      ; TSR is installed
ALREADY_INSTALLED     EQU    2      ; TSR already installed
UNKNOWN_PROBLEM       EQU    3      ; Can't install
FLAGS_NOT_FOUND       EQU    4      ; InDos / CritErr flags not found
CANT_DEINSTALL        EQU    5      ; Can't deinstall
WRONG_DOS             EQU    6      ; Can't handle DOS 1.x
MCB_DESTROYED         EQU    7      ; Memory control block problem
NO_IDNUM              EQU    8      ; No identity numbers available
INVALID_ADDR          EQU    9      ; Free memory block problem
OK_ACCESS             EQU    10     ; TSR accessed successfully
CANT_ACCESS           EQU    11     ; TSR not installed: can't access
BAD_ARGUMENT          EQU    12     ; Unrecognized argument
NO_ARGUMENT           EQU    13     ; No argument in command line
OK_ARGUMENT           EQU    14     ; Okay argument in command line

IFNDEF  FPVOID                      ; Already in DEMO.INC
FPVOID  TYPEDEF FAR  PTR            ; Type for far pointer to void
ENDIF

INTR          STRUCT                ; Structure of handler information
```

```
Num         BYTE ?              ; Interrupt number
Flag        BYTE ?              ; Active flag (for device interrupts)
OldHand     FPVOID ?            ; Address of original handler routine
NewHand     FPVOID ?            ; Address of TSR's handler
INTR        ENDS

ERRINFO     STRUCT              ; Structure of extended error
AxReg       WORD  ?             ; information (see "Preserving
BxReg       WORD  ?             ; Existing Data" in Chapter 11
CxReg       WORD  ?             ; of Programmer's Guide)
DxReg       WORD  ?
SiReg       WORD  ?
DiReg       WORD  ?
DsReg       WORD  ?
EsReg       WORD  ?
ErrResrv    WORD  3 DUP (0)
ERRINFO     ENDS
; Prototypes
Install             PROTO FAR PASCAL,
Param1:WORD, Param2:WORD, Param3:WORD, Param4:FAR PTR FAR

Deinstall           PROTO FAR
; No arguments

InitTsr             PROTO FAR PASCAL,
PspParam:WORD, StrParam:FPVOID, ShrParam:FPVOID

KeepTsr             PROTO FAR PASCAL ParaNum:WORD

FreeTsr             PROTO FAR PASCAL PspSeg:WORD

CallMultiplex       PROTO FAR
; AL = Function number for multiplex handler

CallMultiplexC      PROTO FAR PASCAL FuncNum:WORD, RecvPtr:FPVOID

GetResidentSize     PROTO FAR PASCAL PspSeg:WORD

FatalError          PROTO FAR PASCAL Err:WORD

GetOptions          PROTO NEAR
; ES = Segment of Program Segment Prefix
; AL = Argument character for which to scan
```

/* SERV_DEM.INC */

```
BUFFERSIZE   EQU   2048   ; Buffer size in bytes for disk I/O

MDA          EQU   0      ; Adapter constants
CGA          EQU   1
MCGA         EQU   2
EGA          EQU   3
VGA          EQU   4
```

```
MONO        EQU    0     ; Display constants
COLOR       EQU    1

BACKSP      EQU    08    ; ASCII code for BACKSPACE key
TAB         EQU    09    ; ASCII code for TAB key
LF          EQU    10    ; ASCII code for line feed
CR          EQU    13    ; ASCII code for ENTER key
ESCAPE      EQU    27    ; ASCII code for ESCAPE key
LEFT        EQU    75    ; Scan code for LEFT arrow
CRLF        EQU  0A0Dh   ; Value for carriage return/line feed

; Bit masks for shift status
shIns       EQU  80h
shCaps      EQU  40h
shNum       EQU  20h
shScroll    EQU  10h
shAlt       EQU  08h
shCtl       EQU  04h
shLeft      EQU  02h
shRight     EQU  01h

;* LoadPtr - Macro to load far address into segment:register pair, or
;* near address into register.
;*
;* Params:  sgmnt - Segment to be loaded with segment address
;*          reg - Register to be loaded with offset address
;*          pointer - Pointer to address
;*
;* Shows:   Instructions - lds    les
;*          Directives - MACRO    IF       IFIDNI    ELSE
;*                 ELSE    IFENDIF  .ERR     ENDM
;*          Operators - < >    ;;

LoadPtr MACRO sgmnt, reg, pointer     ;; Macro definition
IF @DataSize                          ;; If far pointer, and
IFIDNI <sgmnt>, <ds>                  ;; if 1st argument is DS,
lds reg, pointer                      ;; load DS:reg with far address
ELSEIFIDNI <sgmnt>, <es>              ;; or if 1st argument is ES,
les reg, pointer                      ;; load ES:reg with far address
ELSE                                  ;; Generate error if not DS or ES
.ERR <First argument must be DS or ES>
ENDIF
ELSE                                  ;; If near pointer,
IFIDNI <sgmnt>, <es>                  ;; and if segment is ES,
push ds                               ;; ensure ES points to
pop  es                               ;; same segment as DS
ENDIF
mov reg, pointer                      ;; Then load reg with near address
ENDIF
ENDM

;* GetVidOffset - Macro to determine offset in video segment that corresponds
;* to given screen coordinates.
;*
```

```
;* Params:  Row - Screen row (top line = 0)
;*          Col - Screen column (leftmost column = 0)

GetVidOffset MACRO Row, Col
mov ax, Row
mov bl, vconfig.cols
mul bl
add ax, Col
shl ax, 1
ENDM

;* Vector - Macro to read current interrupt vector, store it, and replace it.
;*
;* Shows:   Equates - @CodeSize    @code
;*
;* Params:  num - Vector number
;*          old - Pointer to doubleword for storing old vector
;*          new - Pointer to new handler

Vector MACRO num, old, new      ;; Macro definition
push ds                         ;; Save DS and ES registers
push es
mov  ah, 35h                    ;; AH = DOS function number
mov  al, num                    ;; AL = interrupt number
int  21h                        ;; Get Interrupt Vector
mov  WORD PTR old[0], bx        ;; Store it
mov  WORD PTR old[2], es
IF @CodeSize                    ;; If medium or large model,
lds dx, new                     ;;   load DS from parameter
ELSE
mov bx, @code                   ;; Else ensure DS points to
mov ds, bx                      ;;   to code segment
mov dx, WORD PTR new            ;; DS:DX equals new vector
ENDIF
mov ah, 25h                     ;; AH = DOS function number
int 21h                         ;; Set Interrupt Vector
pop es                          ;; Restore ES and DS
pop ds
ENDM

PBYTE     TYPEDEF       PTR BYTE     ; Pointer to byte
PWORD     TYPEDEF       PTR WORD     ; Pointer to word
PSWORD    TYPEDEF       PTR SWORD    ; Pointer to integer
PDWORD    TYPEDEF       PTR DWORD    ; Pointer to integer
NPBYTE    TYPEDEF NEAR  PTR BYTE     ; Near pointer to byte
FPBYTE    TYPEDEF FAR   PTR BYTE     ; Far pointer to byte
FPVOID    TYPEDEF FAR   PTR          ; Far pointer to void
PSEG      TYPEDEF WORD               ; Segment value

; Structure for video configuration
VIDCONFIG        STRUCT
mode             BYTE   ?
dpage            BYTE   ?
rows             BYTE   ?
```

```
cols            BYTE  ?
display         BYTE  ?
adapter         BYTE  ?
sgmnt           WORD  ?
VIDCONFIG       ENDS
PVIDCONFIG      TYPEDEF PTR VIDCONFIG

; Structure for FindFirst and FindNext
FILEINFO        STRUCT
pad             BYTE   21 DUP (?)  ; pad to 43 bytes
attrib          BYTE   ?           ; file attribute
time            WORD   ?           ; file time
date            WORD   ?           ; file date
count           DWORD  ?           ; file size
filename        BYTE   13 DUP (?)  ; filename
FILEINFO        ENDS
PFILEINFO       TYPEDEF PTR FILEINFO
; Structure for disk statistics
DISKSTAT        STRUCT
total     WORD   ?          ; Total clusters
avail     WORD   ?          ; Available clusters
sects     WORD   ?          ; Sectors per cluster
bytes     WORD   ?          ; Bytes per sector
DISKSTAT        ENDS
PDISKSTAT       TYPEDEF PTR DISKSTAT

; Structure for parameter block
PARMBLK         STRUCT
env       PSEG    ?         ; Segment of environment block
taddr     FPBYTE  ?         ; Segment:offset address of tail
fcb1      FPBYTE  ?         ; Segment:offset address of 1st FCB
fcb2      FPBYTE  ?         ; Segment:offset address of 2nd FCB
PARMBLK         ENDS
PPARMBLK        TYPEDEF PTR PARMBLK

; Prototypes from      COMMON.ASM
GetVer                 PROTO PASCAL
GetVidConfig           PROTO PASCAL
StrWrite               PROTO PASCAL Row:WORD, Col:WORD, Sptr:PBYTE
ClearBox               PROTO PASCAL Attr:WORD, Row1:WORD, Col1:WORD,
Row2:WORD,             Col2:WORD
DisableCga             PROTO PASCAL
EnableCga              PROTO PASCAL
SetCurPos              PROTO PASCAL Row:WORD, Col:WORD
GetCurPos              PROTO PASCAL
StrInput               PROTO PASCAL Row:WORD, Col:WORD, Max:WORD, Sptr:PBYTE

; Prototypes from MISC.ASM
WinOpen                PROTO PASCAL Row1:WORD, Col1:WORD,
Row2:WORD,             Col2:WORD, Attr:WORD
WinClose               PROTO PASCAL Adr:WORD
SetCurSize             PROTO PASCAL Scan1:WORD, Scan2:WORD
GetCurSize             PROTO PASCAL
GetShift               PROTO PASCAL
```

```
GetMem          PROTO PASCAL
GetKeyClock     PROTO PASCAL Row:WORD, Col:WORD
VeriAnsi        PROTO PASCAL
VeriPrint       PROTO PASCAL
VeriCop         PROTO PASCAL
SetLineMode     PROTO PASCAL Line:WORD
Pause           PROTO PASCAL Duration:WORD
Sound           PROTO PASCAL Freq:WORD, Duration:WORD
WriteTTY        PROTO PASCAL Sptr:PBYTE, icolor:WORD
Colors          PROTO PASCAL Logic:WORD, Attr:WORD,
Row1:WORD,      Col1:WORD, Row2:WORD, Col2:WORD
Exec            PROTO PASCAL Spec:PBYTE, Block:PPARMBLK,
CtrBrk:PTR FAR,
CtrlC:PTR FAR,
Criterr:PTR FAR
BinToHex        PROTO PASCAL Num:WORD, Sptr:PBYTE
NewBlockSize    PROTO PASCAL Adr:WORD, Resize:WORD
Initialize      PROTO PASCAL
EXTERNDEF       IntToAsc:PROC


; Prototypes from MATH.ASM
AddLong         PROTO PASCAL Long1:SDWORD, Long2:SDWORD
SubLong         PROTO PASCAL Long1:SDWORD, Long2:SDWORD
ImulLong        PROTO PASCAL Long1:SDWORD, Long2:SDWORD
MulLong         PROTO PASCAL Long1:DWORD, Long2:DWORD
IdivLong        PROTO PASCAL Long1:SDWORD, Short2:SWORD, Remn:PSWORD
DivLong         PROTO PASCAL Long1:DWORD, Short2:WORD, Remn:PWORD
Quadratic       PROTO PASCAL aa:DWORD, bb:DWORD, cc:DWORD,
r1:PDWORD, r2:PDWORD

; Prototypes from FILE.ASM
ChangeDrive     PROTO PASCAL Drive:WORD
GetDiskSize     PROTO PASCAL Drive:WORD, Disk:PDISKSTAT
SetDta          PROTO PASCAL Dta:FPBYTE
GetDta          PROTO PASCAL Dta:FPBYTE
ReadCharAttr    PROTO PASCAL Attr:PWORD
GetCurDir       PROTO PASCAL Spec:PBYTE
GetCurDrive     PROTO PASCAL
CopyFile        PROTO PASCAL Imode:WORD, Fspec1:PBYTE, Fspec2:PBYTE
DelFile         PROTO PASCAL Fspec:PBYTE
MakeDir         PROTO PASCAL Pspec:PBYTE
RemoveDir       PROTO PASCAL Pspec:PBYTE
ChangeDir       PROTO PASCAL Pspec:PBYTE
GetAttribute    PROTO PASCAL Fspec:PBYTE
SetAttribute    PROTO PASCAL Attr:WORD, Fspec:PBYTE
RenameFile      PROTO PASCAL Fspec1:PBYTE, Fspec2:PBYTE
GetFileTime     PROTO PASCAL Handle:WORD, Sptr:PBYTE
FindFirst       PROTO PASCAL Attr:WORD, Fspec:PBYTE, Finfo:PFILEINFO
FindNext        PROTO PASCAL Finfo:PFILEINFO
UniqueFile      PROTO PASCAL Attr:WORD, Pspec:PBYTE
OpenFile        PROTO PASCAL Access:WORD, Fspec:PBYTE
CloseFile       PROTO PASCAL Handle:WORD
CreateFile      PROTO PASCAL Attr:WORD, Fspec:PBYTE
```

```
CreateNewFile       PROTO PASCAL Attr:WORD, Fspec:PBYTE
ReadFile            PROTO PASCAL Handle:WORD, Len:WORD, Pbuff:PBYTE
WriteFile           PROTO PASCAL Handle:WORD, Sptr:PBYTE
Rewind              PROTO PASCAL Handle:WORD
GetFileSize         PROTO PASCAL Handle:WORD
GetStr              PROTO PASCAL Strbuf:PBYTE, Maxlen:WORD
StrCompare          PROTO PASCAL Sptr1:PBYTE, Sptr2:PBYTE, Len:WORD
StrFindChar         PROTO PASCAL Ichar:SBYTE, Sptr:PBYTE, Direct:WORD


;* Global variables defined with EXTERNDEF are public in the module
;* in which they are defined, and external in other modules in which
;* they are used.
;*
;* Shows:   Directive              - EXTERNDEF
;*          Predefined text macro - @CurSeg

.DATA
EXTERNDEF  vconfig:VIDCONFIG  ; Video configuration
EXTERNDEF  _psp:PSEG          ; Segment of Program Segment Prefix
EXTERNDEF  _env:PSEG          ; Segment of environment block
@CurSeg ENDS                  ; End .DATA so any subsequent
;  include is outside segment
```

/* PROGRAM SERVER_C.ASM */

```
.MODEL  small, pascal
.DOSSEG
INCLUDE SERV_DEMO.INC
INCLUDE SERV_TSR.INC

.STACK
.DATA
EXTRN BUFFER:DWORD  ;var into which data is read from file
EXTRN TEMP_LOW:BYTE ;signifying the lower nibble transfer
EXTRN TEMP_HIGH:BYTE;and the higher nibble.
EXTRN FILE_PTR:BYTE ;The file pointer variable
EXTRN INT_CNT :BYTE ;EOF counter
EXTRN BYTE_CNT:BYTE ;Signifying lower/higher nibble transfer
EXTRN name_of_file:BYTE; Name of file variable ...

 _CNT BYTE ?         ;Count for the file name length
HOT_SCAN EQU 00h   ;For hot key and install process
HOT_SHIFT EQU 00h
HOT_MASK EQU 00h
ZERO EQU 00h


COUNT_PAR_PORT BYTE ZERO ; Shared variable ....
Handle        WORD  ?  ;Handle for file
.CODE

FILENAMERECV PROC FAR
push ax
push bx
```

```
push dx
push cx

;************ INITIALIZING CLIENT PORTS *****************

mov al,00h
mov dx,0378h
out dx,al
; Receiving the nibbles and decoding as in pooling method
.IF (INT_CNT <=016h )
.IF (INT_CNT >= 00h )
;* To receive the file name for the next 22 int's
add int_cnt,01h
mov dx,0379h
in al,dx
.IF ( byte_cnt == 00h)
mov temp_high,al
and al,080h
.IF ( al == 080h)
and temp_high,070h
.ELSE
.IF (al == 00h)
and temp_high,0F0h
.ENDIF
.ENDIF
.ELSE
mov temp_low,al
and al,080h
.IF( al == 080h)
and temp_low,070h
.ELSE
.IF ( al == 00h)
and temp_low,0f0h
.ENDIF
.ENDIF
.ENDIF

.IF (byte_cnt == 01h)
mov cx,04h
mov al,temp_low
ror cx
or temp_high,al
mov name_of_file[_cnt],temp_high
mov byte_cnt,00h
jmp just_exit
.ENDIF
jmp file_trns_exit
.ENDIF
.ENDIF

.IF (INT_CNT == 016h)
mov byte_cnt,00h ; Reinitializing of byte_cnt variable
.ENDIF
```

```
.IF (INT_CNT == 0FFh)     ; EOF marker .....
mov file_ptr,00h  ; to send to client 0ffh
mov int_cnt ,00h  ; for client to stop interrupting .
pushf
mov al,0f8h
mov dx,0378h
out dx,al
popf

jmp file_trns_exit

.ENDIF
;**********************************************
.IF (byte_cnt < 1)
call OpenfileCopy ; Open File And Set Pointer to next byte
.IF !carry?
call ReadFile ; If no error proceed for byte transfer...
.ENDIF
add byte_cnt,01h
jmp file_trns_exit
.ENDIF

.IF(byte_cnt > 3)
mov byte_cnt,00h
.ENDIF

.IF (BYTE_CNT == 01h)
mov al,BYTE PTR buffer[01h]
and al,0F8h
mov dx,0378h
out dx,al
jmp file_trns_exit
.ENDIF

.IF (BYTE_CNT == 02h)
mov al,BYTE PTR buffer[02h]
and al,0F8h
mov dx,0378h
out dx,al
jmp file_trns_exit
.ENDIF

.IF (BYTE_CNT == 03h)
mov al,BYTE PTR buffer[03h]
and al,0F8h
mov dx,0378h
out dx,al
jmp file_trns_exit
.ENDIF

file_trns_exit:
add byte_cnt,01h

just_exit:
```

```
pop cx
pop dx
pop bx
pop ax

retf
FILENAMERECV ENDP

;************************************************************************

OpenFileCopy PROC

mov  ax,3D00h          ; Request DOS to open file to read from
mov  dx,OFFSET name_of_file ; DS:DX points to file specification
int  21h               ; Open File

.IF   carry?           ; If it doesn't exist,
mov    ah, 3Ch     ; request create file
sub    cx,cx       ; with normal attributes
int    21h         ; Create File

.ENDIF

; .IF !carry?
pushf
mov    Handle, ax ; store file handle
mov    bx, ax
mov    ax, 4200h  ; Request DOS to reset file pointer
sub    cx, cx     ; to next byte of file
sub     dx, dx
mov    dl,FILE_PTR
add    FILE_PTR,04h
int    21h
popf

; .ENDIF


ret

OpenFileCopy ENDP

;************************************************************************
; This procedure reads the contents of the file one byte at a time and
; sends it to the Client..... after decoding .

ReadFile PROC

mov     ah, 03Fh              ; Request DOS Function 3Fh
.mov    cx, 04h               ; CX = number of bytes to READ
mov     bx, Handle            ; BX = file handle
mov     dx, OFFSET Buffer     ; DS:DX points to buffer
int     21h                   ; Write to file
```

```
.IF (ax == 00h)                 ; If EOF is detected
push ax
pushf                           ; Close the file
mov ah,3Eh
mov bx,Handle
int 21h
popf                            ; And exit
pop ax
mov int_cnt,0ffh
jmp read_exit
.ENDIF

.IF    (ax != cx)               ; If number of bytes READ !=

stc                             ;  number requested, set carry

.ENDIF                          ; flag to indicate failure
pushf                   ; Save carry flag

mov     ah, 3Eh         ; Request DOS Function 3Eh
mov     bx,Handle
int     21h             ; Close file

popf                    ; Recover carry

;****************** SEND TO CLIENT *********************


mov al,BYTE PTR BUFFER[0h]
and al,0F8h
mov dx,0378h
out dx,al
jmp ret_exit

read_exit:
mov al,0f8h
mov dx,0378h
out dx,al

ret_exit:
ret

ReadFile ENDP


;*************************************************************************

@CurSeg ENDS

;* INSTALLATION SECTION - The following code and data are used only
;* during SNAP's installation phase. When the program terminates
;* through Function 31h, the above code and data remain resident;
;* memory occupied by the following code and data segments is returned
```

```
;* to the operating system.

DGROUP  GROUP INSTALLCODE, INSTALLDATA

INSTALLDATA SEGMENT WORD PUBLIC 'DATA2'

IDstr   BYTE    'SNAP DEMO TSR', 0      ; Multiplex identifier string
INSTALLDATA ENDS

INSTALLCODE SEGMENT PARA PUBLIC 'CODE2'
ASSUME  ds:@data

Begin   PROC    NEAR

mov     ax, DGROUP
mov     ds, ax                  ; Initialize DS
; Before calling any of the TSR procedures, initialize global data
INVOKE  InitTsr,                ; Initialize data
es,                             ; Segment of PSP
ADDR IDstr,                     ; Far address of multiplex ID string
ADDR COUNT_PAR_PORT ; Far address of memory shared
;  with multiplex handler
.IF     ax == WRONG_DOS         ; If DOS version less than 2.0,
jmp     exit                    ;   exit with message
.ENDIF

;********************DEINSTALL ******************************


mov al,'d'
call GetOptions
cmp ax,NO_ARGUMENT
je installtsr
cmp ax,OK_ARGUMENT
je deinstalltsr
mov al,'c'
call GetOptions
cmp ax,BAD_ARGUMENT
je exit


; This section sets up the TSR's interrupt handlers and
; makes the program memory-resident

installtsr:

push    es                      ; Preserve PSP address

mov     ax, @code
mov     es, ax
mov     bx, OFFSET FILENAMERECV ; ES:BX points to Snap
```

```
;Initializing all variables ...

mov file_ptr,00h
mov _cnt,00h
mov int_cnt,00h
mov byte_cnt,00h
INVOKE Install,          ; Install handlers
HOT_SCAN,                ; Scan code of hot key
HOT_SHIFT,               ; Bit value of hot key
HOT_MASK,                ; Bit mask for shift hot key
es::bx                   ; Far address of Snap procedure

pop    es                ; Recover PSP address
or     ax, ax            ; If nonzero return code,
jnz    exit              ;   exit with appropriate message
INVOKE GetResidentSize,  ; Get size of resident block
es
sti
push ax
push dx
mov al,00h
out 21h,al
mov dx,037ah
mov al,10h
out dx,al
pop dx
pop ax
INVOKE KeepTsr,          ; Make TSR memory-resident
ax                       ; AX = size of block in paragraphs

; This section deinstalls the resident TSR from memory

deinstalltsr:

INVOKE Deinstall         ; Unchain interrupt handlers

.IF    ax > OK_ARGUMENT  ; If successful,
INVOKE FreeTsr,          ;   deinstall TSR by freeing memory
ax                       ; Address of resident seg
.ENDIF                   ; Else exit with message
exit:
INVOKE FatalError,       ; Exit to DOS with message
ax          ; Error number

Begin  ENDP

INSTALLCODE ENDS

END    Begin
```

PROJECT NUMBER THREE - To develop a Key-Diskette for copy-protection

INTRODUCTION

This project aims at developing a software lock using key diskettes for a software application. A few tracks of some sector is made bad by various methods. The software application is loaded only if this key diskette is present in the disk drive.

A program using the BIOS interrupt 13H, function request 04H finds out the bad tracks and sectors. This information is stored in static structure "struct data". Now we have a key diskette. A second program, which must be executed before the application software, checks for the presence of the key diskette, using the static structure obtained from the first program, and loads the application software.

For decoding of key diskette, Terminate and Stay Resident (TSR) programs are used. A sampling TSR, is executed before the INT 13H service by trapping this interrupt. This TSR stores the information about every request made by an software application to the INT 13H and also the results returned by the INT 13H to the software application.

A simulating is then used the information gathered by the sampling TSR and traps INT 13H completely, passes the results directly to each of its request. In this manner it fools the software application into believing that the actual key diskette is present and the software application is loaded.

FLOPPY DISK CONTROLLER

The floppy disk controller (FDC) in the IBM PC is a separate PCB known as the IBM 5 1/4 inch Diskette device Adapter. In the majority of clones, the FDC is part of the multi I/O board, motherboard, multifunction board or HDC board.

A single FDC board can support upto four FDDs. The FDC is linked to the system bus of the PC and appears as a set of I/O ports to the CPU. In addition, it is connected to the Channel 2 of the DMA controller. The FDC interrupts the CPU at level 6. The FDC usually performs data transfer in DMA mode.

The FDC in the PC is designed around an intelligent programmable floppy disk controller IC. The original IBM design used the NEC 765 IC. Intel's 8272, SMC8s FDC 765A and Rockwell's R6765 are the other pin compatible ICs used by various clones. Most of the functions of the FDC are done by the FDC IC. Some additional functions are done by hardware circuits external to the FDC IC. The distribution of functions the FDC IC and the external hardware are listed below :-

1. FDC IC Functions :
   a) Generating MFM format for the data to be recorded
   b) Decoding and executing commands such as seek, read, format etc.
   c) Error detection by CRCC generation/checking
   d) Data synchronisation
2. External Hardware Functions :
   a) Selection of FDD
   b) Switching on motor in the FDD
   c) Resetting the FDC IC
   d) Enabling/disabling interrupt and DMA signals of FDC IC
   e) Data separation logic
   f) Write pre-compensation logic
   g) Line drives for signals to the FDD
   h) Line receivers for signals from the FDD

The FDC IC has provisions to perform device selection and motor-on control by appropriate commands. However the PC design does not make use of this feature. Instead, an external output port is used for performing these functions under software control.

Input/Output Ports

The FDC has three I/O ports; Data port, Main status register control port. The first two are inside the FDC IC and the third port is in the external hardware. The addresses of these three ports are listed in Table

Port Address	Port Name	Location	Port Type
3F5	Data Register	FDC IC	Bidirectional I/O
3F4	Main Status	FDC IC	Input Register
3F2	Digital Control Port	External to FDC IC	Output

Data Port

This port is used by the software for three different purposes :

1. While issuing a command to the FDC IC, command and command parameter bytes are issued to the FDC IC through port. The FDC IC stores the different parameters and the command in its internal registers.
2. After a command is executed, the FDC IC stores a set of status parameters in the internal registers. These are read by the CPU software through this port. The different status bytes are presented by the FDC IC in a specific sequence.
3. In the programmed mode and interrupt mode of data transfer, the data port is used for transferring data between the FDC IC and CPU by IN or OUT instruction.

Main Status Register (MSR)

This port is used by the software to read the overall status information regarding the FCC IC and the FDDs. Before initiating a floppy disk operation, the software reads this port to confirm the readiness condition of the FDC and the drives and to verify the status of the previously initiated command/ operation. The different bits of this register are given below :

Bit 0 - FDD 0 : Busy in seek mode
BIt 1 - FDD 1 : Busy in seek mode
Bit 2 - FDD 2 : Busy in seek mode
Bit 3 - FDD 3 : Busy in seek mode
Bit 4 : FDC Busy; Read/Write command in progress
Bit 5 - Non-DMA mode
Bit 6 - DIO; Indicates the direction of data transfer between the FDC IC and the CPU
Bit 7 - PQM; Indicates data register is ready for data transfer.

Digital Control Port :

This port is used by the software to control certain FDD and FDC IC functions. The bit assignments of this port are listed below :

Bit 0 and 1 : Device number to be selected
Bit 2 : RESET FDC IC
Bit 3 : Enable FDC interrupt and DMA request signals
Bit 4 to 7 : Turn ON the motor in disk drive 0,1,2, or 3 respectively.

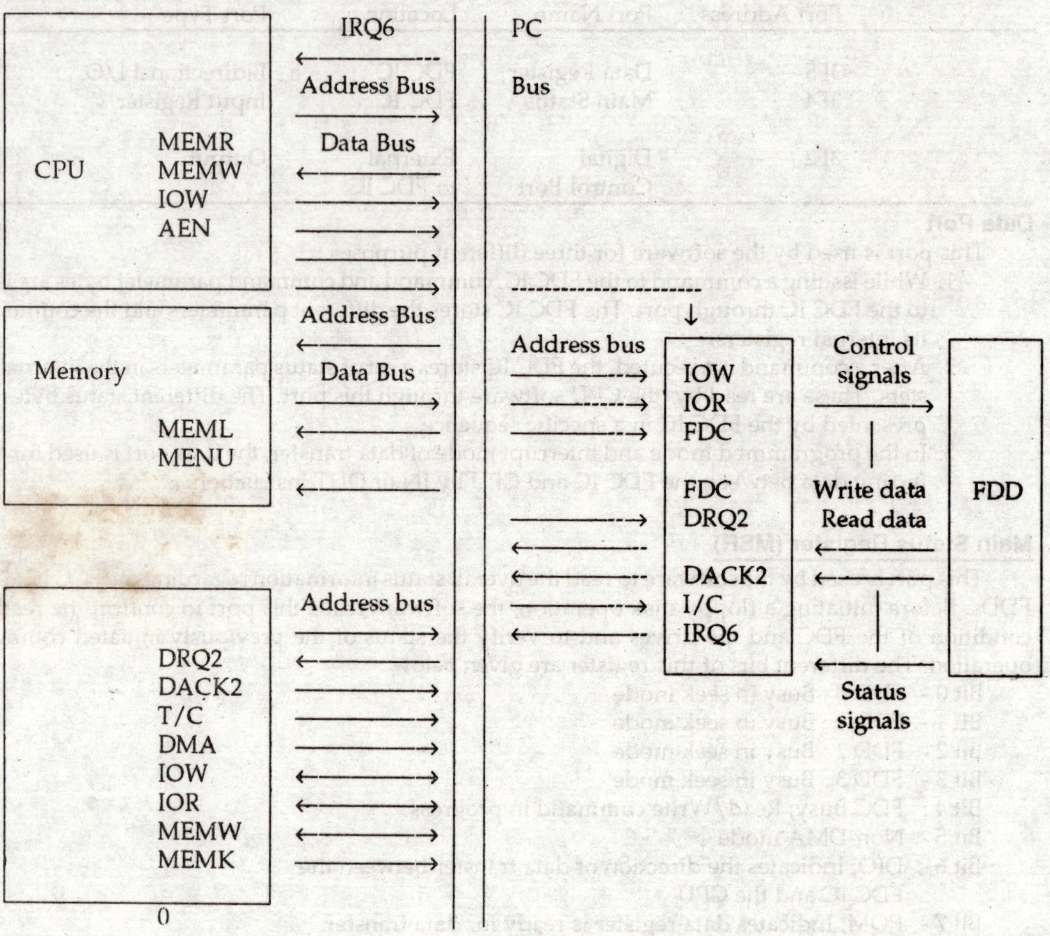

FDC In PC

The BIOS is a set of low-level software routines that forms a buffer or a shield between the hardware and other programs. The BIOS routines themselves communicate with devices directly, but they shield that complicated interface from the user's program by providing a simpler interface by which the user can access them.

These services are provided in ROM on the IBM personal computer, so they are available as soon as the computer starts running.

The BIOS services are invoked by using software interrupts. Some of the services have their own interrupts, while other are grouped together and invoked with the same interrupt.

Invoking the BIOS service :

1) Set up values in certain registers
2) Invoke the service by issuing the INT instruction with the correct interrupt number.
3) Output is placed in the registers or data areas.

BIOS Interrupt 13H :

The BIOS function requests invoked via this interrupt allows I/O operations on disk drives (both flexible and fixed).

There are several functions available via this interrupt.

The function number is stored in the AH register.

AH	Function request
00H	Reset disk

01H	Get disk status
02H	Read disk sectors
03H	Write disk sectors
04H	Verify sectors
05H	Format track
08H	Get current drive parameters
09H	Initialize drive characteristics
0AH	Read long sectors
0BH	Write long sectors
0CH	Seek to cylinder
0DH	Alternate disk reset.
10H	Test for drive ready
11H	Recalibrate drive
14H	Controller internal diagonostics
15H	Get disk type
16H	Disk status change
17H	Set disk type.

For this project we have used the function request number 04H.

This function request verifies the contents of one or more sectors on the disk. This verification does not compare the data with data in memory. It simply determines whether the data can be read without a CRC (Cyclical Redundancy error) occurring.

Input : The following are set before invoking the request.

AH : This register must contain 04H to specify the verify disk sectors.

AI : Identifies the number of consecutive sectors to verify.

DL : This register is set to identify the drive to verify. 0 & 1 identify flexible diskette drives. 80H and 81H identify fixed disks.

DH : This register is set to identify the head number; 0 or 1 for diskettes.

CH : This register is set to identify the low 8 dits of a 10-bit cylinder number. For diskette the track number.

CL : This register is set to identify the sector number of the first sector to be verified.

Error Conditions :

The carry flag (CF) is set to 1, Register AH contains the error code.

If no error, then CF and AL are set to zero.

Error code in Register AH:

AH value	Description
00H	No error occurred
01H	An invalid function request was issued.
02H	Address mark was bad. Sector ID was invalid if not found.
03H	Attempt to write on a write-protected disk.
04H	Requested sector not found
05H	Rest operation failed
06H	Media was removed
07H	Initialization error occurred. Drive parameter activity failed.
08H	DMA failure
09H	DMA boundary error occurred. The data doesn't reside in the 64K byte DMA area.
0AH	A bad sector flag was detected. The sector has been marked as unusable so the I/O operation could no proceed.
10H	A CRC parity error occurred when reading the disk and the Error Correction Code (ECC) could not correct the problem.
11H	Parity error occurred when reading the disk, but RCC corrected the problem.
20H	Controller failed
40H	Seek operation failed
80H	Time-out error occured. Drive failed to respond.
AAH	Drive is not ready

BBH	Undefined error occurred
CCH	Write fault occurred on the selected drive
FFH	Sense operation failed (XT only).

TERMINATE AND STAY RESIDENT PROGRAMS

Microsoft officially maintains that TSRs are not possible but DOS has provided a program called PRINT.COM which allows users to print files in the background. Hence, it turned that DOS was a poor cousine of an actual multi-tasking operating system.

Suppose we are writing a program in a word processor, say Wordstar. To save a program we would press Ctrl-KD. After a fraction of the main menu of the Wordstar. But behind the scenes.

To start with wordstar informs DOS it wants a disk write operation performed. Since DOS is unable to write to disk by itself it in turn tells the ROM BIOS. The I/O routines in the ROM then proceeds to perform the actual write. After it finishes, it notifies DOS, which in turn tells Wordstar and we are back at the menu level.

What we have seen is a process of one entity interrupting another to get its work done. The user interrupts Wordstar, which interrupts DOS which interrupts ROM BIOS, which in turn executes the routine. When we type ctrl-KD, Wordstar interrupts DOS, which may have been performing some house keeping tasks. DOS makes a mental note of what it was doing and goes about interrupting the ROM BIOS. The ROM BIOS stops what it was doing and begins to write to disk. After finishing that, it signals DOS and resumes from where it left off. DOS does the same after passing the message to Wordstar. And we are back at the menu level.

TSRs are possible because IBM designed the PC as an interrrupt oriented machine.

When we work in Wordstar, this program is loaded into memory, just above COMMAND.COM. And when we quit Wordstar, the memory space it occupies is freed by DOS. It can now be used to load any other application we may want to work on.

With a TSR, the rules are slightly different. Once a TSR is loaded into memory, it remains there. For example if we have a TSR above COMMAND.COM and we wanted to work in Wordstar. Wordstar would be loaded above the TSR program. With the press of the Ctrl and Alt keys we can alternate between the TSR program and Wordstar. Of course, it is essential that after loading the TSR program, there is enough memory left to load Wordstar.

TSR should be written in a way that disallows DOS from overwriting it when another application is loaded.

Making a Program Resident in Memory :

Borland's Tubro C offers a very simple and easy way to write TSRs.

Example

```
Main ( )
{
Keep (0,1000);
}
```

After running this program say for about 10 to 15 times, the keep ( ) function reserves memory each time the program run. If we try loading an application now DOS will give a memory error.

The first parameter of keep ( ) is of no consequence, a zero is passed always. The second parameter tells DOS how much memory to reserve. It asks DOS to reserve 16* 1000 =16000 byte of memory. All it does is disallows any other program from being loaded.In the process,it prevents the computer from being used. It usually hangs the machine.A simple reboot is required to free the machine.

Capturing Interrupts :

There is a part in memory called the IVT (Interrupt vector Table). This contains addresses of BIOS routines, that write to or read from disk, that takes keybord inputs that write to screen, verify diskette sectors, etc. (e.g. A table known as IVT (Interrupt Vector Table)) is placed in a part of the memory.

. A program goes to this IVT and replace an address there with the address of its own code. Now a call to a certain interrupt would active this program code, rather than the actual routine.

The functions provided by Turbo C for capturing interrupts are - getvect( ) : This functions searches the IVT for the address of a specific interrupt. The parameter passed by this function is the interrupt number in hexa decimal.The address of every routine in ROM BIOS or DOS is stored in four memory location of the IVT.

setvect ( ) : This function sets a specific address in the IVT to point to the address of a user defined function.

Keep ( ):This function (as explained before) reserves memory for the program.

For example.

```
# include <dos.h>
void interrupt (*old) ( );
void interrupt new ( );
char far *scr = (char far*) 0 x 417;
main ( )
{
old = getvect (0 x 08);
setvect (0 x 08, new);
} keep (0,1000);
void interrupt new ( )
{ *scr =64;
(*old) ( );
}
```

'old' is defined as pointer to a function. It is of type interrupt, which returns nothing.An interrupt function new ( ) is also defined. This function will be excuted first, before the actual timer routine in the ROM BIOS is activated. The routine is INT 08H

Address OX417 contains 8 bits wich are manipulated for turning on CAPS LOCK, NUM LOCK. ALT KEY etc.

The microprocessor has memory location of its own. These are known as registers and there are in all 14 registers of two bytes each.These registers are used to add subtract and even evaluate conditional statements like the 'if' in a program. The registers are used to store address and data. They are thus in a state of constant flux, changing dynamically to reflect the changing state of the computer.

Normally, when a program calls a function only three of these registers are pushed onto the stack. But when a function is defined as being of interrupt, 12 of the 14 registers are pushed onto the stack. We are defining the function as an interrupt function because the routine being dealt with are ROM BIOS routines and are also known as Interrupts service routines.

The next statement is doing what is 'casting'. A variable is defined on one side as pointer to a character and balanced on the other by making it point to a byte only.

In the main part of the program, first the address of the timer routine is assigned to the pointer 'old'. When this program is executed, whenever the timer ticks, the function 'now' is executed.

Redefining interrupt 8, which is the interrupt for the timer and assigning it the function new ( ) causes the line

*scr = 64;

to be executed every 18.2 times (the number of times the timer routine is executed in one second). This results in the 6th bit of the byte 0x417 being set to 1 every 18.2 times a second. Hence, the CAPs lock is turned on forever as long as the machine is not rebooted.

Finally, control is handed back to the timer routine in the ROM BIOS, otherwise the machine will hang. In short, writing TSRs is just a matter of stealing interrupts, reassigning the address in the IVT to point to the function we want to execute and keeping the program resident in memory.

BRIEF HISTORY OF SOFTWARE LOCKING

With the widening scope of computer application in today's world, where almost every sphere of life uses computers in some way or the other, the number of software applications, and types of hardware available are increasing day by day. Numerous vendors and 'brand names' for all kinds of software have entered the market.

Software piracy has become a big business to make quick money. Hence,developers of software applications have resorted to precautions like software and hardware locking methods to present their software from being pirated.

The various methods for software locking being used today are :

1. Writing some data or code in the 41st track of a 360KB disk.
2. Format some particular tracks with different parameters.
3. Removing the magnetic coating from a few tracks of a particular sector using laser or some special liquid.

A combination of hardware and software locking techniques is also used.

1. Programming the I/O controller by directly reading and writing to the floppy disk controller using IN/OUT instructions, which cannot be trapped as the BIOS ROUTINES.
2. Using the ROM BIOS stamp : when a software is loaded on a particular machine, a stamp of the ROMBIOS - manufacturer's name, code, date of manufacture, etc. is taken and used as a code for running the software.
3. PCMICA cards are used. These are the size of credit cards and have to be inserted into a slot provided in the machines hardware.The cards act as locks, unique for each copy of the software.
4. Small infrared transmitters are used, wich can be kept on the table top and the software is loaded only if it receives certain infrared signals from the transmitters.

DESIGN OF SOFTWARE LOCK

1. **Making a key diskette :**
   A floppy disk is taken and some tracks of any sector is made bad arbitarily, by removing the coating on the surface or first making a fine scratch with a needle. A program in C (giving the program listing) is used to sample this key diskette-i.e. find out what tracks of which sector is bad and what is the error code. This information is stored in a static struct data with field - sector number and track number.
2. **Program to check for the presence of the key diskette :**
   A second program then uses the above mentioned static structure 'data' to check for the key diskette. It invokes the INT 13H to check for the specified error code in the track number and sector number specified by the static struct 'data'. The INT 13H also checks if the adjacent sector are good or not. If all the above conditions specified are fulfilled, the application software is loaded.
3. **Integrating the above modules with the application software:**
   An object module of the above program (that checks for the presence of the key diskette) is made after compilation.The object code is then given to the manufacturer of the application software, along with the code the application software.

WARNING : The following section doesn't permit the reader to try breaking locks of commercial softwares. It is merely for understanding the process that this section is included.

DECODING OF A SOFTWARE LOCK

An application software that comes with a key diskette has some code just above the actual software code, that checks for the key diskette. This code invokes the interrupt 13H for disk drive function like read, write verify sector etc. If a particular sector has some specific cylinders or tracks that are bad, and the adjacent sectors are good, then the software is loaded.

Detail of the process:

The code in the application software invokes BIOS routine INT 13H with the appropriate values in the processor registers. The registers contain the following information

AH	=	function request number
AL	=	number of sectors
CH	=	cylinder/track number
CL	=	sector number
Dh	=	head number
DL	=	Drive ('O' for a drive)
es;bx	=	pointer to data buffer

These parameters are passed to the int 13H routine.The control to the IVT which has the starting address of the int 13H suroutine. The instruction of these BIOS subroutine starts getting excuted. After it does BIOS subroutine starts getting executed. After it does the various checks- like looking for bad sector or reading the data stored in a particular sector etc., the results are stored in the above registers.

The result might look as follows:-

Carry flag - if set, denotes error

AH - error code

etc.

These results, after execution of the int 13H, are passed back to the application software. The results are matched against those key diskette will return. If the same result are returned then the application software knows that the key diskette was inserted and the application software gets loaded.

1. SAMPLING TSR PROGRAM : For breaking the lock a sampling terminate and stay resident program is used. The sample TSR traps interrupt 13H, i.e the address of the int 13H routine in the Interrupt Vector Table is changed to point the starting address of this sampling TSR.

So when the int 13H is invoked, control passed to the TSR program the parameters - registers values are sampled by this TSR,which stores them some where in its own memory. Then control is passed to the actual int 13H subroutine. Now the checking of the cylinders/tracks for the requested sector is done and results stored in the processor registers. Again control passes back to the sampling TSR which stores the result for the corresponding request. Now the sampling TSR knows what results to return to the application software to load it - i.e. it knows the code for key diskette used with the application software.

A program in Assembly language or 'C' is written that contains various modules. This program is invoked when applications software is loaded. Command line arguments are used to invoked the program for starting the sampling, stopping the sampling, reporting or printing out the results of sampling etc. This program is called by using the value FFH in the AH register for int 13H. (FFH function request is not used by the BIOS routine). Register AL stores 01,02,03.... for the various options given above. Various modules are used , which execute the required instructions according to the command line argument.

If we send the request with AH = FFH and AL = 00H, then the module that invokes the sampling TSR procedure that stores the request and correspondiing result in memory.

If we send a request with AH = 03 , then the module to print out data stored in memory from above is executed.

Now that we know what results a key diskette returns for a particular request send by the application software we can a simulating TSR program.

2. Simulating TSR program:

This is another program in Assembly language or'C' that again captures int 13H, i.e. its address is stored in the IVT in place of INT 13H routine address.

This program stores the results for the request made by the application software in the required registers.

Now the application software is loaded, the key diskette, and the command to run the application software typed. When the code in the application software invokes int 13H to check for the presence of a key diskette, this TSR program is activated. It matches request sent by the application software with the one it has obtained from the sampling TSR and returns the corresponding results through the registers. The actual int 13H is never invoked at all. Hence, the application software is fooled into believing that the key diskette was used and it gets loaded.Application software usually uses Norton Disk Utilities or PC Tools to check for the particular sector in the key diskette.

The error code returned by a bad sector, using the int 13H is very important. The application software checks for a particular sector which has some specifies tracks /cylinders bad, not just once but 6 or 7 times, as some error might occur in lhose due to some other reasons. The application software could be loading itself only if a particular error code is returned via the AH register.

```
/* INTERRUPT 13H——FUNCTION 04H        VERIFY DISK SECTORS * /
#include<stdio.h>
#include<dos.h>
#include<conio.h>
#inlude<process.h>
#include"data.c"
char check sector(int,int);
void error check (char);
/*struct data {
```

```
int sector;
int track;
};
struct data badsector[20]; */
int count=0;
union REGS inreqs,outreqs;
int track no, sector no;
 /*unsigned char res[39][15]; */
main()
{   unsigned char err code;
int i.k.fleo=1.f1=0;    char c1,c2,c3;
inreqs.h.ah=0x04;
inreqs.h.d1=0;
inreqs.h.dh=0;
for(k=0;k<=1;k++)  {          track no=p1[k].track;
setor no=p1[k].sector;
printf("Verifying track%d\n ",track no,sector no);
/*call a function to check for sectors */
err code=check sector(track no,sectorno);
switch(err code)
{
case 0;{
printf("no error\n");
break;
}
default:{
error check(err code);
/* store sector no & track no. in struct data */
/* ++count ;
bad sector[conut].sector=sector no;
bad sector[count].track =track no; */
}
{
/*check the adjacent sectors*/.
—sector no;
err code=check sector(track no, sector no);
switch(err code)

{
case 0; {}
for(i=0;i<=count;i++)
{
printf("%d /t %d /t/n",bad sector[i].sector sector[i].track);
}
getch(); */
/*check for above and adjacent sectors */
for(i=0;i<=count;i++)

{
c1=check sector [i], track, bad sector [i]. Sector);
—bad sector [i]. sector;
c2=check sector (bad sector (i).track,bad sector [i]. sector);
++bad sector[i].sector;
++bad sector[i].sector;
```

```
c3=check sector(bad sector[i].track,bad sector[i].sector);
if((c2 & c3)==1)
flaq=0;
if(c1 & flag)!=1)
{
printf ("HELLO\n");
f1=0;
}
else
{
printf ("ERROR\n");
f1=1;
}
getch ( );
}
if (f1==0) {
execl ("HELLO.EXE",NULL);
}
else
{
printf ("outside for loop\n");
printf ("ERROR\n");
}
void error check(char e c)
{
switch (e c)
(
case 0x01;{
printf("invalid function was issued\n");
break;
}
case 0x02; {
printf("address mark was bad\n");
printf("sector id was invalid or not found\n");
break;
}
case 0x03; {
printf("diskette is write protected\n");
break;
}
case 0x04: {
printf("sector not found\n");
break;
}
case 0x05; {
printf("rest operation failed \n");
break;
}
case 0x06; {
printf("media removed\n");
break;
}
case 0x07; {
printf("initialization error\n");
```

```
printf("drive parameters wrong\n");
break;
}
case 0x08; {
printf("DMA failure\n");
break;
}
case 0x09; {
printf("DMA accross segment end\n");
break;
}
case 0x0a; {
printf("bad sector flag\n");
break;
}
case 0x10 ; {
printf("CRC.parity error occured\n");
break;
}
case 0x11; {
printf("parity error occured\n");
printf("ECC corrected the problem\n");
break;
}
case 0x20; {
printf("controller failure\n");
break;
}
case 0x40 ; {
printf("a seek operation has failed\n");
break;
}
case 0x80; {
printf("drive failed to respond\n");
break;
}
case 0xaa; {
printf("drive not ready\n");
break;
}
case 0xbb ; {
printf("undefined error\n");
break;
}
case 0xcc; {
printf("write fault occured on the selected drive\n");
break;
}
case 0xff; {
printf("sense operation failed\n");
break;
}
}
}
```

```
char check sector (int tn,int sn)
{
inreqs.h,ch=tn;
inreqs.hcl=sn;
inreqs.hal=1;
int86 (0x13, &inreqs,&outreqs);
res[tn] [sn]=outreqs.hah;
return(res[tn] [sn]);
}

/* INTERRUPT 13H— FUNCTION 04H */
/* VERIFY DISK SECTORS */
/* VERSON 2 */
#include<stdio.h>
#include<dos.h>
#include<conio.h>
union REGS inreqs.outerqs;
main()
{
int track no,sector no;
unsigned char treast;
inreqs.h.ah=0x04;
inreqs.h.d1=0;
inreqs.h.dh=0;
for (track no=0; track no<40;track no++)
{
for (sector no=1;sector no<=9;sector no++)
{
printf("verifying track %d, sector %d\n ",track no.sector no);
inreqs.h.ch =track no;
inreqs.h.cl = sector no;
inreqs.h.al =1;
int86(0x13, &inreqs);
/*  res[track no][sector no]=outreqs.h.ah; */
tres=outreqs.h.ah;
switch (tres)
{
case 0: {
printf("no error\n");
break;
}
default:{
printf("verification failed\n");
if((tres & 0x80)==0x8)
printf("disk did not respond within time out\n");
if((tres & 0x40)==0x40)
printf("seek failure\n");
if((tres & 0x20)==0x20)
printf("error reported by controller\n");
if((tress & 0x10)
printf("CRC error on data read\n");
if((tres & 0x08)==0x08)
print("DMA overrun\n");
if((tres & 0x04)
```

```
printf("requested sector not found\n");
if((tres & 0x02)
printf("disk is write protected\n");
if((tres & 0x01)==0x01)
printf("illegal command given to driver\n");
break;
}
case 0x02: {
printf("address mark was bad\n");
printf("sector id was invalid or not found\n");
break;
}
case 0x03: {
printf("diskette is write protected\n");
break;
}
case 0x04:{
printf("sector not found\n");
break;
}
case 0x05: {
print("rest operation failed\n");
break;
}
case 0x06: {
printf("media removed\n");
break;
}
case 0x07: {
printf("intialization error\n");
printf("drive parameters wrong\n");
break;
}
case 0x08: {
printf("DMA failure\n");
break;
}
case 0x09  : {
printf("DMA across segment end\n");
break;
}
case 0x0a: {
printf("bad sector flag\n");
break ;
}
case 0x10 : {
printf("CRCparity error occured\n");
break;
}
case 0x11 : {
printf("parity error occured\n");
printf(ECCcorrected the problem\n");
break;
}
```

```
case 0x20: {
printf("controller failure\n");
break;
}
case 0x40 : {
printf("a seek operation has failed\n");
break;
}
case 0x80 : {
printf("drive failed to respond\n");
break;
}
case 0xaa: {
printf("drive not ready\n");
break;
}
case 0xbb : {
printf("undefined error\n");
break;
}
case 0xcc; {
printf("write fault occurred on the selected drive\n");
break;
}
case 0xff : {
printf("sense operation failed");
break;
} */
}
}
getch ();
}
}
*MAIN PROGRAM TO CHECK FOR KEY DISKETTE */
#include<stdio.h>
#inciude<dos.h>
#inciude<conio.h>
#inciude<process.h>
#inciude<errno.h>
union REGS inreqs,outreqs;
#inciude"data.c"
#inciude"check se.c"
#include"error ch.c"
char check sector (int,int);
void error check(int);
char err code;
main()
{
int count,track no, sector no,flag1,flag2,flag3;
inreqs.h.ah=0x04;
inreqs.h.dh=0;
inreqs .h.d1=0;
flag 3=1;·
count=0;
```

```
clrscr ();
printf("INSERT KEY DISKETTE\n");
printf("AND PRESS ANY KEY\n");
getch();
while(flag3==1) && (count(11))
{
track no=bad sector[count].track;
sector no=bad sector [count].sector;
err code=check sector (track no,sector no);
flag1=0;
flag2=0;
if(err code!=0)
{
/*    printf("checking for bad sector\n");
printf ("sector %d .track %d\n",sector no,track no);*/
/*call error check */
error check(err code);
flag1=1;
}
else
{
flag3=0;
break;
}
/* check adjacent sectors */
if(flag1==1)
{
++sector no;
/* printf ("sector %d ,track %d\n", sector no. track no);    */ err code=check sector (track no.sector
no );if (err    code==0)
{
/* printf ("no error \n"); */
—sector no;
— sector no;
/* printf("checking adjacent sector 2 \n");
printf("sector %d ,track %d\n,sector no,track no): */
err code=check sector(track no,sector no);
if(err code==0)
{
/* printf("no error\n"); */
flag2=1;
}
else { flag3=0;break;}
}
else { flag3=0; break; }
}
if(flag1==0)
{
flag3=0;
break;
else
{
if(flag1 &&flag2)
flag3=1;
```

```
else flag3=0;
}
++ count;
} /*end while */
if(count==11)
{
execlp("INDIA.EXE",NULL);
perror("file not found\n");
}
else
printf("NOT KEY DISKETTE\n");
}
/*program containing struct intialization */
#include<stdio.h>
struct data {
int sector;
int track;
};
static struct data bad sector[]={
{4,11},
{4,112},
{4,13},
{4,14},
{4,15},
{4,16},
{4,17},
{4,18},
{4,19},
{4,20},
{4,21}
};

/*fuction to check for bad sectors */
/* if sector is bad ,returns an error code */
char check sector (int tn,int sn)
{
int result;
inreqs.h.ch=tn;
inreqa.hcl=sn;
inreqs.h.al=1;
int86(0x13.&inreqs,&outreqs);
result=outreqs.h.ah;
return(result);
}

/*BIOS INTERRUPT NO. 13H */
/*FUNCTION REQUEST NO. 02H - READ DISK SECTORS */
#include<stdio.h>
#include<conio.h>
#include<stdib.h>#include<dos.h>
union REGS inreqs, outreqs;
struct REGPACK addreqs;
main()
{
```

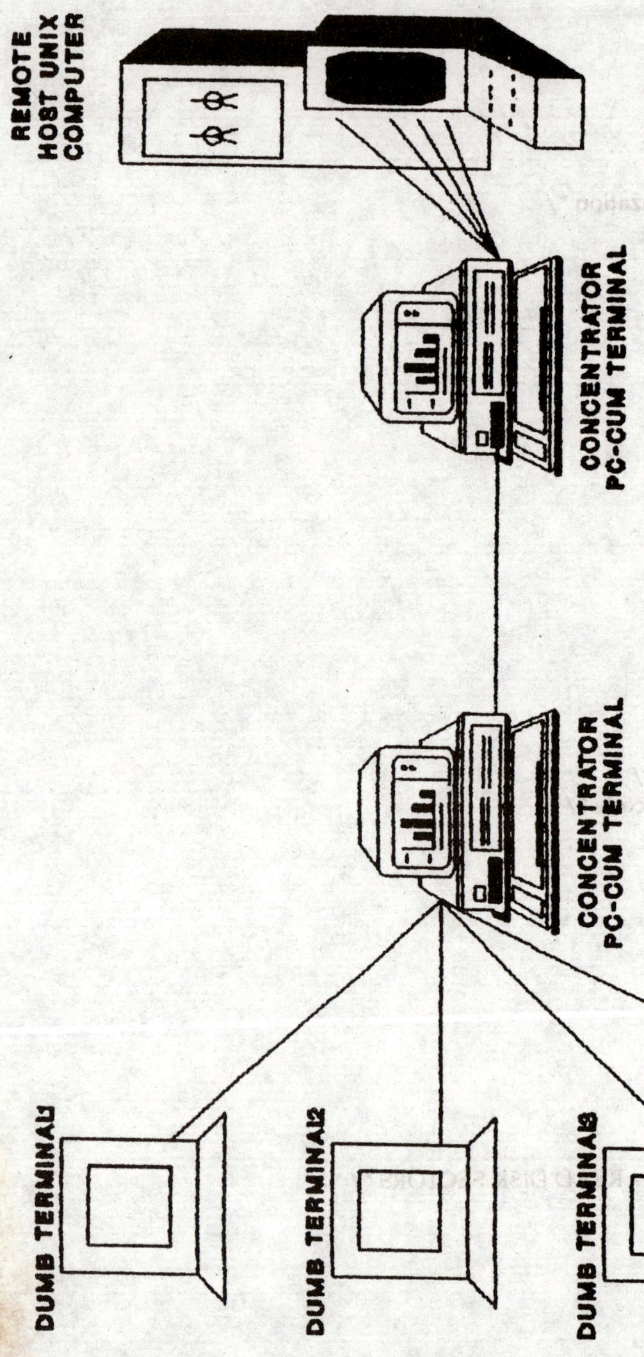

Fig. B : THE IDEA BEHIND THIS PROJECT IS TO BUID TERMINAL SERVER FOR REMOTE COMMUNICATION

```
int track no,sector no, first sector;
int i;
unsigned char result;
printf ("Enter the track number to read\n");
scanf ("%d",&track no);
printf ("Enter the sector no.of the first sector to read\n");
scanf ("%d",%first sector);
printf("Enter the number of the sectors to read\n");   scanf ("%d",%sector no);   inreqs.h.ah=0x02;
inreqs.h.al=sector no;
inreqs.h.d1=0;
inreqs.h.dh=0;
inreqs.h.ch=track no;
inreqs.h.c1=first sector;
addreqs.r es=0x40;    addreqs.r bs=0x50;
int86(0x13,&inreqs,&outreqs);
for(i=0x40;i<0x50;i++) {
result = inportb (i);
printf ("data at 0x%X = 0x%x\n",i, result);
return 0;
}}
```

PROJECT NUMBER FOUR - Development of a Concentrator based network

8250 UART:

Serial communications is so complicated that special chips have been designed to do the work of sending or receiving and timing the strings of bits that comprise serial data. Such a chip is called a universal asynchronous receiver transmitter, or UART. Without UARTs, communications programming would be extremely complicated.

The 8250 UART is the programmable LSI used in asynchronous serial port in the PC. The major features of 8250 are briefly outlined below:

* The 8250 is a programmable asynchronous communication controller. The communication parameters and formats are specified by the software.
* The 8250 provides modem control and status signals.
* The Baud rate is programmble.
* Generates standard baud rates upto 9600 bauds.
* The number of data bits per character is programmable.
* The parity type (Odd, Even or No parity) is programmable.
* The no. of stop bits is programmable.
* The 8250 has seven I/O ports and ten internal registers.
* The 8250 provides double buffering of data both in the transmitter section and in the receiver section.
* Data transfer between the 8250 and the system can be performed either in the programmed mode or in the interrupt mode.
* The 8250 provides separate clock inputs for receiver and transmitter sections thus providing an option of fixing different baud rates for the receiver and transmitter section.
* The 8250 can detect a false start bit.
* The 8250 provides line-break generation and detection.
* The 8250 has multiple pins for each of the following functions: chip select, Read (Data Input Stroble) and Write (Data stroble).
* The 8250 has an internal clock oscillator circuit facilitating direct connection of a crystal.
* The 8250 provides external status signals to indicate when the chip has been selected and when the CPU is reading data from it.
* The 8250 can be programmed to raise interrupts for four different reasons.

Program the 8250 UART chip

DOS supports two communications ports, and hence two UARTS. Their base addresses are kept at 0040:0000 for COM1 and 0040:0002 for COM2. (A base address is the lowest two-byte port address of the group of port addresses by which the UART is accessed). On all machines but the PCjr COM1 starts at 3F8H and COM2 at 2F8H; the PCjr keeps its internal modem at 3F8H and COM1 at 2F8H.

As already mentioned the 8250 has ten programmable one-byte registers by which to control and monitor the serial port. Most are devoted to initializing the port, a process that can be rather complicated. The ten registers are accessed through seven port addresses, numbers 3F8H (or 2F8H-2FEH). In five cases, the register accessed at a particular port address depends on how bit 7 is set in the line control register, which is the only register at port 3FBH. Here are the registers:

3F8H (OUT, BIT 7=0 AT 3F8H) Transmitter Holding register 3F8H (IN,bit 7=0 at 3F8H) Receiver Data Register 3F8H (OUT 7=1 at 3F8H) Baud-Rate Divisor (Low byte 3F8H (IN,bit 7=1 at 3F8H) Baud-Rate divisor (high byte 3F8H (OUT, bit 7=9 at 3F8H) Interrupt Enable Register

3FAH (IN)	Interrupt Identification Register
3FBH (OUT)	Line control Register
3FCH (OUT)	Modem Control Register
3FDH (IN)	Line Status Regisger
3FEH (IN)	Modem Status Register

Of the ten registers, only six are necessary for serial communications. The **transmitter holding** register holds the byte of data about to be sent and the **receiver data** register keeps the most recently received byte of data. The **line control and line status** registers initialize and monitor the serial line, using the baud rate placed in the two baud-rate divisor registers. Of the remaining four registers, the **modem control** and **modem status** registers are used only for modem communications and the two **interrupt related** registers are used only in interrupt-driven routines.

Initialize the serial port

When a communication port is initialized ("opened"), all the parameters by which it operates are set. These parameters include the word length, the number of stop bits, the parity setting, and the baud rate. The **word length** is the number of bits that form the basic data unit.

Line Control Register Initialization

The bit settings for the line control register at 3FBH (or 2FBH) are as follows:

bit 1-0 Character length, 00=5 bit, 01=6 bits
10=7 bits; 11=8 bits
2 Number of stop bits, 0=1, 1=1.5 if the character length is 5, else=2.
3 Parity, 1=parity bit is generated, 0=not.
4 Parity Type, 0=odd, 1=even.
5 Stick parity, Causes parity to always be 1 or 0
0=disabled.
1=always 1 if bit 3=1 & bit 4=0.
or 1=always 0 if bit 3=1 & bit 4=1
or 1=no parity if bit 3=0.
6 Set Break, Causes output of string of OS as signal to remote station, 0=disabled, 1=break.
7 Toggles port addresses of other registers on chip.

Ordinarily bits 5-7 are set to 0. The others are given the values of the desired communications protocol.

Monitor the status of the serial port

The **line status** register of the 8250 UART sets up the communications protocol. This register is located at the port address that is 5 higher than the base address for the particular COM channel. Ordinarily it is constantly monitored during communications activity. During data transmission, the register tells when the prior character has been sent off, lest the program write the next character on top of it. In data reception, the register informs the program when a character arrives, so that the program can remove it before it is overlain by the one that follows. The contents are as follows:

bit 0 1=a byte of data has been received
1 1= received data has been overrun (prior character was not removed in time)
2 1=parity error (probably from line noise)

3 1=framing error (transmission is out of sync)
4 1=break detect (a long string of 1's has been received, indicating that the other station requests an end to transmission)
5 1=transmitter holding register empty (this register is given output data)
6 1=transmitter shift register empty (this register takes holding register data and converts it to serial form)
7 1=time-out (off-line).

PROJECT WORK

The project deals with the software development to emulate a terminal controller. The concepts of terminal emulation, multiplexing and error detection have been incorporated in the our software. The entire project uses the Serial mode of transmission.

Some functions used in the program:

* kbhit ()

It is included in the Library conio.h Checks for currently available keystrokes.

Declaration : int kbhit (void);

Remarks : kbhit checks to see if a keystroke is currently available. Any available keystrokes can be retrieved with getch or getche.

Return value : On success(if a keystroke is available),returns a non-zero integer.If a keystroke is not available, returns zero.

* Inport, inportb, outport, outportb

The above mentioned functions are included in the library <dos.h>.

inport reads a word from a hardware port.
inportb reads a byte from a hardware port.
outport outputs a word to a hardware port.
outputb outputs a byte to a hardware port.

Declarations :

* unsigned inport (unsigned portid);
* unsigned char inportb (unsigned portid);
* Void outport (unsigned portid, unsigned value);
* Void outportb (unsigned portid, unsigned char value);

Remarks :

* inport works just like the 80x86 instruction IN. It reads the low byte of a word from portid, the high byte from portid +2.
* inportb is a macro that reads a byte.
* outport works just like the 80x86 instruction OUT. It writes the low byte of value to portid, the high byte to portid +1
* outportb is a macro that writes value.

Portid :

Inport port that import and inportb read from; outport port that outport and outportb write to.

Value :

Word that outport writes to portid; byte that outportb writes to portid.

If inportb or outportb is called when DOS.H has been included, they are treated as macros that expand to inline code.

Return value :

* inport and inportb returns the value read.
* outport and outportb do not return.

Program (s) description:

* Description of the software for terminal emulation

Port Addresses :

0x02F8 for the transfer of data.
0x02FD for checking the status of the above port.

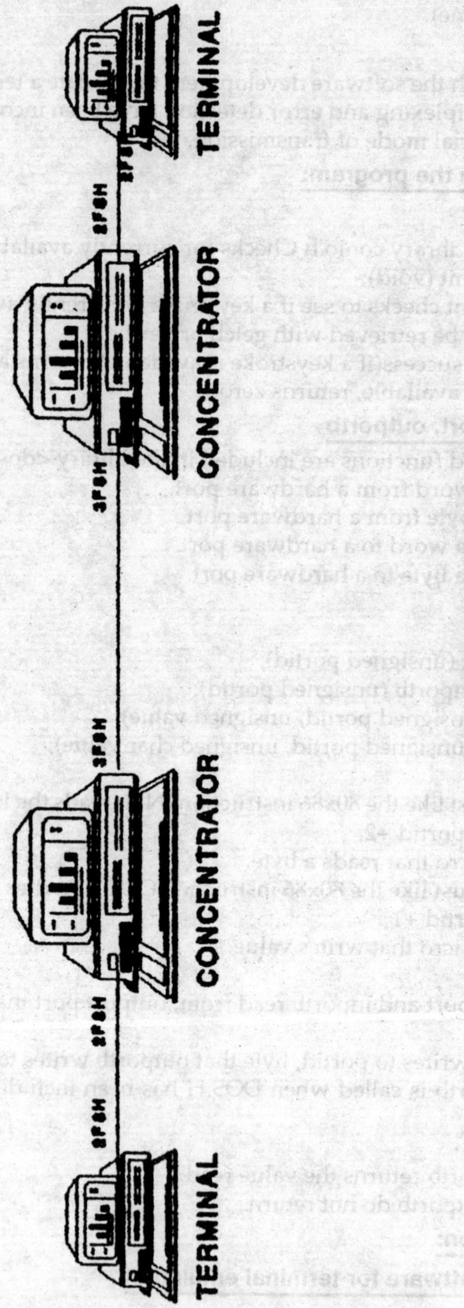

Fig. C : PORT CONNECTIONS
FOR A
CONCENTRATOR BASED NETWORK

Initially the program checks for the keyboard hit. If any input is given to the computer it accepts it and sends it to the other computer. Then the status register is checked for the arrival of data in the port. On the arrival of data, the 0th bit (LSB) of the status register gets enabled, the data is accepted and is displayed on the screen.

*** Description of the software for the multiplexer/CONCENTRATOR**

The software is implemented using two multiplexers (PCs and each of which is connected to a terminal. The multiplexer itself acts like a terminal.

Initially, the multiplexer checks for the source of the input (support terminal or the mux itself). On receiving the input, it accepts a header to it and transmits the data to the multiplexer only if the previous data intended for the other mux has been transmitted. The 5th bit of the status register gets enabled once the data has been sent.

After this, the multiplexer checks whether the data has arrived for the other mux. If so, the 0th bit of the status register gets enabled. It then waits for the arrival of the second character. On it's arrival the header (first character) is scanned and according to it, the second character is either displayed on the screen or sent to the terminal after being assured that the previous character has been transmitted to the terminal. The above procedure is repeated for an infinite number of times.

The same software is run on both the multiplexers.

***Description of the software for the support terminals**

Initially the program checks for the keyboard hit. If any input is given to the computer it accepts it and sends it to the multiplexer after being assured that the previous character has been sent to the mux. Then the status register is checked for the arrival of data. On arrival, it is accepted and is displayed on the screen. The above procedure has been repeated for an infinite number of times.

The same software is run on both the terminals.

*** Description of the software for parity check**

The program for parity check in both the multiplexer and support terminals is the same as programs 2 and 3 respectively except for certain modifications which are common to both.

Initially the contents of the line control register (either 0x02FBH or 0x03FBH) are read. In addition to the previous enabled bits, the 3rd bit is also enabled. The new contents are then sent to the line control register.

After this, parity check is performed before any character is displayed. In case the 2nd bit of the status register is enabled it confirms a parity error, else the data is error free and is displayed on the screen.

FIGURE C

```
/*TERMINAL EMULATION*/
#include<stdio.h>#include<conio.h>#include<ctype.h>#include<dos.h>main()
{
int data_port, status_port, status_value;
char ch, data_value;
C=ckrscr();

/*port addresses*/

data_port=0x02f8;
status_port=0x02fd;
for (;;)
{
/*transmission of data whenever a key is pressed*/

if(kbhit())
{
ch=getch();
outportb(data_oirt,ch);
}
```

```
/*checking for the arrival of data and displaying it*/

status_value=inportb(status_port);
if((status_value & 0x01)==1)
{

data_value=inportb(data_port);
printf("%c", data_value);
}
}
}
```

Program 1.

/*SOFTWARE FOR MULTIPLEXER*/

```
#include<stdio.h>
#include<conio.h>
#include<ctype.h>
#include<dos.h>
main()
{

int st_value;
cha ch, ch1, ch2;

clrscr();
for (;;)
{

/*checking for the arrival of data from the support terminal and transmitting it to the multiplexer
along
with the beader*/
st_value=inportb(ox03fd);
st_value=st_value & 0x01;
if (st_value == 1)
{

ch=inportb (0x03f8);
st_value=inportb(0x02fd);
st_value=st value & 0x20;
while(st_value != 0x20)
{

st_value=inportb(0x02fd);
st_value=st_value & 0x20;
}
outportb(0x02f8, 'e');
st_value=inportb(0x02fd);
st_value=st value & 0x20;
while (st_value !=0x20)
```

```
{
st_value=inportb(0x02fd);
st_value=st_value & 0x20;
}
outportb(0x02f8,ch);

/*transmission of data along with the header to the multiplexer whenever a key is pressed*/
if (kbhit())
{

ch=qetch();
st_value=inportb(0x02fd);
st_value=st value & 0x20;
while (st_value !=0x20)
{
st_value=inportb(0x02fd);
st_value=st_value & 0x20;
{
outportb(0x02f8,'f');
st_value=inportb(0x02fd);
st_value=st_value & 0x20;
while(st_value !=0x20)
{
st_value=inportb(0x02fd);
st_value=st_value & 0x20;
}
outportb(ox02f8,ch);
}
/*checking for the arrival of data from the multiplexer and
either displaying it or sending it to the support terminal
according to the header attached with the data*/
st_value=inportb(0x02fd);
st_value=st_value & 0x01;
if(st_value== 1)
{
ch1=inportb(ox02f8);
do
{
st_value=inportb(0x02fd);
st_value=st_value & 0x01;
}
while (st_vlue !=1);
ch2=inportb(0x02f8);
if(ch1='e')
{
st_value=inportb(0x03fd);
st_value=st_value & 0x20;
while(st_value !=0x20)
{
st_value=inportb(0x03fd);
st_value=st_value & 0x20;
}
outportb(ox03f8,ch2);
```

```
}
else
printf("%c",ch2);
}
}
}
```

Program 2.

```
/*SOFTWARE FOR SUPPORT TERMINAL*/

#include<stdio.h>
#include<conio.h>
#include<ctype.h>
#include<dos.h>
main()
{
int st_value;
char ch;
clrser();
for(;;)
{
/*transmission of data whenever a key is pressed*/
if (kbhit()
{
ch=getch();
st_value=inportb(0x02fd);
st_value=st_value & 0x20;
while(st_value != 0x20)
{
st_value=inportb(0x02fd);
st_value=st_value & 0x20;
}
outportb(ox02f8,ch);
}
/*checking for the arrival of data and displaying it*/
st_value=inportb(0x02fd);
st_value=st_value & 0x01;
if (st_value == 1)
{
ch=inportb(0x02f8);
printf("%c",ch);
}
}
}
```

Program 3.

```
*/SOFTWARE FOR PARITY CHECK IN MULTIPLEXER*/

#include<stdio.h>
#include<conio.h>
#include<ctype.h>
```

```
#include<dos.h>
main()
{
int st_value;
char ch,ch1,ch2;
clrscr();

*/enabling the 3rd bit of the line control register*/
st_value=inportb(0x02fb);
st_value=st_value + 8;
outportb(ox02fb,st_value);
for (;;)
{
/*checking for the arrival of data from the support
terminal and transmitting it to the multiplexer along
with the header*/
st_value=inportb(0x03fd);
st_value=st_value & 0x01;
if(st_value == 1)
{
ch=inportb(0x03f8);
st_value=inportb(ox02fd);
st_value=st_value & 0x20;
while(st_value != 0x20)
{
st_value=inportb(0x02fd);
st_value=st value & 0x20;
}
outportb(0x02f8,'e');
st_value=inportb(0x02fd);
st_value=st_value & 0x20;
while(st-value != 0x20)
{
st_value=inportb(0x2fd);
st_value=st_value & 0x20;
}
outportb(ox02f8,ch);
}
/*transmission of data along with the header to the multiplexer whenever a key is pressed*/if
(kbhit())
{
ch=qetch();
st_value=inportb(0x02fd);
st_value=st_value & 0x20;
while(st_value != 0x20)
{
st_value=inportb(0x2fd);
st_value=st_value & 0x20;
}
outportb(0x02f8,'f');
st_value=inportb(0x02fd);
st_value=st_value & 0x20;
while(st_value != 0x20)
{
```

```
st_value=inportb(0x02fd);
st_value=st_value & 0x20;
}
outportb(ox02f8,ch);
}
```

/*checking for the arrival of data from the multiplexer and either displaying it after performing the parity check or sending it to the support terminal according to the beader attached with the data*/

```
st_value=inportb(0x02fd);
st_value=st_value & 0x01;
if (st_value == 1)
{
ch1=inportb(ox02f8);
do
{
st_value=inportb(0x02fd);
st_value=st_value & 0x01;
}
while (st_value != 1);
ch2=inportb(ox02f8);
if(ch1='e')
{
st_value=inportb(0x03fd);
st_value=st_value & 0x20;
while(st_value != 0x20)
{
st_value=inportb(0x03fd);
st_value=st_value & 0x20;
}
outportb(0x03f8,ch2);
}
else
{
st_value-inportb(0x02fd);
st_value=st_value & 0x04;
if(s_value != 0x04)
printf("%c",ch2);
else
printf("parity error");
}
}
}
}
```

Program 4.

/*SOFTWARE FOR PARITY CHECK IN SUPPOET TERRMINALS*/

```
#include<stdio.h>
#include<conio.h>
#include<ctype.h>
#include<dos.h>
main()
{
int st_value;
char ch;
clrscr();
```

```
/*enabling the 3rd bit of the line control register*/
st_value=inportb(ox02fb);
st_value=st_value +8;
outportb(0x02fb,st_value);
for (;;)
{
/*transmission of data whenever a key is pressed*/
if(kbhit())
{
ch=getch();
st_value=inportb(0x02fd);
st_value=st_value & 0x20;
while(st_value != ox20)
{
st_value=inportb(ox02fd);
st_value=st_value & 0x20;
}
outportb(0x02f8,ch);
}
/*checking for the arrival of data and displaying it after performing the parity check*/
st_value=inportb(0x02fd);
st_value=st_value & 0x01;
if(st_value == 1)
{
ch=inportb(ox02f8);
st_value=inportb(0x02fd);
st_value=st_value & 0x04;
if(st_value != 0x04)
printf("%c",ch);
else
printf("parity error");
}
}
}
```

QUESTIONS

Write 8086 assembly language programs for the following-

Q 1. Subtract (8bit numbers) X from Y? where X=7 & Y=12

Q 2. Find the larger of two given numbers?

Q 3. Count number of 1's available in any register (AH=11110011)

Q 4. Exchange the contents of accumulator & flag register

Q 5. Write a program to generate first 10 odd numbers.

Q 6. Write a program to exchange contents of two memory blocks?

C100=00	C300=FF	such that	C100=FF	C300=00
C101=00	C301=FF		C101=FF	C301=00
C110=00	C310=FF		C110=FF	C310=00
:	:		:	:
:	:		:	:
CIFF=00	C3FF=FF		CIFF=FF	C3FF=00

Q 7. Transfer data between 6-Registers, BH=0, CH=1,DH=2,Dl=3, BL=4, CL=5 such that BH=5, CH=0, DH=1, DL=2, BL=3, CL=4

Q 8. Calculate a value that is four times that of the number in AL.

Q 9. Interchange contents of memory & register ?

C100=08	such that	C100=05
Reg. BH=05		Reg BH=08

Q 10. Calculate a value that is one eigth of the number in AH.

Q 11. Using Add Instruction add the content of Reg B & C & store the result into register D ?

Q 12. Add two 8-bits numbers AL= (03H) & BL= (FFH)?

Q 13. Add 49H & 56H together & store result at memory location 2503H . Let 2501H & 2502H memory location contain 49H & 56H numbers respectively?

Q 14. Write an Equivalent program for XCHG instruction?

Q 15. Describe the utilities of the various flags in the 8086?

Q 16. Why did IBM Corpn. chose the i8088 microprocessor instead of the i8086 inspite of 8088 having 8-bit external data bus against 16-bit data bus of i8086, for it's Personal Computers?

Q 17. Using Dos functions print all the alphabets on the screen?

Q 18. Discuss the IBM PC Tree with reference to the various members of the tree.

Q 19. Give a block diagram representation of a microcomputer and explain each part briefly.

Q 20. Discuss motherboard component recognization.

Q 21. Write briefly on the following :-
i. X86 Family
ii. Pentium Family

Q 22. Discuss briefly the internal architecture of the 8088 microprocessor.

Q 23. Write a short note on support chips.

Q 24. Explain DRAM and SRAM.

Q 25. Write a short note on ROM explaining specifically PROM, EPROM and Flash RAM.

Q 26. Explain wait state.

Q 27. How can the wait problem be solved? Explain.

Q 28. What is memory caching?

Q 29. What do you understand by capacitive keyboards? Explain.

Q 30. Discuss with diagrams Keyboard operations.

Q 31. Explain the various commonly encountered keyboard faults, and explain their remedies.

Q 32. Explain CGA operation in
i. Text Mode
ii. Graphics Mode

Q 32. What do you understand by Super VGA?

Q 33. What is BIT Mapped Graphics?

Q 34. Explain Display unit internals.

Q 35. Differentiate between single density, double density and high density floppy disks.

Q 36. Exaplain the floppy disk drive.

Q 37. Differentiate hard and soft sectoring.

Q 38. Discuss the physical structure of a hard disk.

Q 39. Write a short note on IDE.

Q 40. Differentiate between CD-ROM, Magneto Optical Disks & Flopticals.

Q 41. Discuss tape drives.

Q 42. What do you understand by the word "ports"? Differentiate between serial and parallel ports.

Q 43. Discuss the centronics standard.

Q 44. Discuss the Printer Internals.

Q 45. Differentiate between asynchronous and synchronous data transfer.

Q 46. What are the problems encountered in long distance data communication?
How can they be avoided?

Q 47. Discuss the RS-232 standard.

Q 48. Explain Linear Power Supply (LPS).

Q 49. Explain SMPS and differentiate it with LPS.

Q 50. Using BIOS calls show sixteen colors on your display screen.

APPENDIX A

EVOLUTION OF THE DIGITAL COMPUTER.

The computer evolved after centuries of hard work-the goal was to acheive fast and accurate calculating devices, that would save energy, both in terms of manhours and manpower. We glance into the pages of history to understand the process of evolution of the digital computer.

The earliest evidence of calculating device dates back to around 3500 B.C. This device known as the **Abacus**, an apparatus made of pebbles, who used to perform simple calculations. It was probably used by the Mesopotamian Civilization in the Tigris- Euphrates valley. Other civilizations in Rome, Greece and Egypt had developed similar calculating devices. Various modifications of the Abacus went on to be used by other civilizations that developed. But the whole scenario didn't gain much momentum in terms of development of cleverer calculating devices till the early seventeenth century.

Around 1617, John Napier, a Scottish Mathematician invented a device called the **Napier's bones,** or Card Board multiplier. It was basically a mechanical arrangement of bone strips on which numbers were stamped. This cardboard like arrangement was used to perform multiplications. Blaise Pascal, a French Mathematician, invented a **numerical wheel calculator** around 1642. The numerical wheel calculator was basically a mechanical arrangement of small wheels connected by gears. The wheels had the decimal numbers 0 to 9 embeded on them. This wheel-gear arrangement could be used to perform simple arithmetic operations. Gottfried Wilhelm Van Leibnitz, a German Mathematician improved upon pascals design to make a calculating device known as the **Stepper Calculator**, around the year 1694. These calculating devices were the forerunners of the **Analytic Engine** of Charles Babbage, which in turn is the forerunner of the modern day digital computer.

Charles Babbage, an English Mathematician and Philosopher, started working towards a mechanical calculator, called the "Difference Engine" in the early 19th century. This machine could handle 20 digit calculations, and work with logarithmic tables etc. This machine was operational by the end of 1822. After this engine, Babbage worked on a variety of other machines. He dubbed all his machines as engines. Around 1833, Charles Babbage started working on an machine called the "Analytic Engine". The purpose of this machine was to solve general problems, which were largely analytical in nature. Most of the paper work done by Babbage could never be implemented, and the Analytical Engine never became a reality. But the design of the Analytic Engine was largely implemented in the digital computer design. Considering the constraints with which Babbage worked i.e. no electricity, no ICs, his thoughts and ideas reflect the great genius he was.

With the discovery of electricity, electromechanical devices came into the computing scene. In 1890 Herman Hollerith used a punched card equipment for processing the U.S. Census. Using this equipment the census was processed in record time of about 2 months. With this success the **Hollerith machine** made its entry into other countrics like Austria and Canada. Herman Hollerith founded a Tabulating Machine Company in 1896, which he sold in 1911. After merger with a few other companies, the Tabulating Machine Company was rechristened the International Business Machines,or IBM.

During 1930s electro-mechanical devices started fadding away, paving the way for pure electronics based machines to become available. During this period, the pressures of world war II dictated research in most areas of science. The use of night bombers, submarines, and long range guns on ships meant that the army men had to fight enemies not visible to their eyes. Radar technology was used side by side with powerful computational devices. It was this thrust given by the U.S. Army that promoted the development of the digital computers.

The first electronic computing machine was built in the year 1939, and was known as the **Atanasoff-Berry Computer** after its discoverers. It designed to solve twenty-nine simultaneous equations with twenty-nine unknowns,but it was never able to do its job. The actual work towards development of digital computer began around 1937. Howard A. Aiken of the Haward University embarked upon a project in collaboration with the IBM to develop an electronic computer using existing punch card technology. But it was only in May 1944 that the dreams came true. This original machine was called

Harvard Mark I and was initially used for spealist works of the U.S. Navy.

John Eckert and John Mauchly of the University of Pennsylvania began work on the Electronic Numerical Intergrater And Calculator, or **ENIAC** in 1943. It was the first total vacuum diode based computer and was thousand times faster than Mark I.

Machester Mark I was the earliest stored program computer. It was a small experimental machine with a storage capacity of 32 words, each of 31 binary digits.

Around 1951, **UNIVAC** (Universal **A**utomatic **C**omputer) became the first commercial digital computer to reach the market. It was a general purpose machine, and was widely appreciated in the market.It was primarily a vacuum diode based computer which workec on boolean algebra proposed by George Boole around 1854. It took time of the order of microseconds to complete some of very complex arithmetic calculation. This marked the arrival of the first generation of the digital computer.

APPENDIX B

COMPUTER GENERATIONS AT AGLANCE

Major Characteristic	First Generation	Second Generation	Third Generation	Fourth Generation	Fifth Generation
Years	1949-1958	1959-1965	1966-1975	1975-1990s	1990s
Electronic Circuitry	Vacuum Tubes	Transistors	IC	LSI,VLSI	VVLSI
Size	Room size	Closet Size	Desk-top Size	Laptop Size	Not known
Storage Device	Acoustic Delay Lines	Magnetic Cores and Tapes	High Speed Magnetic cores and disks	Semiconductor memories,CD-ROM disks	Semiconductor memories,High-speed CD-ROM
Speed	Millisecond	Microsecond	Microsecond	Nanosecond	Picosecond
Software	Machine and Assembly languages	High level language:eg Fortran, Cobol, Ada etc.	High level languages: eg Fortran IV, PL/I	High level languages: C, Pascal, Cobol etc.	Artificial Intelligence(AI) based software
Application	Scientific /Business	Business & Engineering	Database Management Systems, all spheres of life	All spheres of life	Every where especially in AI
Early Examples	ENIAC,	IBM 1401 UNIVAC 200	IBM 360 Honeywell	IMB PC-I, Mini Micros, Supermini, Mainframe	Super Super Computer (Expected)

Note : The Table is meant for a rough idea of Computer Generations. **Distinctions between Computer Generations become very difficult, as the transition from one generation to the next is always gradual, which causes overlapping between generations.**

APPENDIX - C

INTEL'S P6

Intel continues its quest for a superchip, which will ultimately be Pentium's successor. Dogged by the clone makers ability to xerox Intel's design, Intel always makes quick transitions to newer high tech chips, P6 being the next in offering.

P6 is expected to hit the market by late 1995. P6 is suppose to be a super microarchitecture based chip which will have two dies, the processor and the cache, mounted in a single pack. These two are interconnected using a highly optimized bus. It will incorporate about 5.5 million transistors using 0.6 micron process and will later bring in 0.35 micron transistor. It incorporates dynamic execution (explained next) and enhances multiprocessing support. It will be able to handle two instruction per clock using its superpipelined design. Pipelines have already been explained with regard to Pentium chips discussion in chapter Two. Most important, it will ensure full compatibility with the X86 family of chips - in the true spirit of Intel's quest for high tech microcomputing.

Let us now consider the working of P6. P6 can be internally described to be consisting of four major sub-assemblies: Fetch Unit, Dispatch/Execution Unit, Retire Unit and Bus Interface Unit. Before the work of these independent units is considered, dynamic execution is to be understood.Consider the following set of instructions:

Instruction No.	Instruction
1	X = a + 3
2	Y = 3 + X
3	S = 4 + 9
4	W = 9 - b

While executing these instructions presented in the sequence above, values of 'a' and 'b' are necessary. Suppose that value of 'a' is not available in memory when the processor tries to execute instruction no. 1. Most linear processor would come to a halt. But dynamic execution makes the processor look ahead. As value of 'a' is not available, 'X' cannot be computed and consequently 'Y' cannot be evaluated. Processor executes instruction 3 and then moves to instruction 4, which is executed if the value of 'b' is available. **This out of order execution of instruction is described as dynamic execution, and consequently P6 is said to have dynamic engines.** P6 is designed with three independent engines to get around with traditional fetch and execute delays.

The Fetch Unit takes the users program in the order it is presented and breaks it into microcode instructions. That is why Fetch Unit is also described as the in-order receiver. The Fetch unit is filled using the same concept of branch prediction, which has been discussed with regard to the Pentium chip. An algorithm called Yeh's algorithm is used to implement branch prediction. Optimized branch prediction increases processor performance manifold.

The Dispatch/Execution unit does all the rescheduling of instruction sequence in accordance to the instruction states. As explained before, instructions 3 and 4 are processed ahead of instructions 1 and 2 by this unit. This unit is thus called the out order section. Results of the microcode instructions are returned to the instruction pool for storage.

The retire unit reorders the instructions in accordance to the order in which they were presented. As already said, the results of execution of instructions 3 and 4 were put in the pool by the Dispatch/Execution unit. When the retire Unit determines that all instructions have been processed, it reorders the instructions and transfers results from instruction pool to the memory.

The Bus Interface Unit is the interface used to establish contact with the various units of the P6 eg: FetchUnit, Dispatch/Execution unit and Retire Unit.

Analysts have been predicting names for the P6 microprocessor.Some hold that it will be an extension of the Pentium Family, while others say that it will start a new family all together. This controversial discussion is not the topic of interest. What is amazing and interesting is the very implementation of 5.5 million transistors on a single chip and the capability to handle about 250 Million Instrucions Per Second (MIPS). When P6 will be released, it is slated to have a clock speed of about 150MHZ, which will be later enhanced to 200 MHZ. P6 with speed, confidence and elegance, is definitely to usher a new era in high tech computation.